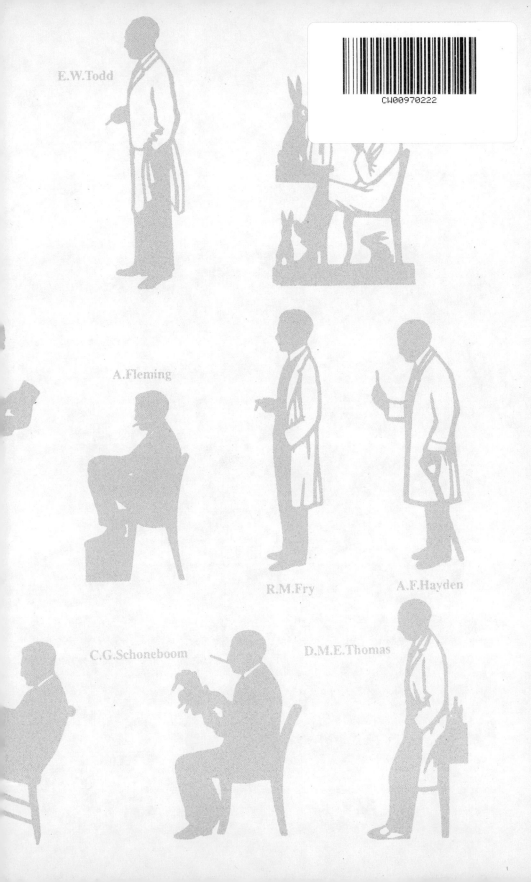

E.W.Todd

A.Fleming

R.M.Fry

A.F.Hayden

C.G.Schoneboom

D.M.E.Thomas

PENICILLIN MAN

ALEXANDER FLEMING
AND THE ANTIBIOTIC REVOLUTION

KEVIN BROWN

SUTTON PUBLISHING

To my parents, Thomas and Lily Brown

First published in the United Kingdom in 2004 by
Sutton Publishing Limited · Phoenix Mill
Thrupp · Stroud · Gloucestershire · GL5 2BU

British Library Cataloguing in Publication Data
A catalogue record for this book is available from the British Library.

ISBN 0-7509-3152-3

Typeset in 11/13pt Sabon.
Typesetting and origination by
Sutton Publishing Limited.
Printed and bound in England by
J.H. Haynes & Co. Ltd, Sparkford.

Contents

List of Illustrations

Preface

This is the book I never intended to write and yet that I was fated to write. When I was appointed Archivist to St Mary's Hospital and Medical School back in 1989, I consciously decided to avoid doing anything at all connected with Fleming. The subject already seemed to have been done to death, and the controversy surrounding the rival claims of Fleming, Florey and Chain still aroused violent passions, especially at St Mary's, where Fleming spent most of his career. It is a lesson never to say 'never'. Very soon I was sweating blood to set up the Alexander Fleming Laboratory Museum and, without intending to do so, I had become something of an authority on Fleming. I resisted all entreaties to write a biography until I could resist no more.

The more I have researched the subject, the more it has seemed that a new approach to Fleming's life and the history of penicillin and a new book are timely. The existing biographies have suffered from too partisan an approach, either glorifying Fleming or knocking him from his pedestal. The more I have learned of the subject, the more unsatisfactory some of these earlier accounts have appeared to be, suggesting the need for an independent and exhaustively researched account that is not partly polemic in intent. There is enough credit to go around and to spare. Any book is partly a product of its own time, and fears that the antibiotic age in medicine ushered in by the work of Fleming may be about to end makes a re-examination at the start of the twenty-first century especially topical.

When I began to research this book, I had not realised just how far I would travel geographically in my quest. Naively, I expected to find most of my material in and around London, with Fleming's papers deposited at the British Library, Florey's at the Royal Society, Chain's at the Wellcome Institute Library and the archives of St Mary's Hospital in my own charge. Instead my mission took me to Sweden, across the United States and to Greece. In the course of this undertaking, I have had the help of many old friends and I have made many new friends, eager to offer what assistance they could.

Fleming himself has been a constant and congenial, if sometimes shadowy, companion throughout. At times his silences have been frustrating, but they have made all the more rewarding the times when those rare but revealing phrases or words of his have unexpectedly brought him vividly to life and given an insight into who he was. Actors say that it is more difficult to play a good character, often a very internalised personality, than an extrovert villain. Equally, it has been a challenge to portray a good, very likeable man, who rarely expressed his feelings and who was often overshadowed by being surrounded by larger-than-life personalities with their hearts too openly on their sleeves. Although it is often said that he was more interesting as a scientist than as a man, what lay beneath the apparently dour, intensely reserved outer carapace has continued to attract and fascinate the public ever since penicillin first found fame. The great challenge is to show why.

Chance famously played a large part in Fleming's life and work; I too have been amazed at some of the unplanned coincidences that have dogged my researches. Indeed, he and penicillin have seemed inescapable even when I haven't sought them out. I remember once visiting Barcelona, walking round the corner from my hotel and finding a bust of Fleming in front of me in a square named in his honour. I was invited to deliver the 2001 Andrew J. Moyer Lecture at the United States Department of Agriculture National Center for Agricultural Utilization Research at Peoria, Illinois, exactly sixty years after Howard Florey and Norman Heatley arrived there to get penicillin production under way in the New World. That was planned, but going to Athens exactly fifty years after Fleming's tour of Greece in 1952 to consult the Fleming papers his widow had taken back to Greece with her was a complete coincidence. Indeed I was only yards away from where he had proposed to Amalia on the same day fifty years before.

There was also a coincidence of atmosphere. My researches into the Second World War development of penicillin in the United States took me to a country where the America of 7 December 1941 had more than a resonance in the nation in the aftermath of 9/11. The sense of impending unease and fears of the threat of terrorist outrages as war against Iraq approached in late 2002 and early 2003 forged a link with the urgency of the mood in the archival documents from sixty years previously that I had been studying in Washington DC, Philadelphia, New Brunswick and New York. There was nothing like being imaginatively immersed in the feel of the time being studied. Working in my day job at St Mary's, the institution with which Fleming was intimately involved for so long, and knowing some of the people who had known him there brought the deepest of all creative links to the past.

Undoubtedly, penicillin was one of the defining discoveries of the twentieth century; it has affected everyone and continues to be relevant to this day. The themes of the importance of individual contributions as opposed to collective effort, the role of war as an agent of change, the role of chance and the story of a man prepared to take advantage of serendipity are all of universal relevance. For contemporary scientists the story of penicillin has lessons about the need to be flexible with different research strategies suitable for different situations and the need to communicate with the public if their work is not to be ignored or distorted. Fortunately for me in retelling that story, penicillin is perhaps one of the most accessible to the non-scientist of almost all discoveries. It is something we can all relate to. I vividly remember as an 8-year-old first learning the story of Fleming and a teacher demonstrating the discovery of penicillin with a mouldy orange. With hindsight I am also conscious that I myself might not be here without penicillin. As a young woman my mother had meningitis at a time when antibiotics were coming into use to treat this sometimes lethal infection. Perhaps this gives me all the more incentive to look behind the accepted story of Fleming and try to establish what really happened.

While this interpretation of the penicillin story and of Fleming is my own, I owe a deep debt of gratitude to many people around the world who have given me assistance in so many ways. I can only apologise in advance to anyone whom I may have inadvertently missed out. Dr Robert Fleming, son of Alexander Fleming, has always been supportive of, and interested in, the various forays I have made into aspects of his father's life and work. Although this is in no way an official biography, the generosity with information and the support for my task from Robert have been greatly appreciated, and this book would have been the poorer without them. Biography, by its nature, if it is to tell the truth, must be intrusive, and I am grateful to all who knew Fleming who have shared their memories of him with me. He was a man who compartmentalised his life and rarely showed himself in the round to others. Only by talking to a range of the people still alive who knew him in different spheres have I been able to see how others perceived him and connect the different aspects he showed to them. I wish to thank, in particular, Bill Frankland, Barbara Gammon (née Parry), George Bonney, Keith Rogers, Felix Eastcott, John Ballantyne, John Crawford Adams, the late Jack Suchet, the late Andrew Matthews, Frank Diggins, Giles Romanes, Wolfgang Suschitsky, Phyllis French (née Norton), Iain Craddock, Diana Morley, Margaret Parfitt, Barbara Webb, John Hofmeyr and Edith Dee. Unfortunately Norman Heatley, the last surviving member of the Oxford team, was too frail to be interviewed again for this book. Boyd Woodruff has kindly shared with me his memories of wartime production at Merck in the United States and, with David Pramer, of Selman Waksman of Rutgers University, who coined the very word 'antibiotic'. Tom Lees and Elmer Gaden have shared with me something of the atmosphere at Pfizer, where modern fermentation methods of penicillin production were first introduced on an industrial scale. Margaret Child and Jessie Carter have both vividly described what it was like to be the recipient of penicillin in the early days. Gilbert Shama has drawn my attention to material on wartime German involvement with penicillin. Over the years I have had many discussions on Almroth Wright with his biographer Michael Dunnill.

At St Mary's, I must express my gratitude to St Mary's NHS Trust for encouraging me in the writing of this book. There has been interest in my progress from many people throughout the Trust, but I wish to thank in particular Julian Nettel, Chief Executive, the Baroness Hanham, Chairman, and Jill Blowers for their interest in the project. Nor can I forget Alasdair Fraser, who has constantly urged, if not nagged, for many years that this was a book waiting for me to write it. The St Mary's Hospital Association has given some sponsorship, for which I am grateful. In thanking the then Chairman of the Association, Averil Mansfield, I wish to thank all the Executive Committee and alumni who make up the membership. I must also thank the Lord Glenarthur for his interest in Fleming and this book, going back to his time as Trust Chairman, when he, Simon, was a keen supporter of the idea of setting up the Alexander Fleming Laboratory Museum. It was from this time too that I owe a debt to Professors Alan Glynn and Charles Easmon for their elucidation of the bacteriology behind Fleming's work. Stuart Philip has also helped with my understanding of the practical side of this science at various times over the years. If I have got any of it wrong, it is my fault alone. Evi Kalodiki has communicated her enthusiasm for her compatriot Amalia Fleming and the Greek connections of Fleming. Tony Rippon has offered practical help and shown a keen enthusiasm, which I have much appreciated. Simon Newman has experimented with digital imaging for copying some fragile material. I would also like to express my appreciation of all the volunteer guides who enthusiastically work in the Alexander Fleming Laboratory Museum and have shown such a keen interest in my progress with this work throughout, as has former assistant archivist Tudor Allen.

At the National Center for Agricultural Utilization Research, Peoria, Illinois, I was made to feel both like an adopted member of the NCAUR family and like an honoured VIP guest during my visit as 2001 Andrew J. Moyer Lecturer and in all my subsequent communications with them. I am grateful for their wholehearted help, given in much the same spirit as it was for a much more important project back in 1941, when the foundations of modern antibiotic production were laid there. I especially wish to thank Peter Johnsen, Director, Kate O'Hara, Technology Communications Officer, and Joyce Blumenshine, Librarian. Cletus Kurzman, Head of the United States Department of Agriculture, Agricultural Research Service Culture Collection, and Steve Peterson, Curator of *Aspergillus* and *Penicillium* collections, showed me the national culture collection originally established by Charles Thom, especially the strains relating to the development of penicillin, and the accompanying documentation.

I have enjoyed great cooperation from the pharmaceutical industry, which has opened its doors surprisingly willingly. At Pfizer (UK), I am indebted to John C. Adams for facilitating my visit to their Sandwich plant and to Ian Cording, Assistant Records Manager, for access to the Kemble Bishop records held there and for his investigation of other sources of material within the company. At Pfizer in New York, my thanks go to Robert J. Fanteux, Veronica Plucinski and Gustavus Barrientos of the Corporate Affairs Division for access to the records of Pfizer. At GlaxoSmithKline, I wish to thank Danita Onräet for her encouragement and contacts, Bill Smith and Tony White. Brian Ward of Merck in the United Kingdom similarly eased my route to Joe Ciccone, Archivist at Merck Corporate Archives at Whitehouse Station, New Jersey, who has been helpful despite staffing difficulties. Brian Davis of Bristol Myers Squibb, New Brunswick, New Jersey, has kindly supplied material relating to his company's involvement in penicillin.

At Rutgers University, I owe a great deal of gratitude to Douglas Eveleigh, who took considerable pains to facilitate my researches in the New Jersey area and for his nominating me as Pfizer Visiting Professor. My visit to Rutgers was a pleasure as much as a labour and was smoothed considerably by Doug.

At the Alexander Fleming Biomedical Sciences Research Centre at Vari, Greece, I am grateful for the cooperation and hospitality of the Centre proffered by John Volanakis, the then Director. In particular, I must mention the help from George Panayotou, who went out of his way to make my stay there and my researches as comfortable and productive as possible. I am also appreciative of the access to Fleming's papers given by Elsa Rokofillou, President of the Hellenic Foundation for Basic Medical Research Alexander Fleming, and for sharing her memories of her friend Amalia Fleming.

In Italy, I have had much help from Maria Luisa Messa of Brescia, who has long had an interest in Fleming, and also from Michele Francaviglia, Medical Director of the Fleming Laboratories. In Spain, Lluis Martinez, sub-Director of *Avui* in Barcelona, has been assiduous in collecting for me material relating to Fleming's visit to Barcelona in 1948 and in generously translating documents from Catalan into Spanish for me, becoming a friend in the process. Some of the material he gathered was supplied from Manuel Escudé Aixelà, Chair of the History of Medicine at the University of Barcelona. My thanks also go to Carlos Flores Varela, Director of the Archivo General at the Universidad Complutense Madrid, for access to material relating to Florencio Bustinza Lachiondo, one of Fleming's greatest admirers. I must also thank Marika Hedin, then of the Nobel Museum in Stockholm, for advice on sources relating to the Nobel Prize. Hans Jörnvall, Director of the Karolinska Institute, granted access to the 1945 Nobel archives, despite his disastrous summer and near fatal car accident. Material from the Nobel Archives was kindly provided by the Nobel Committee for Physiology or Medicine. Maria Lorentzon, with whom I have collaborated on issues of nursing history, translated those documents that were in Swedish for me into English over a couple of bottles of wine.

Inevitably, though, much of the research has been conducted in libraries and archives. I would like to thank the staff of the British Library, the Wellcome Institute and Royal Society Libraries and Archives, the Bodleian Library, Library of Congress, Public Records Office (now the National Archives, London), and National Archives and Records Service of the United States, as well as those other librarians and archivists mentioned by name. At the National Academy of Sciences, Washington, DC, Daniel Barbiero and Janice Goldblum were helpful. Arlene Shaner, Reference Librarian at the New York Academy of Medicine, enthusiastically showed me her relevant holdings. Thomas J. Fusciano, University Archivist at Rutgers University, and his staff facilitated access to the Waksman papers. Monica Blank, Archivist at the Rockefeller Archive Center, has been ever ready with help. Clem Webb of the London Scottish Regiment facilitated my access to the regimental library. I also wish to thank Amey Hutchins of the University of Pennsylvania Archives for her unsuccessful search for references to the Alexander Fleming Memorial Fund. Over the years, I have enjoyed the facilities and friendship of the staff of the Library at St Mary's Hospital Medical School (now the St Mary's Campus Library of Imperial College Faculty of Medicine), especially the help of Nigel Palmer and Sally Smith, the former and present librarians, and their staff, in particular Rachel Shipton and Dinah Akan. Bernadette Tallon, formerly of St Mary's Audio-Visual Services, has always been helpful regarding photographs of Fleming and ensured that the collection was saved and passed to my care on the regrettable closure of her department, just as Cathy Ison was a guardian of Wright and Fleming relics until my advent. I am also grateful to Professor Herman Waldmann, Head of the Sir William Dunn School of Pathology at Oxford, for freely making available photographs of the ground-breaking work done there.

Robert Peberdy I wish to thank for first suggesting Sutton Publishing as a firm that might be interested in this book and for advising me on publishing issues. At Sutton, my thanks go to Jaqueline Mitchell, who has been an enthusiastic commissioning editor and has made constructive comments. Also I wish to thank Hilary Walford and Mary Worthington for helping me to make this a better book.

Completing this book amidst the flurry of activity surrounding celebration of the seventy-fifth anniversary of the discovery of penicillin has underlined for me the continued importance of Fleming's discovery. Amidst a series of television appearances ranging from BBC *Breakfast* to a news item on Catalan television, newspaper interviews, a competition sponsored by the Royal Society of Chemistry to find Britain's mouldiest mug, a summer festival marking the anniversary at St Mary's Hospital, the merchandising of the inevitable anniversary memorabilia and delivering special lectures, I seemed to spend much of the anniversary week at the scene of the discovery talking about Fleming. It all left little time for drawing breath, let alone thought, yet a rare quiet moment to myself for reflection in Fleming's laboratory exactly seventy-five years after the discovery was enough to remind me of the importance of what had happened there and of why I had written this book: to retell a story that has never lost its drama but where sometimes the truth has slipped behind the myth.

London
3 September 2003

ONE

'That's funny!'

It was the bane of many a bacteriologist's life – the contamination of a culture plate by a fungus. Yet this mysterious mould was destined to change the world and to revolutionise medicine in a way the scientist who noticed it could never have predicted that early September day. It would also change his own life and bring him the fame and public attention he would never have intentionally sought for himself. Forty-seven-year-old Alexander Fleming had only just returned from holiday that Monday morning, 3 September 1928, after spending August with his wife and 4-year-old son at their country home in Suffolk. His appointment as Professor of Bacteriology at St Mary's Hospital Medical School, part of the University of London, had commenced on Saturday 1 September, but, whatever pride he may have had in his new status, he was really returning to a department he had worked in for over twenty years and he did not expect too many changes to his way of working. If anything, he was more interested in the research that had absorbed his attention before he went away.

Before him on the bench of his cramped laboratory, crowded with the tools of his bacteriologist's trade, were some discarded petri dishes containing *Staphylococcus aureus*, a fairly common bacterium which can cause nasty though not lethal abscesses and boils. He had finished working on these cultures before his holiday and now had no further use for them, but settled down to examining them for one last time before asking his laboratory technician to sterilise them so that the glass plates could be reused. The culture plates were stacked in an overflowing shallow enamel tray for examination and after inspection would be transferred to an adjacent tray, containing lysol, a strong disinfectant.[1] Many bacteriologists liked to dispose of their discarded culture plates as soon as they had finished with them, but not Fleming. His usual practice was to leave them for a few weeks until the bench was overcrowded with forty or fifty cultures just to see what, if anything, might have happened. He teased any of his more orderly colleagues with the charge of excessive tidiness if they cleared their benches and discarded test tubes and culture plates for which they had no further use at the end of each day.[2] Fleming's approach was about to be vindicated.

He was busy examining his plates under a hand-held magnifying glass when a visitor popped his head around the always open door of the laboratory. Merlin Pryce, then a research scholar, had helped Fleming with his earlier work on *Staphylococcus aureus*, but had left the laboratory in February 1928 to work as a pathologist in the Department of Morbid Anatomy at St Mary's, leaving Fleming to continue with the work himself. Fleming, ever anxious to encourage the careers of younger associates, indeed wished to make him co-author of the resultant publication, but Pryce refused as he believed he had not contributed enough to the work on staphylococci to merit such distinction. Fleming continued to sort through the plates, a number of them contaminated with colonies of yeasts and moulds, as he chatted to his visitor, chiding him for having left him to do all this work himself and occasionally pulling out an interesting specimen at random to show to his colleague. Indeed he had come very close to discarding the culture plates without inspecting them when his visitor arrived, but Pryce urged him to continue to look at them.[3] Suddenly, Fleming noticed something unusual and paused to examine much more closely one of the plates he was about to hand to Pryce. 'That's funny!' he said. He had discovered penicillin.[4]

Fleming showed Pryce what had interested him. Colonies of staphylococci cluster together like bunches of grapes and the plate should have been densely covered with these colonies on nutrient agar jelly. What the two men saw was that the plate had become contaminated by a mould. There was nothing unusual in that, as contamination was an occupational hazard. It would have been easy to have glanced at the contamination and immediately set the culture aside without a further glance.[5] However, Fleming had noticed something that caught his attention much more than the big blob of mould. There were no staphylococci growing close to the fungus and beyond this zone of inhibition there were signs that the bacteria were being lysed or dissolved. The fungus was producing a substance capable of inhibiting the bacteria. That substance Fleming at first called 'mould juice'.

Indeed it was the signs of lysis that perhaps interested Fleming more than anything. Pryce confessed himself to have been unimpressed by the plate that had so excited Fleming: 'I didn't know what was going through his mind, but for my own part I thought that the lysis was due to acids produced by the mould . . . But pandering to the great man, I actually said "That's how you discovered lysozyme." He made no comment, but with automatic hand he took his platinum loop and subcultured the mould into a tube of broth.'[6] Unconsciously, Pryce had hit upon the very factor which had attracted Fleming's interest. The circumstances in which he had made the first of his great discoveries, that of the body's own antiseptic lysozyme, almost seven years earlier, were very similar to the discovery of penicillin. In both discoveries, a chance observation of a natural phenomenon on a petri dish was the starting point. Fleming was always to claim that much of his best work had been done on lysozyme but its therapeutic value was limited. Now here was another substance with lytic activity, one that was perhaps more potent than lysozyme. Certainly, in attacking *Staphylococcus aureus* it had shown itself capable of destroying a common pathogenic organism. It was well worth pursuing.

An acute observer of natural phenomena, Fleming at once took action and subcultured a minute sample of the fungus from the culture plate into a liquid growth medium rather than the solid agar of the petri dish. The test tube in which he placed his specimen was filled with Sabouraud's medium, a mixture of peptone–agar used for culturing fungi, though he later found that an ordinary meat broth would have done just as well. He also took pains to preserve the original plate, photographing it and exposing it to formalin vapour both to kill and to fix the mould and the bacteria. He was to keep this original plate for many years, even when there were few people who believed that penicillin would prove to be anything more than an interesting phenomenon or useful laboratory tool. Dried up and brittle, it is now a national treasure in the British Library, where it was deposited in 1965 with Fleming's papers.[7] It was obvious that, from the beginning, Fleming considered the plate interesting and important enough to be preserved.

He also thought it worth sharing with his colleagues. It was shown to anyone who called into his laboratory that day, including E.W. Todd, who had just returned from New York, Hurst Brown, a Canadian Rhodes scholar, and C.J. La Touche, an Irish mycologist who occupied the laboratory immediately below his own. They were politely interested but no more. He even took it to the main laboratory up the stairs from his own room and, standing in front of the open fire with the ever-present cigarette dangling from his lip, proudly showed his colleagues the plate. Once again it was greeted without any enthusiasm. Everyone dismissed it as another of Fleming's interesting curiosities of bacteriology that they had seen so many times before and that were without much significance. Almost as soon as they had seen the plate, they forgot about it. Thirteen years later, when the clinical importance of penicillin had been truly established, they were all to remember this moment.[8]

With hindsight it may have been a Eureka moment, but Fleming was not by nature a very demonstrative man nor one to show excitement. His laconic comment on making the observation that it was funny was typical of a man given to few words. Affectionately nicknamed 'Flem' by his colleagues, Alexander Fleming was considered by many to be the typical dour Scot, revealing little of what he actually thought. One of his research assistants, Frederick Ridley, was to say that 'in seeking to recapture something of Fleming's personality, one is up against almost a brick wall'.[9] Fleming's biographer André Maurois was to describe him as a shy man, but Ernst Chain, the biochemist who was to contribute so much to bringing penicillin into clinical use, disputed this: 'I knew him sufficiently well to say with certainty that he was anything but shy . . . he was a taciturn Scot, and small talk did not come easy to him. He was oligophasic.'[10] It is something of an overstatement, but it is true that, fond as he was of company, he was always a better listener than a talker. His favourite snooker partner at the Chelsea Arts Club, the artist Vivian Pitchford, was stone deaf, rendering small talk unnecessary.[11] A conversation with him was 'like playing tennis with a man who, when he received a service, put the ball in his pocket'.[12] Fleming was equally comfortable with silence and could stand staring at someone without exchanging a word and without showing the slightest embarrassment or discomfort, making his conversations 'masterpieces of brevity'.[13] Taciturn though he may have been, he was sociable and generally ready to attend scientific meetings, give lectures and socialise with his colleagues, visiting scientists and his friends outside work. Ever accessible, he invariably left his laboratory door open. Visitors were always welcome. If no one called in on him and he felt like some company, he would wander into the main laboratory, often doing little more than watch what was going on. Occasionally, he would make some comment on the state of the stock market, the marriage of a colleague or some scandal in the scientific world, but generally he was not given to gossip and he had no time at all for the smutty stories of the locker room.[14] Nor was this practical and down-to-earth man likely to inspire his colleagues with the excitement of his discovery.

He was a small man, only 5ft 6in in height, with blue eyes and greying hair, once fair and now well on its way to being white.[15] He was very conscious of his lack of stature and sensitive to the disadvantages of being small and of needing to prove himself. He once commented to his friend and stockbroker Anthony Ritchie that Ritchie's son Brian 'doesn't need to bother about exams – he's tall and tall people can do anything, go anywhere'.[16] Yet, despite his stature, his head was large and dominated by a boxer's bent nose that had been broken when he was a boy and by the intensity of his stare through large and noticeable searching blue eyes, features that were often remarked on.[17] He had a disconcerting habit of keeping his eyes closed when talking and then suddenly opening them, only to stare at the person he was talking with.[18] Although he had lived in London since the age of 16, he had never lost the soft lilt of his Ayrshire accent and had a slight speech impediment when pronouncing his 'r's.[19] Often he would sing at his work.[20] There was a 'swing in his walk, almost a jaunty lift of the shoulder', and, while attractive to women, he was considered 'very much a man's man'.[21] His one affectation of individuality in dress was always to wear a brightly coloured bow tie.[22] Very rarely was he seen without a cigarette in his mouth. He smoked sixty cigarettes, which he often rolled himself, during a working day alone, and on his lab bench there was always to be seen an upturned glass petri dish pressed into use as an ashtray, overflowing with cigarette butts and ash.[23]

By modern twenty-first-century standards his laboratory was primitive in the extreme. He had shared it with his colleague E.W. Todd since his return in 1919 from the First World War, and, though it was small, no more than 12ft by 10ft, the two men had appreciated being able to work with little or no disruption from their colleagues in the larger open-plan laboratory.[24] Fleming sat facing three windows, which covered one entire south-facing wall of the laboratory, giving him a good source of the natural light he needed. If he needed extra light, he used an electric light improvised from a low-powered bulb covered by a cigarette tin with a hole cut in it. He used an old monocular Beck microscope, which was not much use for any photographic purposes. Much of the equipment was either handmade or improvised by Fleming or the laboratory boys. Pipettes and other delicate items of glassware were hand blown and Fleming would often teach the new lab boys the art of glass blowing.[25] Indeed one of Fleming's party tricks for children was to use his glass-blowing skills to make little animals for them. The laboratory would have been cramped enough even without Fleming's craze for hoarding things that might come in useful at some time or other, including string, elastic bands, old cigarette tins and blackened cotton-wool plugs. On the bench was a clutter of oil baths, copper water baths, an opsonisation bath for estimating the activity of leucocytes, hand-drawn pipettes, test tubes plugged with different coloured cotton wools to indicate their contents, conical flasks, culture plates, staining bottles, jars of reagents, Wright's capsules for separating blood cells from serum, medical flats (flat-bottomed flasks) in which bacteria were grown in meat broth, a bench-top incubator, an asbestos Seitz filter and all the other paraphernalia Fleming needed for his experiments. It may have seemed a jumble, but Fleming, who had a remarkably sterile technique as a bacteriologist, knew where to lay his hands on anything he required and he liked everything to be handy on his crowded mahogany work bench. It was only when he went away on holiday that Dan Stratful, his laboratory boy (as the technicians were then called irrespective of age) since 1921, could tidy the bench and completely clean it by wiping it down with a disinfectant.[26]

The laboratory, with its walls half-tiled with plain yellow tiles that were easy to wipe down and that were crowned with a dado of floral-patterned green tiles, was on the second floor of a turret of the Clarence Memorial Wing of St Mary's Hospital and had never been designed to house a laboratory. The wing had been planned in 1892 as a memorial to Queen Victoria's grandson the Duke of Clarence, who had been attended in his last illness by a St Mary's physician, Sir William Broadbent, and nursed by two of the hospital ward sisters. The intention had been to give St Mary's a grand public frontage onto the main thoroughfare of Praed Street, Paddington. The hospital, founded in 1845, had suffered from obscurity in facing a mean back street and it was even claimed that the usually omniscient London taxi drivers could rarely locate it. The foundation stone was laid in a great flurry of publicity by the Prince of Wales on 17 December 1892, and his surviving son, the Duke of York, whose life had been saved from typhoid by the same team from the hospital that had tended the Duke of Clarence in his last illness, became President of the Hospital. Unfortunately, the name of the late Duke of Clarence was not the fundraising draw the hospital had hoped and by 1898, when the basement of the wing was opened as a new Outpatients Department, the money had run out for further building work. Irreverently named the 'amputation stump' by the students, this much truncated building had a roof that was let out as a stand for spectators watching the return of the City Imperial Volunteers from the Boer War in 1900. A bequest of £25,000 on condition that the hospital could find an equivalent amount within six months enabled the building's completion by 1904. The only problem was that the hospital could not afford to open any of the wards until 1907. Sir Almroth Wright, founder of the Inoculation Department in which Fleming worked, had seized the opportunity to expand his own empire by leasing space for laboratories and a research ward in the Clarence Wing using privately raised funds.[27]

Old-fashioned as it was, it was perhaps only in that small, cramped, musty and dusty laboratory that Fleming could have discovered penicillin, or so he himself thought. Years later at the end of the Second World War, when shown around the modern, state-of-the-art Pfizer plant at Brooklyn, Fleming was asked by a journalist what he thought of the laboratory facilities. The expected answer was what marvellous work Fleming could have done with the most sophisticated of facilities compared with what had actually been available to him in 1928 in his old-fashioned laboratory back at St Mary's. However, that was not how he saw it at all: 'I could never have discovered penicillin here. Everything is much too clean and tidy.'[28] His lab boy may not have appreciated this casual dismissal of his best efforts at keeping the laboratory free of the dust and pollution of Paddington, amidst Fleming's clutter, but without the possibility of contamination there would have been no penicillin.

It was not just the physical environment of the laboratory that made Fleming's workplace so conducive to him making the discovery. He had the freedom to pursue something that interested him and, working as an individual in the tradition of the nineteenth-century lone researcher, was able to follow up a chance occurrence in a way denied to the modern researcher tied by the tight deadlines that come with research grants. Fleming himself was very conscious of this advantage and often in later years was to stress that none of his detour to study penicillin would have been possible had he been part of a team, though he admitted that teams rather than one individual were needed for the subsequent development of the drug: 'Suppose, however, I had been part of a team at the beginning and I was being directed on a certain piece of research which I was engaged on, and the accident happened which led to penicillin. In this circumstance I would have chucked the thing away and gone on with my research. Fortunately I was an individual . . . the only way to do it is to give a man a free hand for a portion of his time and let him do as he will.'[29]

It was in connection with an invitation to write a chapter on the staphylococcus group of bacteria for a prestigious nine-volume publication, *A System of Bacteriology*, by the Medical Research Council that Fleming had prepared the culture plates he was working on when he discovered penicillin.[30] He was a recognised authority on this micro-organism, but his detailed prior knowledge did not absolve him from the hard labour of collecting and reading references to the subject and confirming through practical laboratory experiments the observations he wished to make in his paper. Although his mentor and the head of the Inoculation Department at St Mary's in which he worked, Sir Almroth Wright, was firmly of the school that raised reason over observation and believed that 'one observation suffices if properly performed to establish the truth of a principle',[31] Fleming adopted a much more thorough approach to his research, putting careful practical observation above a logic that might perhaps be faulty and lead one astray. He had begun work on his studies of staphylococci for the book in 1927, with the help of Merlin Pryce.[32] His acquaintance Joseph Bigger of Trinity College Dublin had recently done some work correlating the virulence of staphylococci with the variations in the colours of their colonies, which intrigued Fleming and prompted him to repeat the experiments. Bigger and his colleagues had suggested that, if culture plates were left for days and weeks at room temperature rather than incubated overnight at 37°C as usual, the bacterial colonies might change their colour and that such colour changes might indicate their virulence.[33]

However, staphylococcal variation was not Fleming's main concern; it was his curiosity about something that appeared to dissolve bacteria that actually made him look at the plate with interest rather than annoyance, as he himself admitted: 'Now had I been intensely interested in staphylococcal variation and not in antibacterial substances I would have cast out the plate, possibly with suitable language, and carried on with my original programme. However, it was the other way about – I was much more interested in antibacterial substances than I was in staphylococcal variation, so I subcultured the mould and the staphylococcus and proceeded to see why the mould colony should have acted as it did.'[34]

If it was the evidence of lysis or of the bacteria being dissolved that attracted Fleming's initial interest, there is a problem with the exact process by which he made the discovery. Penicillin has no effect upon mature bacteria. However, it does inhibit the growth of developing colonies of microbes. For there to be signs of lysis, the plate must have been contaminated before the staphylococcus was plated or at an early stage of the growth of the bacteria and not after the colonies were mature and exposed to the air, as Fleming had seemed to suppose. Fleming had himself been aware in the 1940s of the difficulties of reproducing his culture plate if mature bacteria were exposed to contamination by the mould. However, it was left to Ronald Hare, who as a research student in the Inoculation Department had been one of the first to be shown the mould, to reproduce the discovery of penicillin in 1966. When Fleming went on holiday at the end of July, space on his bench had been cleared so that his latest research assistant, Stuart Craddock, could work there during his absence. The enamel dish containing the petri dishes awaiting examination had been put to one side but otherwise left undisturbed. The plates were left at normal room temperature for the next month or so. Hare believed that the penicillin plate had never been placed in the incubator, following the methods reported by Bigger. However, very strict environmental conditions were still necessary if there were to be any signs of lysis on the plate. If the temperature had been less than 98.6°F (37°C), the growth of the staphylococci might have been very slow, allowing penicillin from the mould to attack them during growth. If the room temperature had been any higher, the conditions would have been impossible for replicating Fleming's culture plate. At first Hare had thought the very specific conditions necessary for the growth of the mould would have made it impossible to reproduce the plate in summertime. However, Meteorological Office records showed that temperatures were unusually low for nine days after 28 July 1928, with maximum daily temperatures of only 68°F (20°C). Fleming's turret room was also a target for cold winds from the east and south. The conditions for the growth of the penicillium mould were just right and then a heat wave from 10 August on had been conducive to the growth of the bacteria beyond the zone of inhibition.[35]

Another mystery that has exercised the imaginations of young and old ever since the discovery of penicillin is exactly what was the source of the mould that changed the world. In the urge to clarify the matter, journalists came up with some bizarre explanations that could only be immediately discounted. One newspaper claimed that Fleming, cast in the role of the absent-minded scientist, ate a mouldy cheese sandwich that cured a boil on the back of his neck.[36] Rather than cure a boil, it would have been more likely to cause a gastrointestinal upset. The *Evening Standard*, with a total disregard for chronology, reported that there was reason to say 'Thank you, Luftwaffe', claiming that during the bombing of nearby Paddington Station in 1940 the force of the blast had disturbed some cultures, one of which became contaminated by a mould.[37] Since Fleming had not discovered some form of reverse time travel to whisk his contaminated culture back some twelve years to 1928, the weakness of the explanation is only too obvious, although it does reflect the interest there was in finding some easily understandable explanation for the source of the mould. However, the most popular and frequently repeated explanation is that the mould came through an open window from the street outside. The public house opposite, the Fountains Abbey, even lays claim to having been the source of the contaminant, not the best of advertisements for a pub. Fleming himself even supported the idea of the spores having come through the window.[38] The only problem was that the window was rarely opened. As a bacteriologist, Fleming preferred to work in a still atmosphere, and ventilation was supplied by the ever-open door onto the staircase.

If the open window and the street outside were not the source of the mould, where did it come from? This was not a question that gripped Fleming. He was more interested in establishing whether other fungi produced anything similar to penicillin. He collected samples of mould from wherever it could grow – mouldy walls, jam jars, leather,

Wellington boots and even cheese.[39] He also obtained samples from a mycologist, or mould specialist, Charles La Touche, working in the laboratory below his own. La Touche had been appointed by John Freeman, Director of the Allergy Department at St Mary's, to study the effects that fungi could have on asthma. Freeman had attended a lecture at St Thomas's Hospital by the Dutch allergist Storm van Leuwen in which he suggested that some sufferers from asthma had their allergy brought on by moulds growing in the foundations and floorboards of their homes. La Touche's task was to isolate moulds from the homes of asthma patients, identify the mould and make extracts from it that could be used to desensitise the patient. Fleming asked him for help in identifying the mould and for samples he could test to see if they also produced anything similar to penicillin. Only one strain of mould produced penicillin and it was one of those supplied by La Touche, the same strain of *Penicillium notatum* as that which had contaminated Fleming's culture plate, although the mould was misidentified by La Touche as *Penicillium rubrum*. The most likely explanation would be that the spores of mould had entered Fleming's laboratory on someone's clothing or had been airborne.[40] Ronald Hare suggested that the ultimate source of the contaminant may have been the basement of the townhouse of one of Freeman's private patients living in Belgravia, Mayfair or Kensington, but it has also been suggested by A.W. Frankland, who succeeded Freeman as head of the Allergy Department, that the mould may have been among those acquired by La Touche at the start of his work from Professor Harold Raistrick of the London School of Hygiene and Tropical Medicine, a pioneer in the study of fungi.[41]

Chance had undoubtedly played its part in the circumstances of the discovery, but it would be wrong to say that Fleming was merely lucky. His detractors, however, continue to charge him with no more than being in the right place at the right time in their attempts to topple the idol from his pedestal.[42] Fleming himself freely admitted the role that chance had played:

My important part in the story was that I saw something unusual and appreciated something of its importance so that I set to work on it. I have no doubt that the same phenomenon had been presented by accident to other bacteriologists, but they were not interested and so the chance was missed . . . Further than that, if my mind had been occupied with other things I might have missed it; I might have been in a bad temper; my chief might have insisted that it was not worth pursuing this strange path. Then I would probably have thrown away the culture and thought no more about it.[43]

The discovery of penicillin is perhaps the classic case that can be used to illustrate Pasteur's often quoted dictum that chance events favour only the prepared mind.[44] Training as a doctor and twenty years' working experience as a bacteriologist made him receptive to the interesting phenomenon, but it was factors in his own life that made him more likely to grasp its significance. For Fleming this was almost a discovery waiting to happen. It was to lead him down paths that no one could ever have imagined and take him a fair distance from his simple origins.

TWO

Doctor in the Making

'For Pasteur, 1881 was a memorable year; so it was for me, for it was then that I was born,' Alexander Fleming was later to say in his characteristically dry and laconic style.[1] Scientifically, it was an exciting time. Louis Pasteur, that titan of nineteenth-century science whose work had laid the foundations of modern microbiology, had successfully vaccinated sheep against anthrax in June 1881, validating his belief in immunisation.[2] Like immunology, the science of bacteriology, in which Fleming was to make his mark, was in its infancy. Alexander Ogston, a fellow Scot, had just described the bacterium staphylococcus against which Fleming's penicillin was to prove so effective. The work in France of Pasteur and in Berlin of Robert Koch, who was the first scientist to show that a specific disease could be caused by a specific micro-organism, had demonstrated the existence of harmful bacteria and showed how they could cause disease. This led to a search for chemicals that could kill bacteria without doing more harm than good to the patient, a search that was later to attract the attention of Fleming. The work of Joseph Lister on such antiseptics as carbolic acid supported Pasteur's germ theory of infectious disease and laid a basis for modern surgery.[3]

In both community and hospital, death from infection was common, and many people suffered from such bacterial infections as septicaemia, pneumonia and peritonitis. Lobar pneumonia was common and frequently fatal. Tuberculosis killed 65,000 in 1896 in Britain and left many young adults permanent invalids. The sexually transmitted diseases gonorrhoea and syphilis were prevalent. Women died of puerperal sepsis after childbirth. Children were prone to whooping cough, scarlet fever, diphtheria and middle-ear disease, which could cause permanent deafness. Typhoid fever had killed Prince Albert and was to endanger the life of his grandson Prince George, the future King George V. Mortality in hospitals was high, with a quarter of all surgical patients dying from gangrene or mortification of the wound.[4] There were no antibiotics to fight these diseases. Alexander Fleming was destined to play a major part in the conquest of many of these infections, although in 1881 that lay far in the future.

His life, which was to have such an impact on this fight against disease, has often been depicted all too readily as the classic rags to riches story of the humble farm boy made good.[5] It is an attractive story with an enduring appeal, but like many of the myths that have grown up around Fleming it is not true. Like another Ayrshire success story, that of the ploughboy Robert Burns destined to become the Scottish national poet, Fleming's story is much more complex than the modern version of the Dick Whittington myth might suggest.

He was born on 6 August 1881 at Lochfield Farm near Darvel, Ayrshire, the second youngest of the eight children of a hill farmer. Since 1855 his father, Hugh Fleming, had rented the 800-acre farm from the Earl of Loudoun. Sheep farming was the main activity at Lochfield, but there were some 40 or 50 acres of arable land and a small herd of cattle. Life at Lochfield was spartan by modern standards, but the Flemings were as prosperous as any Ayrshire tenant farmers of the time. Tempting as it has been for some authors to write of the poor farm boy who went barefoot to school, the truth is that the Flemings were comfortably situated, if far from wealthy. The sons of the family could be launched onto the first rungs of successful professional or business careers, albeit that small sacrifices had to be made in order to do so. Their home was comfortable if not luxurious. Lochfield was substantially built of immaculately whitewashed stone, with barns and byres forming three sides of a courtyard, and had three bedrooms for the four adults and four children living there in the 1880s. Compared with the two-roomed cottages of some of their neighbours in nearby Darvel, the Flemings had a spacious home.[6]

Hugh Fleming, born in 1816, had been married twice. His first wife, Jane Young, died of pulmonary tuberculosis in 1874 after giving birth to her fourth child, Mary. Her eldest child, Jane, had been born in 1862, followed by Hugh in 1864, Thomas in 1868 and Mary in 1874. Left a widower with four young children to bring up and a farm to run, Hugh Fleming remarried in 1876. His second wife, Grace Morton, born in 1848, daughter of a neighbouring farmer, was to bear him another four children: Grace born in 1877, John in 1879, Alexander (known always to his family as Alec) in 1881 and Robert in 1883. As was common at the time in large families, the eldest daughter, Jane, helped her stepmother to bring up her siblings, some twenty years her junior, until she left home to be married when her youngest brother, Robert, was still a baby. Sadly, she was to die of smallpox within a year of her marriage to Dr Lyon of Darvel. Grace Fleming nursed Jane during her illness, regardless of the risk to herself but characteristic of the strong-willed and generous-minded woman, as concerned about her stepchildren as her own offspring.[7]

Grace Fleming was at the heart of the entire family, praised by her own children and her stepchildren alike as an excellent and cheerful mother, housekeeper and cook. She was practical and ready to join in with her children's fun in the games they loved to invent. Grace Fleming united the children of both marriages as if they were her own, and there were no signs of the friction that could have arisen between them. They seem to have been close to each other, as they were to remain throughout their lives.[8] Alec Fleming himself later said, 'I have to render great thanks to my mother – one of the best women who ever lived – for my upbringing.'[9] A happy upbringing and family life were to form the foundations of Alec's background.

When Alec was 7 his father had a stroke and, after a short period as an invalid, died at the age of 72. Alec and Robert were later to remember their father only as a kindly, grey-haired old man confined to a chair by the fireside.[10] He remained a shadowy figure in the memories of his younger children. Much more important for their upbringing was the partnership between their dynamic mother, Grace, and eldest brother, Hugh, who at the age of 23 had now inherited the tenancy of Lochfield and headship of the household. The second son, Tom, was a medical student at Glasgow when his father died, but was later to assume some responsibility for the care of his younger brothers when they were old enough to leave Darvel to seek their fortunes elsewhere. Until then Hugh was to take on the role of guiding them through their childhood.

Life on the farm was idyllic for the younger children, who were allowed to roam the local moors and hills unfettered by parental worries about their safety. The farmland covered an area approximately 2 miles long from east to west and a mile wide. The eastern boundary, corresponding with the border of Ayrshire and Lanarkshire, was marked by a fence, but the northern boundary was formed by a natural feature, a large bog known locally as Juck's Haggs, which separated Lochfield from neighbouring Overmuir Farm. Three streams crossed the Lochfield land, Glen Water, a tributary of the River Irvine, forming the western boundary, and Calder Burn forming the southern boundary of the Flemings' land. Close to the farmhouse was the Loch Burn. Separating the glens through which these streams ran were Lamb Hill, Rough Hill and Whiteknowe, about 900ft high. Higher hills were to be found to the north of this wild, remote countryside, scattered with the ruins of tiny farmsteads abandoned during eighteenth-century enclosure. The Fleming children were able to roam over this rough terrain in their free time, tobogganing down the peat slopes, bathing in the deep pools and clambering over the waterfalls.

Danger meant nothing to them, nor did such escapades as raiding a neighbour's turnip field on the way home from school.[11]

Alec and Robert were inseparable during their childhood at Lochfield. Robert did not remember Alec ever acting the heavy-handed part of the elder brother, but even as a child Alec was to show a determination to win at competitive games. Keen to prove himself the one who could roll fastest downhill in one of these games, he chose a steep slope ending in a sheer drop to a rock-strewn gully. Watched with fascinated horror by his brothers and sisters, he rolled out of control and came to a stop only on the edge of the drop, merely remarking 'Ah cam doun tha quick.'[12] Such pawky understatements were to remain his trademark, just as a quietly competitive streak was to show itself at times throughout his life.

Hunting and fishing provided many hours of amusement for the boys, when they were not helping with sheep shearing or performing other small chores on the farm. Too young to use guns, they would catch rabbits with their bare hands. The boys noticed that rabbits would stay still in the undergrowth if they thought themselves unseen, and so would play a game with these rabbits by pretending not to notice and then swiftly diving on their unlucky prey. They would also collect plovers' eggs to sell for 4d each to a Darvel grocer, who sold them on to his customers for 5s each. However, one thing they would never consider either as sport or as a source of pocket money was to act as beaters for the game shoots on the estates of the Earl of Loudoun, because they sympathised with the birds during this annual slaughter for sport. They also thought snares and traps to be too cruel to use in their own sporting expeditions. What the boys firmly believed in was giving their quarry a sporting chance. If an activity did not involve some measure of agility and skill, it did not interest them.[13]

Fishing was Alec's favourite sport, because it involved some degree of technical skill and dexterity in the construction of home-made rods with worm-baited hooks, just as there was some skill involved in guddling or tickling the trout to catch them. Manual dexterity was an attribute of the young Alec for which he was to be noted throughout his life. One Sunday morning Alec and Robert went fishing and caught several fine trout. Games and sports of all kinds were frowned upon on the Sabbath in Presbyterian Ayrshire and the boys could not take the fish home without expecting a good telling-off, so they hid them in a pool. The next morning, they went out early and recaught the trout in time to produce them for breakfast, a feat that astonished their mother, who commented on how 'clever and quick' they must have been that morning, although, like the rest of the family, she obviously knew full well what had really happened, but chose to turn a blind eye. Her attitude was generally tolerant so long as the offences were minor and kept well away from where she could be expected to see them. Robert said that 'to tell the truth we could do anything within reason so long as we did it down the Glen out of sight of the house and neighbours'.[14]

Birdwatching became another keen interest of Alec's, surrounded as he was by swallows nesting in the barns and lapwings near the grazing pastures. He soon learned to recognise hawks, golden plovers, curlews, larks and thrushes on the moors, sand martins near the streams, sandpipers, herons and snipe in the marshes, and wild ducks and gulls nesting on Juck's Haggs. Hunting and fishing also encouraged him to observe the behaviour of the local wildlife so that he could anticipate their movements before catching them. Similarly the annual necessity of finding and digging out the sheep buried during severe winter snowstorms demanded some awareness of the signs of where the sheep had found shelter in hollows. Alec Fleming himself was to consider that he had unconsciously learned a great deal about nature that would have been impossible anywhere but on a remote farm. Abilities that he developed in childhood were to serve him in good stead in later life: 'My powers of observation were sharpened by my search for peewits' eggs in the fields and moors, my patience increased by the guddling for the trout in the Glen Water.'[15]

Schooldays began when Alec was 5 and he was sent off to the small village school of some ten pupils in a crofter's cottage at Loudoun Moor, a mile from Lochfield. There was only one schoolmistress, usually a young girl starting out her teaching career and soon progressing to a larger school or giving up teaching for marriage. One of Alec's early teachers at Loudoun Moor School, Marion Stirling, was to write to him from South Africa many years later when he was a household name, congratulating him on his discovery and the honours it had brought him, whom she remembered as 'a dear little boy with dreamy blue eyes'.[16] One neighbour of the Flemings, William Morton, remembered that 'Alex was a fine little chap, fair-haired, blue-eyed with a beautiful smile inherited from a wonderful mother'.[17] Of all the boys, Alec was the one most likely to be found with his head buried in a book or making things with his hands, while both John and Robert preferred to attach themselves to their older brother Hugh.[18] At this small village school lessons were relaxed and fairly informal, around the peat fire in winter and sometimes out of doors by the Glen Water in summer, especially when Lizzie Haddow from nearby Newmilns was the teacher. During one of these open-air lessons the Inspector of Schools from Ayr was observed approaching the school for a snap inspection. Quickly and surreptitiously, pupils and teacher climbed into the schoolroom through a back window to be in their places – albeit breathless – when the Inspector arrived. Such collusion between pupils and teachers, far from destroying any sense of discipline, reinforced the cohesion of the group, as 'Lizzie was one of the family, the inspector was a foreigner from Ayr or some remote and uncultured place'.[19]

The quickest route to the school was over the moors by a rickety plank bridge across the Glen Water, a way often impassable when the river was in flood. In wet weather, the Fleming children would take with them a change of boots and socks slung around their necks, and when it was fine they would go barefoot. This was not, as it has often been depicted, a sign of early hardship and poverty, but was rather a practical measure suitable for healthy, sturdy children. They kept their boots and socks dry for school and, being hardy, the boys came to no harm. In winter the ever-practical Grace Fleming would give her sons two hot potatoes to keep their hands warm during the walk; the potatoes then gave them a warm meal on arrival at school. One winter, the children got lost in a snowstorm, but eventually managed to find their way home.[20] Alec was to attribute his physical stamina to this upbringing and to say that it encouraged him to be observant. In his own opinion, the walk to school was the best education he had for life: 'it was not wasted time because we learned things. You might go up the Glen, you might take a shortcut across the fields and you picked up many interesting things about wild nature that you might not have learned at school.'[21]

There was a limit to what a small moorland school could teach apart from the basic 3 Rs and a little history and geography, despite the legendary excellence of the Scottish education system. Accordingly, at the age of 10 in 1891, Alec was sent to a larger school in the small mill town of Darvel 4 miles away, a school kept by Mrs Fleming's cousin Peter Gorrie. It was at Darvel that Alec acquired his 'boxer's nose'. Running around a corner without, for once, looking where he was going, he bumped into a smaller boy charging in the opposite direction. They collided and Alec's nose was broken.[22] Like his intense blue eyes, it was to be a physical feature much remarked upon in later years.

After two years at school in Darvel, Alec was sent to Kilmarnock Academy in late August 1894.[23] Loudoun Moor and Darvel had given him a good grounding in the basics, but could not go beyond that. The move to Kilmarnock Academy took him away from home for the first time. It was too far from Lochfield for daily commuting and the nearest railway station was at Newmiln, 6 miles from the farm, though a railway line between Kilmarnock and Darvel was in the course of being constructed. During the week he stayed with an aunt, Grace Fleming's sister, in Kilmarnock and returned home from Friday evening to early Sunday morning, walking the 6 miles to and from Newmiln Station. At that time there were 700 day pupils at the school, with class sizes of fifty to sixty pupils. The curriculum at Kilmarnock was comprehensive for a fee of 10s per subject each quarter, averaging £10 a year in total fees: English, Latin, Greek, German, French, history, geography, geology, astronomy, arithmetic, algebra, geometry, trigonometry, mechanics, chemistry, physics, biology, agriculture, domestic economy, bookkeeping and phonography (shorthand). While Kilmarnock Academy was advanced in teaching science at all, mainly through the personal initiative of the headmaster, Dr Dickie, the study of it would appear to have been very basic and primitive and it is doubtful how much actual benefit it was to have for the future scientist.[24] Nor could any of his fellow pupils remember any great desire on the boy's part to know more about science than he was taught.[25] Alec was ahead of his contemporaries by about a year, as he had been at Darvel, but does not appear to have exerted much effort in pursuing his studies. Blessed with a good memory and the critical faculty of getting to the heart of a subject and extracting the salient information, he was able to sail through his lessons in the time he spent at Kilmarnock before leaving his native Ayrshire for a new life in London.[26]

Lochfield could not offer a livelihood to all the Fleming boys, and Hugh, as the eldest son, had been marked out from birth as the one to take over the farm. Farming it until his death at 79 in 1943 and having purchased the freehold in 1921 for £3,750, Hugh always considered himself the luckiest of the brothers to be the one able to stay on at Lochfield, despite the later successes of his siblings in their respective fields.[27] However, for the younger boys, plans had to be made for their futures and it was now the turn of their older brother Thomas to help them make a start in life. After graduating as a doctor from Glasgow University, Thomas had briefly gone into general practice in Wigton, Cumberland, but this had not been a successful venture and his health broke down. After a visit to South Africa to recuperate, he had established himself as an oculist at 144 Marylebone Road in London, and his sister Mary moved to London with him to act as his housekeeper. In 1893, 15-year-old John Fleming joined him and was apprenticed to an optical firm that supplied his practice with spectacle lenses.

Then, in the summer of 1895, Alec too was invited to seek his fortune in London, to be joined six months later by Robert, who was also later to follow John into the optical business. When Mary Fleming married a veterinary surgeon, James Douglas, in 1898, her place was taken by her younger sister Grace. At this time, with his practice thriving, Tom

Fleming moved to a bigger house at 29 York Street and then moved his consulting rooms to 142 Harley Street. When Hugh Fleming got married in 1903, his stepmother Grace Fleming decided to move to London and make a home for her own younger children in Ealing, where she bought a small house. Relieved of the responsibility for his younger brothers, Tom then moved into a smaller flat, but was a frequent visitor at his stepmother's home and continued to be close to the younger boys. Until their schooldays were over, the Fleming brothers would also pass long holidays at Lochfield, which made their exile in London more bearable.[28]

London was an exciting change of tempo for the young Flemings, very different from that of a Scottish hill farm or small country town. The house in which they lived at 144 Marylebone Road would shake each time an underground train passed by. With very little pocket money to spend, Alec and Robert considered a ride on a horse-drawn omnibus a great treat; they liked to sit close to the driver and did not really care where they were going provided they could watch him and listen to his often colourful exchanges with other drivers and jaywalking pedestrians. The thrill of exploring the hidden nooks of the capital helped the boys to overcome any homesickness they might have felt for the hill farm they had left for ever. Robert commented many years later that 'the romantic school might say that the hearts of the boys bled for the heather and they pined away . . . but with so many of us assembled together in one house we wanted to have a good look at London before we pined right away'.[29] Their free time was taken up with visits to all the tourist spots, such as the Tower of London, Westminster Abbey, the British Museum and the Museums at South Kensington. Never very talkative, Alec would point out anything he thought interesting to his younger brother but rarely expanded on what he saw.[30]

Tom Fleming, more extrovert than his younger brother, made sure that the boys had a lively home life and led them in inventing a wealth of new games. History and geography competitions stimulated them with their education, but Tom would also encourage them to play whist, solo bridge and even poker. He also bought one pair of boxing gloves and for several weeks there were one-handed boxing matches between the four brothers until their sister Mary, finding this new craze of Tom's too violent and 'near to disturbing the brotherly co-existence', binned the gloves once and for all.[31]

Their new life in London was not all fun and games. John was already working, while his younger brothers went to school at the Regent Street Polytechnic. Founded by the educational philanthropist Quentin Hogg in 1882 and housed in the former buildings of the

Polytechnic Institute where mid-Victorian audiences had been treated to theatrical demonstrations of such marvels of science as the magic lantern, the Regent Street Polytechnic offered day and evening courses for nominal fees. Anxious to establish himself in practice as an oculist and disillusioned by the rebuffs facing any young professional just setting out in a medical speciality, Tom discouraged his brothers from aiming at a professional career and steered them towards business.[32] Alec was entered into the commercial division of the Polytechnic, which covered most subjects including foreign languages but did not include Latin, then a sine qua non for university matriculation requirements. He was rapidly moved up the school according to ability rather than age and after two weeks there was admitted to the second top form, in which he was the youngest pupil.

When he left school at the age of 16, it was to the world of business that Alec was dispatched. However well meaning Tom's motives may have been, this was a mistake. Alec was not suited to the world of commerce and had no great interest in it. He found a job as a junior shipping clerk in the offices of the American Line in Leadenhall Street. The ships of the American Line, the *St Paul*, *St Louis*, *City of Paris* and *City of New York*, were among the largest and fastest of the Atlantic liners. The work was routine and dull, mainly concerned with the copying of letters and other documents, the entering of accounts into ledgers, the preparation of cargo lists and the booking of the steerage passengers. It may only have paid 2½d an hour, but it was a job with future prospects for any young man wanting to make a career in the City of London. It was one step above the role of office boy and Alec was to prove diligent and capable. The only problem was that he hated the job, which bored him. It was enlivened by occasional visits to other firms to deliver vital documents. He made no lasting friends among his colleagues and sought a more adventurous life with his brothers outside work.[33]

In 1900, at a critical stage in the Boer War, with the British forces in South Africa virtually at the mercy of the Boers and besieged Mafeking, Kimberley and Ladysmith daily expected to fall, Lord Roberts launched a recruiting drive for the territorial regiments for home defence and possible service in South Africa. Nineteen-year-old Alexander Fleming and his older brother John were among the first to answer the call to arms, while Robert Fleming also enlisted as soon as he reached the age of 18.[34] The London Scottish Regiment, which they joined, had had its origins as the Highland Armed Association of London in an earlier national crisis when invasion was expected from Napoleon. It had then re-emerged as the London Scottish Rifle Volunteers during the Crimean War. For Private 6392, Fleming A., it offered an antidote to the boredom of his bitterly hated job as a shipping clerk and gave him an opportunity to show his patriotism. The London Scottish sent three detachments to the Cape but none of the Flemings was posted overseas. Within a year the tide of war turned for the British and it was no longer necessary to draft any further territorial volunteers to the war zone.

More than anything, membership of the London Scottish Regiment gave Fleming the opportunity to socialise in a club-like atmosphere with his fellow Scots, though his brothers were still to remain, as they had been and always would be, his closest friends. The downside of being part of such a close family was that there was little incentive to make deep friendships outside the family circle. Since leaving Ayrshire for London, he had made few new friends, but now for the first time he had the opportunity to mix with young men of the same age and interests. The regimental headquarters in Buckingham Gate offered the social amenities of a gentlemen's club open to all ranks and to young Scots making their way south of the border. As for many expatriates, their sense of identity was sharpened in the English capital, notwithstanding the 1707 Act of Union. The uniform of the regiment was similar to that of the regular Highland regiments, but the kilts worn were of hodden grey to avoid all clan rivalries and unite all the volunteers by their Scottishness in London not by allegiance to any particular tartan. Off duty, officers mixed freely with the other ranks. Indeed the other ranks' mess was preferred to the officers' as a social centre. Among the privates were city clerks, doctors and lawyers, more than happy to exchange their city suits for the swirl of the kilt and the skirling of the bagpipes.[35]

The London Scottish Regiment was to be at the heart of Fleming's social life for the next fourteen years. Part-time military training at the weekends and in the evenings, route marches and summer camps, including one particularly gruelling 60-mile trek in pouring rain from Aberdeen to Blairgowrie in August 1901, as well as off-duty socialising, were to play a major part in his life.[36] Throughout these years, Fleming never rose above the lowly rank of private and nor did he have any higher ambitions for status within the military hierarchy. Rather, he seems to have enjoyed watching others climb the ladder of worldly success by differing means. He was, however, awarded the Territorial Force Efficiency Medal in 1913[37] and, as he himself put it, maintained his immaculate kit 'by bloody hard work'.[38]

H Company, to which all three Flemings were assigned, was not the most distinguished company within the regiment. Fleming himself was later to comment that in his time no one in the other companies had heard of H Company and that it marched so far to the rear of a column of one thousand men that they could never hear the bagpipes and kept in step only by sheer will-power.[39] It was later to be one of the highlights of his 1951 tour of Pakistan and consolation for missing out on the pipe music in his youth that he was able to choose the music to be played by the Pipe Band of the Pakistan Army Medical Corps at a London Scottish reunion at Karachi.[40] Even if not in the foremost company in the regiment, the men of H Company prided themselves on their reputation: that they were 'self-opinionated, egocentric and obeyed no rules but their own'. Such individualism appealed to Fleming and made such men congenial to the taciturn small Scot, well able to hold his own among taller and burlier young men, who adopted him as something of a company mascot. On long train journeys in crowded carriages, his fellow other rankers would hoist him up to the comparative comfort of the luggage rack.[41]

Membership of the London Scottish was to have a crucial bearing on the future career of Fleming. It taught him how to swim and indirectly brought him to St Mary's Hospital, the institution that was to be the field of his labours for the next fifty-four years. He joined the regimental swimming club and was soon a member of the water polo team. Most of the matches they played were scratch affairs and neither Alexander nor Robert Fleming was ever to claim more than moderate prowess. One of their games was against a team from St Mary's Hospital Medical School. Something in the camaraderie and team spirit of the medical students was to impress itself on Fleming and so when the opportunity to study medicine arose it was to St Mary's that he applied. His choice of medical school was partly determined by proximity to his then home in York Place, off Baker Street. This gave him the choice of Middlesex, University College and St Mary's Hospitals. Equally ignorant of the merits or otherwise of all twelve of the London medical schools, Fleming remembered that water polo match and it was that which clinched his choice of St Mary's. It was to be a decision that neither Fleming nor St Mary's was to regret.[42]

It was only after four detested years at the shipping company that Fleming was able to take up the study of medicine. One enduring story in the rags to riches tradition sets out to explain how Fleming was able to make a career switch and study medicine in 1901. The story first appeared in the American press before taking on an enduring life of its own, remaining an attractive one for all believers in the romance of coincidence or anyone who wishes to point out the moral that out of one act of goodness comes future good.[43] In one version of the story old Hugh Fleming saved a nobleman's son from drowning, and in another version it is Alexander himself who saves the boy's life when the two of them are out swimming together. In gratitude the nobleman paid for

Alexander's medical studies. Many years later, it is Fleming's penicillin that again saves the life of the boy, now wartime Prime Minister Winston Churchill. The story is full of improbabilities and has no basis of truth. Churchill was seven years older than Fleming, and the grandson of the Duke of Marlborough was not likely to have had any contact with the son of a Scottish hill farmer. Fleming himself considered it a 'very nice fable'.[44]

The truth is much more prosaic. In 1901, Alec Fleming inherited a legacy of £250 from his Uncle John Fleming of Low Ploughland Farm. This gave him the opportunity he needed to give up his job in the City. Advised by his brother Tom, whose hostility towards the professions had now evaporated with increasing success just as quickly as it had grown through rebuffs and false starts, he decided that the study of medicine would be his most interesting and promising option.[45] However, his lack of Latin, the result of following the commercial course at the Regent Street Polytechnic, was to prove a drawback if he wanted to pass the matriculation examinations necessary for entry to a medical school affiliated to the University of London. Undaunted, he arranged for private coaching in Latin, gained without any problems the Diploma of the College of Preceptors, which was considered an acceptable alternative to the University of London Matriculation examination, and was admitted to St Mary's Hospital Medical School in October 1901. However, his legacy alone was not sufficient to fund his studies and living costs and in 1902 he applied for an entrance scholarship in the natural science examination worth £145, which covered exactly the cost of his fees for his entire course. Without any difficulty he came first in the examination and won his scholarship. The second place went to Charles Aubrey Pannett, whom he first met in the examination room and who was to become a lifelong friend as well as a colleague at St Mary's. Pannett put Fleming's success down to an uncanny ability to predict the questions that the examiners were likely to ask and later commented that he himself had to work much harder to gain second place than had Fleming to come first.

Once again Alec Fleming was to prove himself an outstanding and talented student. Throughout his life he gave the impression that things came easily to him. His early academic success was not achieved by poring over textbooks and notes in all his waking hours, as he always preferred to take part in the family games in the evenings instead of intensive study. He did work diligently, but gave the impression that he did not need to do so. What he did possess was the ability to skim through the pages of a textbook and take in the salient points as he went along. His brother Robert believed that he had a selective and

penetrating mind, which could arrange facts logically and in a structured
fashion that could be easily memorised.[46] He did not have the
photographic memory that some people imputed to him. In writing, as in
speech, he was brief, concise, clear and went straight to the point. These
qualities brought him success in his medical school examinations and
were to be repeated when he came to write professional scientific papers.

At 20, he was two years older than most of his fellow medical
students, who had come to medicine straight from school, but
experience of life outside medicine was to make him a more rounded
doctor. It was not so long since his own education had ended that he
was unable to settle down to study once more and he buckled down to
work without any fuss. He was one of forty-eight new students to enter
St Mary's Hospital in 1901. Of these, 12 had been born in London, 27
elsewhere in the British Isles and 9 came from various parts of the
British Empire.[47] As well as Charles Pannett, who became a
distinguished surgeon, some of the other students who entered with
Fleming were to go on to distinction and be future colleagues. Charles
Wilson was to become Dean of St Mary's in 1920, President of the
Royal College of Surgeons and become best known as Winston
Churchill's physician. Leonard Colebrook was to make his name for his
use of the drug sulphanilamide in the 1930s for the treatment of
infections in childbirth. E.H. Kettle was to become Professor of
Pathology at St Mary's and win an international reputation for his work
on silicosis, which was the scourge of coal miners. As for Fleming, like
Kettle destined to become a Fellow of the Royal Society, little could he
have known that St Mary's was to be the centre of his working life for
the next fifty-four years.

St Mary's Hospital was the youngest of the twelve teaching hospitals
in London. It had been founded in 1845 to meet a need for a medical
facility for the deserving sick poor of the rapidly expanding west and
north-west areas of London. As a voluntary hospital dependent upon the
annual subscriptions of its supporters, upon donations and legacies in
order to survive, it to some extent enjoyed a precarious hand-to-mouth
existence. Indeed its original buildings had been completed only because
a local builder had deferred his bill until the hospital could afford to pay
him, following a catalogue of disasters in which one builder had died,
another had gone bankrupt and the committee overseeing the foundation
of the new hospital had run out of money. Ambitious plans and lack of
money to accomplish them were to be a *leitmotiv* of the new hospital. It
was also all too conscious of its junior status among the other London
teaching hospitals and strove to give simultaneously an air of modernity
and of venerability to add to its dignity. While depicting itself as up to

date and in the forefront of modern medical advance, starting with the appointment of the first ear, nose and throat specialist in the country to have beds in a general hospital, St Mary's also adopted as its emblem a curiously medieval-style crest depicting the Virgin and Child. Such cod-medievalism put it alongside genuinely medieval foundations such as St Bartholomew's and St Thomas's Hospitals.

The hospital also prided itself on having been founded as a teaching hospital from the beginning, unlike other institutions that had only later acquired medical schools. The first two students had been admitted to walk the wards in the traditional fashion when the hospital opened in 1851, while in 1854 a purpose-built medical school was established. The hospital had been built by the architect Thomas Hopper in the style of a grand country house, giving it an imposing entrance hall but inadequate wards, ward kitchens and sluices.[48] The medical school buildings have justly been compared to the stable block of a mansion. Edmund Owen, a student at St Mary's in the 1860s and subsequently a surgeon there from 1872 until 1902, described it as being 'hidden away in the space between the Hospital, the Great Western terminus and the canal . . . as difficult to find as Meckel's ganglion'.[49] David Carmalt-Jones, a contemporary of Fleming as a student, described the hospital in his time as 'a gloomy place . . . quite without any aesthetic attractions' and was even more scathing about the medical school, which 'was worse, shabby, squalid rooms, ill-lighted and coarsely furnished'.[50]

It was a rough-and-ready masculine world that Fleming entered, but it was one that was congenial and to some extent familiar to the private in the London Scottish regiment. There was an emphasis on sport, especially the rugby for which St Mary's was to be renowned, and on gamesmanship, which would have appealed to Fleming. Although not a rugby player himself, Fleming followed the fortunes of the hospital team, while he himself took part in the activities of the swimming and rifle clubs. Pannett commented that, although he had not himself been a member of the same clubs as Fleming, it was there that 'he revealed his true nature at these times. He seems to have excelled in any game or sport he took up. I don't mean that he reached the front rank, but that he always became proficient in the essentials, and so was more than an averagely good proponent.'[51] He also took part, when a houseman, in the Christmas play in December 1908 when he played Fabriquette, a sprightly French widow, in a production of Pinero's *Rocket*, a performance in which he made his character 'considerably more attractive than that unprincipled female deserved'.[52] His small stature, fresh complexion and rather delicate features at this time made his casting inevitable.

His first two years were spent in the laboratories and classrooms of the medical school without any direct contact with patients in the hospital. There he studied chemistry, physics and biology, sitting for his University of London matriculation, before going on to the study of physiology, histology, pharmacology and anatomy.[53] The idea was that the student should gain a grounding in basic sciences and an understanding of the human body before having any contact with living patients. In the latter half of the nineteenth century, the study of medicine was increasingly becoming scientific and theoretical in its basis, whereas earlier much of it had been based on experience. A student was now expected to understand both the causes and the effects of disease. He was expected to know how to employ the technology used in diagnosis such as the microscope and petri dish. He needed to understand how to evaluate the action of the drugs he would be prescribing in the future. Despite this new emphasis on scientific understanding, in practice much of the work still involved rote learning of parts of the human body. Students were encouraged to spend the maximum amount of time in the dissecting room, which required a strong stomach. Each student would pay a fee for use of the body assigned to him for the year. Many students would smoke heavily during their sessions in the dissecting room, the fumes of tobacco helping to disguise the stench of the arrayed ranks of corpses. If they could not gain experience of the living patient, they soon became well acquainted with the dead.

Most of the teaching was carried out on a part-time basis by members of the hospital honorary staff. Traditionally anatomy was taught by a practising surgeon. Fleming's anatomy teacher was James Lane, a man renowned for the dullness of his lectures, which consisted of little more than an hour-long recitation from memory of the relevant pages of *Gray's Anatomy*.[54] Fleming does not appear to have had any great problems with this pedestrian approach, nor with mastering the vast corpus of facts and figures about every bone, muscle, tendon, ligament, nerve, blood vessel and organ in the human body. He mastered the textbooks with their Latin names for the body parts, observed them in practical sessions in the dissecting room and carried off both the Anatomy Prize in 1902 and the Senior Anatomy Prize in 1904.[55] He also became a prosector, or junior demonstrator, in anatomy.[56] Such prowess may have encouraged an early inclination towards surgery.

Much more stimulating than Lane's anatomy lectures was the study of physiology, which required a more logical approach compared with the mechanical, repetitious demands of anatomical studies. The lecturer in physiology was one of the unsung heroes of medicine. Unlike

Fleming, who gained full credit for his initial discovery of penicillin, Augustus Desirée Waller was to be one of the forgotten men of medical advance. Lecturer in physiology at St Mary's since 1884, Waller had discovered the electrical reactions of the human heart in 1887. This discovery was later developed into the electrocardiogram by Willem Einthoven, who was awarded a Nobel Prize for the work. Everyone today is familiar with the electrocardiograph, but very few people have heard of Waller. Unlike Lane, he was a full-time research scientist and a Fellow of the Royal Society. Fleming responded well to this inspiring teacher and was awarded the 1902 Physiology Prize.[57]

Yet another prize that he walked off with in these first two pre-clinical years was the Histology Prize.[58] The study of the minute structure of the different tissues and organs involved the cutting of sections of the tissue being studied. These were then smeared onto microscope slides and stained with different coloured dyes so that they could be better examined under a microscope. Students were expected to purchase their own microscopes, as well as textbooks and dissecting equipment. Fleming obviously treasured the microscope he used as a student and kept it for many years until he gave it to one of his own students.[59]

Biology was taught by W.G. Ridewood, a zoologist and Director of the Natural History Department of the British Museum. The lecturer in chemistry was a young physician, William Willcox, who was in later years to cut such a dash as an authority on the use of poisons in the medico-legal world in such notorious murders as the Crippen case that he came to be nicknamed the 'King's Poisoner'. As part of the study of chemical physiology, Fleming learned about the chemical basis to respiration, digestion and muscle contraction. In physics, he was taught about heat, light, mechanics and sound. There was also mention of electricity and the new scientific curiosity of X-rays. Discovered by Röntgen in 1895, within a year they were first used at St Mary's in 1896 when A.P. Laurie, who was then lecturer in chemistry, took an X-ray photograph of a patient's bladder.[60] While it was not until 1913 that the hospital established an X-ray department, it was quick in being receptive to new ideas at a time of great change in medical knowledge.

The expansion in the bounds of science teaching in pre-clinical medicine meant that medical schools such as St Mary's had constantly to update both curriculum and facilities. New laboratories for pathology and practical pharmacy were constructed three years before Fleming entered the school to cater for the increasing emphasis on the scientific basis of medicine, while a new chemical pathology laboratory was actually opened in the year of his entry.[61] Such facilities were necessary if a medical school was to keep up to date with the demands of a modern medical education and offer the students the knowledge and skills that were increasingly demanded of them. However, it all came at a cost, and the beginning of the twentieth century saw St Mary's faced with a financial crisis that for a time threatened the school with closure. It had arisen as the result of a period of over-ambitious expansion spearheaded by the then Dean, George Field, between 1883 and 1899. Not only were existing laboratories updated and new ones established, but also a residential college was set up and there were grandiose schemes to put up a new public frontage for the hospital by building the Clarence Memorial Wing. By the time of Field's resignation as dean in 1899 the financial outlook of the school was bleak. The costs of medical education were rising but not the income of the school, while the residential college was draining resources. Closure of the college could not avert the crisis and the Board of Management of the hospital instigated an inquiry into the financial situation of the school. Only narrowly was it saved in Fleming's first year as a student.[62]

He had won prizes in anatomy, physiology and histology together with the Junior General Proficiency Prize for the best all-round student of his year, and it only remained for Fleming to cap his pre-clinical years by sweeping the board with the Pharmacology and Organic Chemistry Prizes for 1904.[63] He then sat the Intermediate Bachelor of Medicine (MB) examination of the University of London in July 1904. As might be expected, he passed effortlessly, with distinctions in physiology and pharmacology.

Now came a new phase in Fleming's medical education. He entered the wards of the hospital as a clinical student, at last let loose on the patients. Whereas pre-clinical teaching used comparatively up-to-date facilities and new ideas and knowledge, clinical medicine was still taught in ways that would have been familiar to a student entering St Mary's fifty years earlier. It was a vestige of the old apprentice system where students would attach themselves to a hospital consultant and walk the wards. In 1904, clinical students learned from attachment to the firms, teams of doctors led by a member of the honorary staff. These firms formed an entourage for the physician or surgeon, who would visit patients on the wards or clinics attended by registrars, house officers and several students, dispensing wisdom and patronage in equal measure. Over the three clinical years, the student would be attached to a number of different firms in order to gain practical experience of all branches of medicine, learning at the feet of a number of masters. What was taught was not always consistent. Fleming was attached for a time to the firm of Dr David Lees, who treated pneumonia with ice packs as he firmly believed that the cold discouraged the growth of the bacterium pneumococcus, which caused the infection. One of his patients had lobar pneumonia of the left lung and was prescribed the usual ice-pack treatment. Lees then went on holiday and in his absence the patient developed pneumonia of the right lung. The physician who had temporarily taken over Lees's case load was a firm adherent of the more generally accepted view that the application of a hot poultice was a more effective treatment and prescribed accordingly. The result was extreme discomfort for the patient who had ice packs on the left side of his chest and hot poultices on the right.[64] It never occurred to anyone that these two courses of treatment might be contradictory, nor to challenge the Olympian decision of a consultant once it had been made.

Ward rounds were conducted with great ceremony. The surgeon or physician was met at the entrance of the hospital by his houseman. On entering the ward, he was greeted by the ward sister, who conducted him to each of his patients. Behind them walked a probationer nurse carrying a chair for the great man to sit on; many consultants were so confident of the chair being in the right position that they did not deign to look behind them before sitting. There at the bedside of the patients, the senior clinician would demonstrate the mantra of diagnosis by 'inspection, palpation, auscultation and percussion'. Then the students themselves would prod, probe and feel the patient to observe what their teacher had told them to expect. It was an initiation into the medical mysteries closed to the layman, and, as they were the recipients of a charity, the patients were not in a position to complain. Students were also taught how to question patients and take their case history, which helped with diagnosis. As well as this clerking of patients, students were expected to make themselves useful and gain practical experience of such minor procedures as lancing boils, draining abscesses, stitching up cuts, dressing wounds, extracting teeth, inserting catheters and treating minor fractures.

It was not only from these part-time consultants that these fledgling doctors learned their trade. Much closer to them in age were the junior medical staff, resident in the hospital and on whom much of the routine work fell. Generally these were young, ambitious men climbing the ladder of professional progression at a time when most of the consultants at a teaching hospital had been former students, house officers and registrars in that one institution. There may have been something incestuous about such a system, and indeed several generations of the same family were elected to positions on the staff of St Mary's, but it did encourage group solidarity. Equally loyal to their hospital was the nursing staff, and in the absence of medical supervision the students often learned a great deal from the ward sisters. Indeed one departmental sister, known throughout St Mary's as 'Granny Casualty', claimed to have trained all the surgeons in the hospital in her long reign over the Casualty Department. Fleming was one among many who had come under the wing of this larger-than-life character, who left any cases she considered 'not quite nice' to innocent young student nurses and refused admission to Casualty to anyone she considered to be malingering and in search of a free bed or merely inebriated.[65]

Contact with the seedy and seamy side of Paddington was not confined to Casualty. Students often had a profound culture shock when they were sent out to the slums of Paddington to gain experience of obstetrics. The dangers of cross-infection and of puerperal sepsis meant that few acute hospitals had maternity wards. St Mary's established a labour ward only in 1920. While there were some specialist maternity hospitals such as Queen Charlotte's Hospital, which was then located on the Marylebone Road not all that far from St Mary's, most babies were born at home.[66] However, medical students were expected to deliver a certain number of babies as part of their obligatory obstetrics training. They were sent out to the 'maternity district' served by the hospital and thus saw the environments from which many of their patients came.

Once again, Fleming continued to scoop up most of the prizes available to clinical students at St Mary's, including the Pathology, Medicine, Medical Jurisprudence, Second General Proficiency, Third General Proficiency and Psychological Medicine Prizes.[67] At this stage he was considering specialising in surgery, although his brother Robert considered that temperamentally he was not altogether cut out for it. Nevertheless, surgery did have a certain amount of glamour attached to it that was lacking in the career of a physician. Surgery was active and allowed for interventional treatment, whereas medicine at the beginning of the twentieth century was very much a case of allowing the disease to take its course in the absence of effective therapies. Moreover, Fleming had a sound and detailed knowledge of anatomy, while he was even as a student noted for his manual dexterity. It was natural that he should take the Primary Examination for the Fellowship of the Royal College of Surgeons in January 1906, and equally natural that he should once more pass with flying colours.

Although there was no limit on how long it took a student to qualify as a doctor, provided he paid his fees promptly, and some took as long as thirteen years to qualify if indeed they ever did, Fleming was ready after the minimum five years of study to sit his final examinations and begin his career as a doctor. Although he was registered for the University of London qualification and had already passed his first MB, he chose to sit for the Conjoint Board examinations of the Royal

College of Physicians and Surgeons in July 1906. This was considered an easier route to qualification and many students who entered for the University of London course ended up with the Conjoint Board, either because they were not academically able to pass the more rigorous university examinations or because, for financial or personal reasons, they wished to qualify as soon as possible. Sitting the Conjoint Board examinations was also insurance against failure in the London examinations and gave the student time for further study once qualified. Fleming's record of academic success could have given no one any doubt about his ability. Once more he sailed through his examination papers, practical examinations and viva voces to emerge with the letters MRCS, LRCP after his name that gave him the status of a qualified doctor.

Such a record of unqualified academic success did not stop Fleming from being popular. Rather it made him an object of interest to younger students, who looked up to him as an exemplar and role model rather than the focus of envy. G.W.B. James, who entered St Mary's in 1907, in particular was an admirer: 'he seemed to us in our time a model of success and I recall discussions on his career among the students of my year.' His intravenous injections, which were then a new and memorable procedure, in particular elicited admiration, as did his participation in the sporting and social life of the hospital and medical school.[68]

If it was his interest in the sport of water polo that swayed Fleming's decision to study medicine at St Mary's, it was another sporting activity that brought him into the bacteriology laboratories and the field in which he was to make a major impact. The choices facing a young, newly qualified doctor at that time were usually confined to going straight into general practice or seeking a highly prized house job at the teaching hospital at which he had studied. Both choices required money. It was not cheap to buy into general practice, while house jobs were unpaid, though they did offer free board and lodging. Fleming was not wealthy and needed to earn a living as well as secure financial support for the further period of study necessary for his University of London degree, which offered greater choice for his future career path than the Conjoint Board qualification he already possessed. There were some paid positions in the Poor Law infirmaries, though they tended to be looked down upon by the medical profession for the very reason that they were salaried. There was, however, at least one person keen to keep Fleming at St Mary's. John Freeman was a doctor working in the Inoculation Department of the hospital and also a keen member of the St Mary's Hospital rifle club. Anxious that the club should not lose such a first-rate shot as Fleming, he was keen to make sure that he remained at the hospital and, above all, that he did not go elsewhere and join a rival hospital team. The team had won the Hospitals Cup in 1905 and there was a chance of success in the Armitage Cup at Bisley, which the loss of Fleming might well jeopardise. Luckily for Freeman, there happened to be a salaried vacancy for a junior assistant in the very department in which he himself worked and he managed to persuade his chief, Almroth Wright, to offer it to the young Scotsman. Fleming also had to be persuaded that a temporary job as a bacteriologist in the Inoculation Department would be a good place to watch out for any suitable surgical opportunities.[69]

Over the next two years Fleming continued his studies and in May 1908 sat for his MB, BS examinations. He was awarded the University of London Gold Medal as top medical student in the university.[70] It was a valued achievement but not the only one to come his way in 1908. In later years, Fleming was to say that among his many honours one of the most prized was to have been a member of the victorious *Daily Telegraph* Cup team competing for the London Scottish Regiment at Bisley in 1908.[71] Before that shooting competition there was a forced march of 12 miles from Weybridge to Bisley on a very hot day. Other teams, including the Life Guards, fell by the wayside. The London Scottish was the only team to arrive complete and on time. The following Monday Fleming was examined for his final Bachelor of Medicine examination and was asked a question on the relative humidity of air and its effects on human exertions. Claiming to know very little on the subject, Fleming cannily told his examiners the story of Saturday's march and compared the kilt with trousers as a comfortable and effective marching uniform. He got honours in that subject, and four others, but his characteristic comment when recounting the tale in 1942 was that 'perhaps the examiner was a Scotsman'.[72] Still intensely conscious and proud of his Scottish origins, Fleming was now ready to enter on a professional career that was to make him a household name.

THREE

Republic of Science

It was without any great enthusiasm that Fleming had begun his duties in the Inoculation Department in the summer of 1906. His professional goal was still to become a surgeon, yet he was to become so engrossed in his new sphere of work that not only was he inspired to change his career plans but he was to remain a member of that department for the next forty-nine years.

Almroth Wright, head of the Inoculation Department, a brilliant and inspirational figure who brought an intellectual excitement to St Mary's,[1] liked to see his laboratory as a republic, in which everyone was equal and debate was conducted in a democratic spirit, 'as all the world ought to be'.[2] What he in fact presided over was a benevolent dictatorship in which the cardinal sin was opposition to the Old Man's most cherished ideas. Aged 45 in 1906, he was at the height of his career with a worldwide reputation as a pioneer in the war against infection. His eminence was recognised by official government circles and within the scientific world with a knighthood and election as a Fellow of the Royal Society in the same year that Fleming joined his department. As a mentor to the younger man, he was to become perhaps the most important scientific influence and inspiration on the fledgling bacteriologist, although this had not been inevitable. Fleming had first come into contact with Wright as a medical student when he had attended his lectures. Although, like most of his contemporaries, he had been enthralled by the virtuosity of these lectures, Fleming had retained a healthy scepticism, which enabled him to see beneath the eloquence and enthusiasm with which they were delivered. While interested in the ideas expressed, he realised that much of what he heard was little more than airy generalisations whereas what he himself demanded was facts to support the ideas.[3]

Working more closely with Wright, even the more down to earth and empirically minded Scot was not immune to the infectious enthusiasm that pervaded the laboratory and the conviction that they were about to effect a revolution in medical science. Already impressed by Wright as a teacher, Fleming became one of his loyal disciples. In 1909 *St Mary's Hospital Gazette*, the monthly magazine of the hospital and medical school, wrote that 'Mr Fleming, who recently was bracketed for the Gold Medal at the MB, BS and who seems to have merely taken the Fellowship in his stride, is one of Sir Almroth Wright's most enthusiastic followers and we see great distinction in store for him in the future'.[4] It was a prescient remark, in terms of both Fleming's future achievements and his continuing loyalty to the chief who was so often to overshadow him.

Wright was a charismatic if irascible figure able to inspire either loyalty or loathing among the many who came within his sphere of influence. His abrasive personality and contentious opinions did not make him universally popular with his professional colleagues, who derided him as the Praed Street Philosopher, the Paddington Plato, Sir Almost Right and Sir Always Wrong.[5] He in turn prided himself that 'I make it a principle never to write anything that won't give offence to someone'.[6] When giving evidence before a military tribunal, he told the president: 'I have given you the facts, I can't give you the brains.'[7] He warned his colleagues at St Mary's that 'unless the physicians of the future soon learn to do something, they will be relegated to little better than head nurse', to the delight of medical students, including Fleming, attending a meeting of the St Mary's Hospital Medical Society.[8] These views were expanded in newspaper articles arguing that 'after food and shelter, the most urgent need in a civilised community is for medical research', coupled with condemnation of the wealthy, fashionable, complacent and ineffective doctors of Harley Street.[9] It was little wonder that he was unpopular within his own profession, but he did enjoy the devotion of his followers. John Freeman believed that 'his personality seemed like a draught of wine to the young men of that day: his freedom of thought, freedom of manner and freedom of language, while distasteful to the more orthodox elders, was a heady but stimulating brew for us youngsters'.[10]

His appearance alone was overwhelming. Tall, ungainly and bulky, with rounded shoulders from stooping over a laboratory bench, he had the heavy and clumsy movements of a bear, yet was surprisingly deft and precise in performing delicate laboratory procedures. William Bulloch, a pathologist at the London Hospital in Whitechapel and a close friend of Wright's, described him as being 'within a narrow shade of being acromegalic'. One of his protagonists, Major Greenwood, compared his face to that of the lion 'blinking lazily at Alice' as depicted by John Tenniel in his illustrations for *Through the Looking Glass*.[11] Above his sandy moustache and steel-rimmed spectacles, his expressive eyebrows indicated his various emotions. With the sick and suffering he could be gentle and patient, whereas with his colleagues he was capable of utter brutality. Physically, he was made for acrimony and his career had never been free from controversy.

Born in 1861, the son of an Irish curate and of the daughter of a Swedish professor of organic chemistry, Almroth Wright had shown an independence of spirit from early childhood. The only person he was ever afraid of was his mother and she had confessed that Almroth was one of her failures, as she could never make him do what she wanted if he was intent on going his own way.[12] His early career path was erratic and unconventional, veering from the humanities to the sciences and back again. He graduated from Trinity College Dublin in 1882 with first-class honours, having studied modern languages and literature. Concurrently with his literature studies, he read medicine and qualified in 1883. A scholarship to study at Leipzig for a year brought him into contact with German medical research at a time when advances were being made in methods of clinical investigation in pathology and physiology. Then he had switched from medicine to law, before turning his attention once again to medical research. Working as a civil servant at the Admiralty by day, he spent the early mornings and evenings studying blood coagulation at the Brown Animal Sanatory Institute, unpaid work which brought him the offer of a paid post at Cambridge as demonstrator in pathology in 1887. The University of Cambridge was not the most congenial environment for Wright, mainly because no one there shared his personal estimation of his own abilities, and in 1888 he seized the opportunity of a Grocers' Company Scholarship to study at Marburg and Strasbourg. Then, newly married, he accepted a post as demonstrator in physiology at the University of Sydney only to return jobless to London in 1891 after two years in Australia.[13]

By now Wright had definitely settled on a career in medical research, but opportunities for salaried appointments in the field were limited. Yet he was appointed Professor of Pathology at the Army Medical School at Netley, overlooking Southampton Water, in 1892.[14] A civilian with little experience as yet in the field of pathology, Wright at 31 was younger than many of the army officers passed over for the post, causing inevitable resentment, which was to fan the hostility towards his ideas. During his decade at Netley, Wright's popularity with the army medical establishment did not increase, although his work there was to bring him professional success and acclaim. Cholera, typhoid, typhus and dysentery were of pressing concern to the British Army, as well as the pathology of wound infections, since the lives of more soldiers in war were lost from infection than from direct enemy action. In treating wound infection, army medical officers had an almost unshakeable faith in the therapeutic value of chemical antiseptics, an approach that Wright abhorred and was to wage a lifelong fight against, later ably assisted by Fleming. Enjoying minimal teaching obligations, Wright was able to spend most of his time on pathological research at Netley, becoming increasingly interested in bacteriology, which he had had to teach himself in order to lecture on the subject to his students.

Perhaps his first important advance in bacteriology was to develop a reliable diagnostic test for Malta Fever.[15] However, Wright was not content with mere diagnosis, but was intent on finding a vaccine that would offer protection against this prolonged, relapsing illness. When he tried this vaccine out on himself and then tested his immunity against the infection by injecting live organisms, he went down with Malta Fever. His illness did not discourage his faith in the principle of vaccination, although he did not pursue his work on this particular disease, turning instead to the problem of producing a vaccine against typhoid fever. However, there were even greater dangers in injecting a human being with this virulent organism, in however attenuated a form, since it had a mortality rate of 20 per cent and was killing some 5,000 a year in Britain and 35,000 in the United States.[16] Yet he had the courage to develop a heat-killed vaccine, which he tested on himself and on sixteen trainee army medical officers.[17] More extended clinical trials following an outbreak of typhoid at the Maidstone Insane Asylum in 1897 and with the Indian Army in 1898 were encouraging but too sketchy and incomplete to confirm conclusively Wright's faith in his vaccine.[18] It was the outbreak of the Boer War that gave him the opportunity to test the vaccine in wartime conditions. It was offered to volunteers, but there was a less enthusiastic take-up of the inoculation on offer than Wright had expected and many frontline medical officers believed that inoculation had actually caused the fever in the first place.[19] Concern about the severity of the initial reaction to inoculation, which could leave a soldier unfit for duty for several days, was enough to provoke military hostility, and in some cases supplies of vaccine were actually dumped over the sides of the troopships leaving Southampton Water within sight of Wright at Netley.[20] The result was that only 14,000 out of 330,000 troops were inoculated, too small a number for accurate statistical analysis of the results of using the vaccine.[21]

Wright, never a great believer in statistics, was himself an advocate of compulsory anti-typhoid vaccination of troops, but this only played into the hands of his enemies in the military hierarchy. David Bruce, discoverer of the cause of Malta Fever and one of the disappointed candidates for Wright's post at Netley, was particularly hostile to inoculation and persuaded an army board advising the War Office on scientific issues to recommend that voluntary inoculation be suspended in 1902.[22] Moreover, Wright's methods of analysis were attacked by the statistician Karl Pearson.[23] In the long term his views were to be triumphantly vindicated and compulsory anti-typhoid vaccine was to be a life-saver during the First World War. However, the struggle to gain official recognition of the value of vaccination was to take up most of his energies until 1914 even after he had left Netley for St Mary's. The spice of controversy may have rallied Wright's younger disciples, including Fleming, around him, but it was to create enemies in the army medical hierarchy who would later seek revenge in attacking the work Wright and Fleming undertook on wound infection during the First World War.

Wright's position at Netley was not comfortable and he was in dispute with the army authorities over their hostility to his anti-typhoid vaccine, which despite his grand ambitions was perhaps his most lasting achievement. Fortuitously, St Mary's Hospital advertised two vacancies for a pathologist and a bacteriologist, and Wright applied for, and was appointed to, both positions. The combined annual salary of £400 was £200 less than he earned at Netley, while the laboratory facilities were of the most basic, but, seeking greater freedom and independence to further the cause of medical research unshackled by the bureaucracy of Netley, he was eager to accept. St Mary's was equally anxious to appoint so distinguished a figure, considering that 'it will be invaluable to the Hospital to obtain the services of so skilled a pathologist and to the best interests of the Medical School to add to its teaching staff so eminent a scientific investigator and so able a teacher'.[24]

St Mary's offered Wright the perfect opportunity to develop his big idea, which he had started work on while still at Netley, that he could effect a revolution in medicine through what came to be known as vaccine therapy, the use of inoculation to treat disease as well as prevent it. Such therapeutic vaccination had advantages over prophylactic inoculation in that it was a more direct and immediate way of waging bacteriological warfare and its results could be expected to be more immediate. If he could apply these ideas in a general hospital, then there was a chance that he could prove his ideas to a sceptical medical profession and make a difference in the fight against illness.[25]

He lost no time in developing a new theory of bactericidal action in the blood performed by a new substance that Wright called an opsonin. Discovery of opsonins allowed him to reconcile two different theories of immunity that were prevalent at the turn of the twentieth century, the cellular and humoral theories, burning issues of the day, keenly followed by the young Fleming. The cellular theory was based on the work of the Russian zoologist Elie Metchnikoff. In 1883 he had demonstrated the way in which the white blood cells or leucocytes swallowed bacteria, a process he termed phagocytosis.[26] He likened these white blood cells to an army fighting infection. While this cellular theory of immunity was taken up by the French scientific community with the approbation of Louis Pasteur, it met with strong opposition from German researchers such as Robert Koch, Emil Adolf von Behring and Paul Ehrlich, who argued that rather than being waged by the white blood cells it was in the blood serum that the battle was actually fought. This humoral theory, so called because it involved the body fluids or humours, was based on the observation that blood serum taken from patients who had recovered from, or who had been inoculated against, a particular infection could kill those bacteria within a test tube, even though the serum had been separated out from the red and white blood cells. The blood serum, in which antitoxins were formed in reaction to toxins, thus had a bactericidal power. Koch went so far as to suggest that the leucocytes were in fact a fifth column through which germs spread through an organism.[27] National rivalries ranged these opposing theories against each other just as there had been tension in Franco-German relations since the Franco-Prussian War.

It was left to Wright, who maintained contact with currents of thought on the Continent, to resolve the debate about the role of the components of the blood. He observed that, while the blood serum could produce antitoxins, it had no bactericidal effect on staphylococcus or plague, whereas the leucocytes did ingest these particular bacteria, which seemed to support the cellular approach. However, he also noticed that the leucocytes alone were not so effective unless combined with blood serum, which suggested to him that the serum did actually have a role to play in facilitating the bactericidal power of the leucocytes, as in the humoral theory. Loving to coin new words and to display his vast knowledge by doing so, Wright gave the name opsonin to the elements in the blood serum that produced this effect, from the Greek word *opsono* meaning 'I prepare victuals'.[28] According to Wright, the opsonins coated the surface of the bacteria in such a way as to make them more digestible to the leucocytes, what George Bernard Shaw was to describe as 'butter' for the phagocytes.[29]

The discovery of opsonins provided Wright with a practical means of assessing the action of his vaccines in boosting immunity by charting *in vitro* changes in the patient's defence mechanism. Microbes would be mixed with serum taken from the patient so that they could be coated with opsonins. The mixture was then added to the leucocytes in a pipette. The average number of microbes swallowed by the leucocyte was then calculated, and the process was repeated using normal serum instead of the patient's blood serum. The resultant

Opsonic Index was a mathematical ratio of the two averages, denoting the presence of specific opsonins capable of enhancing the ability of the leucocytes to engulf specific bacteria. Wright argued that vaccination was necessary to increase the production of opsonins and so fully to stimulate the body's immune system against the infection, whereas his opponents believed that to inject more of the same organism that had already caused an infection would be useless if not positively harmful. It was easy for Wright to ignore such criticism coming from those he deemed ignorant of the finer points of his methods. He had found that there was a natural swing in the Opsonic Index of a patient and concluded that vaccination would be effective only at the peak of the natural cycle. Similarly, he found that the Opsonic Index varied according to whether the patient was at rest or in motion and concluded that movement helped to circulate the bacteria and leucocytes through the body system.[30] Skilled and experienced pathologists were essential for the successful application of vaccine therapy. It was a labour- and time-intensive process and its results on patients were inconclusive, yet Fleming and his colleagues were to work enthusiastically through the night on these tests, for which they had more faith than evidence-based proof. It was a faith that Fleming never entirely lost, even after penicillin had relegated vaccine therapy to little more than a cul-de-sac in the history of medicine. Wright's ideas were the basis of his own scientific career and he was to attempt to reconcile them with later developments that threatened their viability. Meanwhile, Wright's own department at St Mary's became the high temple of vaccine therapy and Fleming never wavered in his allegiance to the high priest.

Ever the publicist and increasingly a public figure, Wright rarely missed an opportunity to bring vaccine therapy and his own work at St Mary's before as wide a public as possible. As a result a large number of patients flocked to him for treatment and he was able to argue for improved facilities for his work at the hospital. Indeed in the early days the facilities in which Wright worked were scarcely adequate. When Fleming began to work with him, he occupied one small basement room, which shook when underground trains passed underneath it – not the best of conditions for microscopy.[31] He had demanded and obtained more equipment and more space, succeeding in 1905 in persuading the hospital to establish a Department for Therapeutic Inoculation, to which patients could be transferred from the hospital or apply to it directly.[32] Wright was even allowed to charge fees to those able to pay, and thus plough the money back into his department, at a time when the hospital did not levy fees in any other unit.[33]

He was also able to count on the support of an influential circle of friends and patrons among London society and the intelligentsia of the capital, including the former Prime Minister, Arthur Balfour, the Appeal Judge Lord Moulton, the Minister of War, Lord Haldane, the brewer Rupert Guinness, the banker Max Bonn, the actor Harley Granville-Barker and the playwright George Bernard Shaw. It was to this group that he turned when the opportunity arose in 1904 to extend his department into the newly built Clarence Memorial Wing at St Mary's. The hospital was unable to afford to open the wards in the new building and Wright had a pressing need for research beds and laboratory space. The obvious answer was for Wright to find the money to lease the space he needed. In April 1908 Balfour convened a meeting at the House of Commons to form an Inoculation Department Committee,[34] and within a few months more than £17,000 had been raised, allowing Wright to fund a research ward of thirty-one beds. Although the nursing staff were supplied by the hospital, the responsibility for the treatment of the patients was his alone. Not only had it given him the research beds devoted to vaccine therapy that he craved, with the ward as an extension of the laboratories, but the new arrangement effectively had given him a semi-autonomous research institute, attached to a general hospital but under his control.[35] For Fleming and his fellow researchers the new facilities were a vast improvement on the cramped basement they had enjoyed for the previous couple of years.

If the Inoculation Department were to retain its autonomy, it required a continuing source of income. Wright could not continue to rely solely upon the generosity of his friends and private patients. Vaccine production provided the answer. The department, which had popularised the use of inoculation, was producing vaccines for its own clinical research, and it was an easy matter to extend this production for wider distribution to the medical profession. An agreement was entered into with the pharmaceutical firm Parke, Davis and Company for the distribution of vaccines for acne, pyorrhoea, boils, pneumonia, bronchial colds, influenza, sore throats, intestinal trouble, gonorrhoea, tuberculosis and even cancer. There was also a public-school vaccine against a variety of childhood illnesses. All were marketed as having been 'prepared in the Vaccine Laboratory of the Department of Therapeutic Inoculation, St Mary's Hospital, W2, under the supervision of the Director Sir Almroth Wright, M.D., F.R.S.'.[36] Production was the responsibility of Stewart Douglas, who had accompanied Wright from Netley, though Fleming was later to assume this vital role, without which the department would not have been viable. Such commercial activity as vaccine production underpinned many of the research institutes on the Continent with which Wright aspired to be compared, including the Pasteur Institute.[37] It would be a mistake, though, to see the Inoculation Department or the other research institutes turning themselves into production units as being driven purely by their commercial links, as the purpose behind these arrangements with commerce was to further the work of research rather than to make profit an end in itself.[38] Wright was capitalising on the strengths of his department and was intent on furthering vaccine therapy, using one aspect of it to fund the necessary research, a policy with which Fleming wholeheartedly agreed. Undoubtedly, the agreement with Parke Davis remained the financial mainstay of the survival of the Inoculation Department for many years to come, supplemented by donations from Wright's wealthier patrons.

All Wright's friends were active on his behalf, but it was Shaw who was to immortalise him in literature as the origin of Sir Colenso Ridgeon in the play *The Doctor's Dilemma*, first performed at the Royal Court Theatre in 1906.[39] The play itself remains as topical as when first performed, dealing as it does with the question of how to decide who should be treated when medical resources are scarce. Shaw had been inspired to write it during one of his many visits to the laboratory at St Mary's when the issue of Wright's having more patients than he could cope with had arisen and Wright had replied that he would have to make the moral judgement as to whose life was most worth saving.[40] In the play, Sir Colenso Ridgeon of St Anne's Hospital, a very thinly disguised Wright, is faced with the dilemma of whether to treat an honest, decent but otherwise mediocre general practitioner or an artistic genius but worthless scoundrel by the successful method of vaccine therapy with which he has built his professional reputation. Attracted by the artist's wife, he nevertheless decides to treat the humble doctor, leaving the treatment of the artist to an eminent but stupid royal physician, who utterly fails to understand the importance of determining the Opsonic Index before attempting to 'stimulate the phagocytes' and manages to kill off his patient. It may have been a brilliant satire on the medical profession, but Wright was less than tolerant when it came to being portrayed on stage himself and he walked out on the first night, declaring that Shaw's interest was not in the truth but in circus tricks.[41]

Amazingly, the friendship between Wright and Shaw survived Shaw's dramatic portrayal of his friend and the fact that the two men differed in their opinions on most conceivable subjects. One such subject was the burning question of women's suffrage. Wright had a misogynistic contempt for women's abilities, though he enjoyed their company socially, and would not allow them to work in his department. His view was that 'ill-groomed and ugly women annoy men and good-looking women trouble them'.[42] Never afraid to court controversy, he could not resist the opportunity to add his voice to the opposition to the vote for women and in 1913 published *The Unexpurgated Case against Woman Suffrage*, prompting the composer Ethel Smythe to attempt to break his windows.[43] Earlier in January 1910 Wright had crossed swords with Shaw at a well-attended debate before the St Mary's Hospital Medical Society. Wright's assertion that women were intellectually and physically unfitted to participate in democracy was countered by Shaw's argument that it was unfair to exclude women, who were admittedly intellectually inferior to Shaw and his opponent, but then so were most men and they still had the vote.[44] Neither side conceded the laurels to the other, but their sparring kept Fleming and his contemporaries amused. Fleming well knew the dangers of crossing Wright on this subject and in later years was to warn a less cautious colleague, R.M. Fry, against supporting the continued admission of women students to the medical school in 1924 for fear of incurring the wrath of the Old Man.[45] His own attitude to women in medicine and science was much more relaxed and, when he was eventually in a position to employ women scientists and doctors, he did so, though not until Wright was safely retired.

Although Wright's Inoculation Department was an exciting place to work, humming with both medical research and intellectual and political discussion, it was also a place where everyone worked hard, often into the small hours, enlivened by teatime discussions in the small and cramped library on any topic that interested Wright from philosophy to gardening, and later by midnight tea parties to discuss the results of the day's work. The routine work of the Inoculation Department relied upon the labour of junior staff for opsonic work and vaccine preparation, but Wright was insistent that this staff should be medically qualified. Lab technicians were allowed to clean glassware and prepare media and stains but were forbidden to examine or prepare slides. Much of the work was done at night, when there were fewer interruptions. Wright, himself a prodigious worker, did not shirk such unsocial hours and by his example encouraged others to work late hours, despite the hospital cutting off the electricity supply at 6 o'clock every evening until it was agreed in 1904 to leave it connected until 9 o'clock. In later years Wright was able to pay for an unlimited supply of current.[46] John Freeman found Wright in his laboratory one evening 'in semi-darkness, the only light coming from two smoky yellow flares from the bunsen burners with the air cut off from their base. He was swearing heartily as he tried to perform some delicate manoeuvres with a capillary glass tube and mercury.'[47] Freeman immediately went off to buy some gas mantles to place over the bunsen burners so that the laboratory could be better lit. Wright's response was the comment that he could now work all night. Able to push himself to the limits, Wright expected no less from his juniors. David Carmalt-Jones, one of his team, could never recall him giving a direct order but he was still able to ensure that his wishes were obeyed. Carmalt-Jones remarked that 'A chief who, without orders given, kept a team of young men out of their beds till past midnight several times a week, and for years on end, had some remarkable qualities'.[48]

This then was the man whom Fleming was to regard as his mentor with a loyalty that was not always to be deserved, a man able to attract a team of young researchers, whom he paternalistically referred to as his 'sons in science' and who in turn affectionately nicknamed him 'the Old Man'.[49] These were young men in whose careers he interested himself and whom he initially envisaged as the nucleus of a school of medical scientists owing their inspiration and ideas to him as their chief, though it was rare for him ever to give praise for any outstanding piece of work. Mistakes, on the other hand, brought forth constructive but vituperative criticism. One man described having 'had Falstaff quoted to me about having my brains taken out and buttered and given to a dog for a New Year's gift'.[50] Among these young men, Fleming at first stood out as someone different. Most of the others were tall and articulate, whereas he was small and very quiet. Some of them had been educated at public schools and Oxford or Cambridge. A number of them too had military backgrounds, though as officers they were quite distinct from Private Fleming of the London Scottish Regiment.

Foremost among them was John Freeman, who had first recommended that Fleming join Wright's band of disciples. A tall, good-looking and charming athlete born in 1877, he had interrupted his medical studies at Oxford to join the Oxfordshire Light Infantry at the outbreak of the Boer War. On completing his medical studies, he came under the influence of Wright and indeed until his marriage in 1907 actually lodged with him. Freeman, although socially adroit, was mercurial in temperament and easily upset if any of his ideas were challenged, so much so that 'he blew in, blew up and blew out'.[51]

Freeman had also attracted another crack shot, his old school friend from Charterhouse, Leonard Noon, to come to work in the Inoculation Department. Noon was considered to be one of the most outstanding and brightest of the stellar team surrounding Wright and did sterling work on allergic disorders with Freeman. However, he was to die of

tuberculosis in 1913 at the early age of 35.[52] He was not the only one of
the young men who flocked around Wright to die young while still
under the Old Man's spell. John Herbert Wells was among the bright St
Mary's students, like David Carmalt-Jones, William Parry Morgan and
Fleming, to be 'gathered in to Sir Almroth Wright's net', as *St Mary's
Hospital Gazette* described it.[53] While working in the Inoculation
Department, Wells accidentally inoculated himself with the glanders
bacillus. Inspired to the last by Wright's ideas, he saw his own fatal
decline from this equine illness charted with Opsonic Indices until his
death at the age of 30 in 1909.[54]

Fleming, much quieter and more reserved than his co-workers, soon
found his feet in this exciting new environment. He had never been a
great conversationalist and his contributions to the discussions were
rare. This silence puzzled Wright, who claimed that Fleming could
speak only Eskimo and that he would have to learn the language if he
wished to communicate with him. Wright did indeed teach himself
Eskimo, though this had no connection with his taciturn assistant. He
also teased Fleming for being a Scot and for not knowing the poetry
of his fellow Ayrshire man Robert Burns by heart. On one occasion,
he declaimed some lines he had composed himself and was delighted
when Fleming said that he supposed they must be from Burns.[55]
Nevertheless, despite all the chafing, Wright came to have some
respect for his assistant. When he did speak, it was invariably to the
point, and he had quickly become a popular member of the team
ready to join in everything. Above all, what commended him to
Wright was the manual dexterity that enabled him to devise any item
of equipment or invent an ingenious method that his chief, himself a
great deviser of new equipment,[56] fancied that he needed for his work.
He was also quick to point out when some grandiose idea was too
impractical. Wright, unused to contradiction from his own team,
would then repeat his explanation as if Fleming had misunderstood
him, but Fleming was not afraid to stand his ground, and more often
than not his judgement would be proved sound. It was respected when
he asked if a job could be found in the laboratory for a wheelchair-
bound friend, A.F. Hayden, whose career as a doctor had been
blighted when he was struck down with polio.[57] Fleming by then was
himself an invaluable member of the team to be relied upon for both
technical skill and well-reasoned judgement.

Fleming, despite his initial scepticism about Wright and his ideas,
soon became as loyal a proponent of them as any of the team. In 1907
he was co-author with Wright, Douglas, Freeman and Wells of a paper
on 'Therapeutic Immunisation' in the *Lancet*[58] that marked his debut in

the field of medical publication. It was followed a year later by another paper in the *Lancet*,[59] written with Leonard Noon, on the accuracy of Wright's method of measuring Opsonic Indices, and a similar paper in the *Practitioner*[60] bearing Fleming's name alone. Essentially these articles were defences of Wright against criticism of his ideas, which were now shared by Fleming. He also won the Cheadle Medal for Clinical Medicine awarded by St Mary's Hospital Medical School for an essay, 'The Diagnosis of Acute Bacterial Infection',[61] reflecting his work in the Inoculation Department.

He also took his work home with him and even practised on his family, who had now moved from Ealing to a flat at 125 Clarence Gate Gardens near Regent's Park and 15 minutes' walk to St Mary's. If any of his siblings had a sore throat or cold, he would take swabs and blood samples from them for analysis in the laboratory and would return with a vaccine to inject into them. His brother Robert complained that 'I must have had my arm punctured and injected with hundreds of different kinds of dead microbes in those days. Alec must have jabbed killed microbes into himself many more times . . . He could insert the needle of a syringe into you so that you hardly felt it.'[62]

As well as having become convinced by vaccine therapy, Fleming also developed his own personal interest in the treatment of acne by these methods. He studied the bacteriology of this potentially disfiguring condition, which could cause great distress for those adolescents affected by it. He then isolated the acne bacillus, *Corynebacterium acnes*, and produced a vaccine that appeared to give good results.[63] It was solid and lucid work if far from earth-shattering or life-saving, but it did indicate that Fleming was more than capable of working independently and on projects that were all his own rather than merely following the instructions of others.

Despite his enjoyment of the new field of bacteriology, Fleming had not yet given up his original aim of becoming a surgeon. His post in the Inoculation Department had little permanency attached to it and was not originally meant to be full-time. He had already passed the primary examinations of the Royal College of Surgeons while still a medical student, but to progress further he required some practical experience. In 1908, he applied for, and was appointed to, a six-month post as Casualty House Surgeon, which gave him practical experience of minor operations and allowed him to assist at major operations. He sat for the Fellowship of the Royal College of Surgeons in June 1909 and passed with his usual ease. He now had to make the final and crucial decision about the future path his career would take. He could set up a practice as a surgeon and seek an appointment on the staff of a voluntary hospital, or he could continue as a bacteriologist. Significantly, he had continued to work in Wright's laboratory while serving as Casualty House Surgeon and, having caught the bug of bacteriology, he could not easily return to surgery as his career field. His post in the Inoculation Department also offered him an annual honorarium of £100, while the rewards of a successful career in surgery were potentially greater but could have meant financial stringency while he established himself.[64]

Fleming's friend and contemporary Charles Pannett believed that it was perhaps his failure to be appointed as surgical registrar at St Mary's that finally decided Fleming against pursuing a career in surgery.[65] Such a post would have been a significant rung on the career ladder to eventual election to the honorary surgical staff of a major teaching hospital. Not to be appointed to the post when he possessed such obvious ability was a setback and must have reinforced doubts that Fleming had about pursuing a surgical career. He had argued with Zachary Cope, who was more successful in this direction, as to whether a surgeon could ever do anything more than cut up a patient.[66] Bacteriology, by contrast, seemed the way forward in treating disease. Ideas of a career as a surgeon were quietly dropped. In the event, this decision was to mean that he was able to contribute more to surgery than if he had become a surgeon rather than merely priding himself on being 'the only FRCS never to have done an operation'.[67] However, the consequences of his decision were far off in the future, and for now Fleming was more concerned with his work in the Inoculation Department.

It was an exciting atmosphere for him in which to work and for a time it seemed that Wright had created the first real clinical research school to be established within a British voluntary hospital. There was contact with the mainstream of European medical research, with visits from Elie Metchnikoff, August von Wassermann, Robert Koch and Paul Ehrlich. Signed photographs of these pioneers of microbiology lined the walls of the Inoculation Department, and Fleming himself later always hung a photograph of Metchnikoff in his own lab, a sign of his respect for his predecessors in research. Fleming noted that in his first six months in Wright's laboratory, there were visiting research workers from Canada, the United States, Germany, France and South Africa.[68] In 1907, forty-six clinicians and pathologists came to St Mary's to observe his techniques. They then returned to their own hospitals, medical schools and laboratories full of enthusiasm for vaccine therapy. Other hospitals quickly jumped onto its bandwagon and opened their own opsonisation departments, though not everyone accepted Wright's views as being entirely orthodox.[69] Nevertheless the publication of all this work on vaccine therapy, which was if anything even more popular in the United States than in the United Kingdom,[70] cemented Wright's reputation as perhaps the 'godfather of British microbiology'.

Wright was above all an immunologist in his ideas about the treatment of disease and had very little sympathy for any of the other approaches that were common at that time to the treatment of infection in patients. He had serious doubts about the use of antiseptics, which killed off any form of living cell, and indeed Fleming was later to demonstrate the limitations of their use. He also had very little time for chemotherapy, which involved the use of particular chemicals that could be active against specific causes of infection without doing major damage to the other body cells. It was this scepticism on Wright's part that paved the way for Fleming to take his first step towards making an independent reputation for himself far beyond the walls of St Mary's.

Paul Ehrlich, during a visit to London in 1909 to lecture on chemotherapy, gave a sample of salvarsan to his friend Almroth Wright. Salvarsan, compound 606, developed by Ehrlich and Sachachiro Hata in 1909, was the first effective use of chemotherapy and held its own until the development of the sulphonamides in the mid-1930s.[71] This 'magic bullet' was targeted at syphilis and offered a much more effective and less dangerous replacement for the centuries-old treatment of this venereal disease with mercury salts, especially calomel, or else copper iodide salts and chalk. Though there was now no risk of mercury poisoning, salvarsan too had its limitations and was never quite the single dose of a chemical capable of overwhelming bacteria and ridding the body of infection that Ehrlich had envisaged. What he was looking for was something that would hit only its target without harming other tissue. He had tested 605 different chemical compounds before finding success on his 606th attempt with salvarsan. Unlike antiseptics, which were applied only topically, salvarsan was injected into the human body and so could reach the syphilis-causing spirochaetes wherever they might be found. Its main limitation was that it worked only against these particular bacteria and not on any other virulent organisms, but this in itself was a great advance in the treatment of sexually transmitted diseases.

Having little sympathy for any form of chemotherapy, Wright lost no time in handing over the sample of salvarsan he had been given to Fleming and his colleague Leonard Colebrook, who were to have great success in injecting salvarsan into patients at a time when few doctors knew much about intravenous injections. Fleming and Colebrook published a note in the *Lancet* on 'The Use of Salvarsan in the Treatment of Syphilis' and were for a time the only doctors in England to use salvarsan to any great extent.[72] Effectively, they enjoyed a

monopoly at first. This and his skill in injecting directly into the vein
was to enable Fleming to build up a successful and lucrative private
practice administering salvarsan to wealthy patients in the years leading
up to the First World War. He rented a consulting room at John
Freeman's house in Devonshire Place. His practice kept him busy, but
between appointments he would play pitch and toss with Mrs Freeman
to while away any idle moments. Among Fleming's patients were fellow
volunteer soldiers in the London Scottish Regiment. These young
professional men and part-time soldiers were to nickname him 'Private
606' and this was how the artist Ronald Gray caricatured him in his
regimental kilt, the inevitable cigarette drooping from his lip, and armed
with a syringe in place of a rifle.[73]

As a result of his work with salvarsan, Fleming was gaining a
reputation as a 'pox doctor' and seemed well on the way to becoming a
specialist in the pathology of sexually transmitted diseases. In 1911, he
was elected pathologist to the London Lock Hospital, founded in 1788
for the treatment of venereal diseases and located next to the
Paddington Workhouse and Infirmary close to the Grand Union Canal.
The London Lock Hospital had a strong reformatory character with
compulsory chapel attendance for the inmates, who wore very
distinctive flannel uniforms to mark them out as morally flawed.[74]
There had long been strong links between St Mary's and the London
Lock Hospital, though St Mary's tended to keep quiet about its cases of
venereal disease, despite being located in a notorious red light district
close to a major railway terminus. The Laws of the Hospital, unlike
those of some other voluntary hospitals, did not exclude VD cases, but
it was still considered wisest not to say too much about those treated,
for fear of losing subscribers to the charity. The presumption generally
was that the voluntary hospitals were intended for the 'morally
deserving poor', and no one ever considered the prostitutes of
Paddington and their clientele in that light. Cases would present
themselves to the Outpatients Department with other outpatients and
they were seen by surgeons.[75] No separate record was kept of such
cases. Indeed it was considered more appropriate for such cases to be
treated at specialist Lock Hospitals. There was a tradition for members
of the Honorary Surgical Staff at St Mary's to hold posts at the London
Lock Hospital, including George Gascoyen, E.K. Chambers, Sir Edward
Sieveking, who also attended the Prince and Princess of Wales, and
father and son James R. Lane and Ernest Lane. James Lane, nephew of
one of the strongest promoters of the foundation of St Mary's, was one
of the first surgeons to be appointed to St Mary's in 1851 at the age of
26 and his expertise in VD was to ensure that cases were seen at

St Mary's from the earliest days. After his career had been cut short (probably by syphilis), his son Ernest followed him at both St Mary's and the London Lock Hospital, and was to head the first VD clinic to be established at St Mary's in 1917, with the assistance of Fleming, his colleague from the London Lock Hospital.

Fleming's expertise in the study of venereal diseases brought his first exposure to the tincture of controversy that was never far from Almroth Wright. Many doctors in the nineteenth century had found the diagnosis of VD difficult, especially in women patients. As late as 1898 many of them were not confident about distinguishing between gonorrhoea and urethritis. It was not until the late 1880s that it was generally recognised that syphilis might be a specific infection caused by a microbe rather than an inflammatory poisonous disease or moral scourge, even though Philippe Ricord had established the specific natures of syphilis and gonorrhoea as long ago as 1837. Albert Neisser had identified the bacterium gonococcus, which causes gonorrhoea, in 1879 and in 1905 *Spirochaeta pallida* (now known as *Treponema pallidum*) was identified by Fritz Schandinn and Erich Hoffman as the cause of syphilis. A breakthrough in diagnosis came in 1906 with the development of the complement fixation test by August von Wassermann, revealing the presence of infection even when the disease was quiescent, which gave emphasis to the role of the laboratory in medicine. The problem with this test was that it needed more blood for testing than could easily be taken from a skin prick. In 1909 Fleming turned his attention to this difficulty and devised a modification of the Wassermann Reaction Test. By using a very small quantity of serum obtainable from one or two drops of blood, he argued that it would now be possible for most hospitals to carry out the test.[76] Fleming, as a result of this work, found himself in demand as a diagnostician of syphilis from both venereologists at other London hospitals and Harley Street specialists alike. However, a rival group of pathologists at the London Hospital tested the modification and concluded that it gave the wrong results in a quarter of all cases and was inaccurate compared with the full Wassermann Test. They challenged Fleming to prove that his technique worked by publishing a series of cases and investigating those cases where his test seemed to have failed. When Fleming did not rise to the challenge, a research student, R. Donald, undertook the work and concluded that Fleming's modification was flawed.

Throughout 1912, the dispute was played out in the pages of the *Lancet*.[77] Fleming and his supporters argued that Donald's technique rather than the modification itself was to blame, as he had apparently failed to wash the serum with saline first. Donald's defenders at the

London Hospital replied that he had actually followed Fleming's instructions to the letter and could not really be criticised for having failed to use a trivial procedure that was considered essential by someone else but that had never been described in detail. Fleming's supporters defended him on the grounds that the test required experience and that the first hundred or so cases were bound to be statistically unreliable. However, given experience and the optimal conditions for the test, it was a reliable method. P.W. Bassett-Smith actually admitted that initially he had himself been very critical of the modification, but after performing more than 900 tests he found it to be invariably correct. Fleming himself argued that, if the modification was as unreliable as his critics from the London Hospital claimed, his 12,000 diagnostic tests performed at St Mary's between 1909 and 1912 would have produced 900 false positives and 'the method would have been absolutely discredited by the clinicians of St Mary's Hospital from whom I have had almost all of my material'.[78] Fleming placed clinical judgement above statistics in the assessment of this work and made little attempt to quantify his clinical experience, though, as always, he was to be very precise in describing his experiments and laboratory results. Like many disputes, this one soon fizzled out, with neither side able to claim victory.

Fleming's colleagues, however, gave him their unstinting support. There was an easy-going camaraderie and team spirit among Wright's team of enthusiastic disciples. Not only did they work long hours in the laboratory without complaint, but they also went away together for more social 'lab weekends' away from St Mary's, where they could cement their close-knit professional solidarity. Since 1905, Leonard Colebrook and his sister Dora had rented a cottage for half a crown a week at Golters Gap, Kimmeridge, near Swanage. It was to this cottage that he invited members of the Inoculation Department for two weekends away from London in October 1909 and March 1910. Accommodation was basic in a cottage originally built to house blackstone miners before it was discovered that the local bituminous oil shale had no commercial value. There was no gas or electricity and the water was collected from a standpipe. The visitors were put up in rows of spartan iron bedsteads. Colebrook managed to take an intimate snapshot of Fleming in his nightshirt lounging on one of these bedsteads half-covered by the bedding and looking as if recently roused from sleep.[79]

The weekends were active ones, despite the relaxed mood. Leonard Noon was an experienced and adventurous rock climber. On one of the weekends in Dorset, he took Colebrook and Fleming out with him to Lulworth Cove for an after-lunch climb. When Noonie and Coli had reached the top of Gads Cliff, they found a recumbent Fleming already there, pipe in mouth rather than the more usual cigarette. He had found an easier and quicker way up. On another occasion, the entire party had spread itself out along the seashore only to get caught by the tide. Hurriedly reassembling, they were alarmed to discover one of their number missing – Fleming. After scrambling up the cliffside to escape the incoming rush of water, they made their way back to the cottage to find an unconcerned Flem happily making and burning toast. He had noticed the tide coming in and had returned to the cottage to avoid getting wet.

By contrast with his younger colleagues, Wright was not fond of hard exercise other than swimming, but he found plenty to interest him in the botany of the Dorset coast. Fleming and Colebrook also pursued less strenuous activities as they both had an interest in photography, but they joined in all the sports of their colleagues. The locals were intrigued by 'those six gentlemen who didn't look like gentlemen', all of them in their late twenties or early thirties and led by the very distinctive and much more mature figure of the Old Man.[80] As ever, whether in the lab or on the beach, Wright gave them the stimulation of his thoughts on anything and everything, but overall the atmosphere was one of horseplay and high spirits.

Life was not all hard work for the young Fleming, who was able to enjoy a full life outside the confines of the Inoculation Department, despite its long hours. As well as socialising with his fellow workers in the St Mary's Hospital Rifle Team, Fleming continued to be an active member of the London Scottish Regiment. However, his social life outside work was also expanding beyond medicine and the territorial army. An Australian colleague of his at St Mary's, Dr Page, introduced him to an artistic circle centred on the Pegrams, who lived in Warwick Gardens, Maida Vale. Fred Pegram was an etcher and illustrator, while one of his brothers-in-law, Townsend, was the art editor of *Punch* and another, Ronald Gray, was a painter. He made an instant hit with Pegram's small daughter Marjorie, for whom he devised 'terribly exciting' games of miniaturised golf and who considered him the 'ideal companion to a twelve year old girl', even if he could not cure her asthma.[81] His simplicity of manner and lack of affectation made him a perfect foil to a much more sophisticated and cosmopolitan society and he was soon a popular member of the Pegram circle. While generally silent and a good listener in the midst of a sparkling and voluble artistic group, he was not afraid of correcting the author George Moore when he mispronounced the name of the prophet Ezekiel during a lunch party. Such social contacts did not impress the young bacteriologist, who accepted people as they were, irrespective of wealth or social status.[82]

He became even closer to the Pegrams after he successfully treated Ronald Gray by vaccine therapy for tuberculosis of the knee. While treating Gray, who had been staying at the home of his merchant banker friends the Hammersleys, Fleming came into contact with a higher stratum of society than hitherto. Mrs Richard Davis, wife of a Bond Street antiques dealer, in particular, was very taken with him, feeling that the serious and solemn young man 'needed some frivolity in his life'. She asked him to her parties, where he came into the orbit of the wealthy connoisseurs, the Wertheimers. Their palatial house was 'full of beautiful furniture and rare porcelain, with a perfectly trained staff and a table which abounded with delicious food and wine', and they encouraged an appreciation of fine arts and good furniture that he was to share with his wife in later years. Mrs Davis made sure that he learned to dance, however awkwardly, and was not taken aback when visiting him at St Mary's to be greeted with, 'I am so glad to see you; I badly need some of your delicious blood.'[83]

When he recovered from his illness, a grateful Ronald Gray introduced his doctor to the congenial milieu of the Chelsea Arts Club. This had been founded in 1890 as a social centre for the artists who at that time had established themselves in Chelsea. Membership was restricted to men professionally engaged in the visual arts, and women were banned from the club, along with dogs and bicycles. Fleming felt at home in this bohemian environment and soon made himself popular with Gray's fellow members. He also treated some of the Chelsea artists for minor illnesses, and they resolved to make him a member as Honorary Bacteriologist in return for free treatment for club members. It helped that Fred Pegram had been President from 1904 to 1906. However, in order to regularise Fleming's membership, it was considered necessary that he should paint a picture, exhibit and sell it. Fleming happily complied. Marjorie Pegram, although only a child at the time, remembered that it was a painting by Fleming of the children's ward at St Mary's that her uncle Ronald Gray submitted to a futurist gallery.[84] However, other acquaintances of Fleming's at the time were equally adamant that it was a painting of a cow.[85] Whatever the subject may or may not have been, Gray took it to a gallery exhibiting modern art with one of his own, which he had deliberately painted badly. To Fleming's delight, one critic is said to have described it as an example of 'sophisticated naivety', but no one wanted to buy it until Gray sent one of his friends along with an offer of the purchase price and the wherewithal to buy it.[86] Having qualified for membership, Fleming was to be a regular attendee at the Chelsea Arts Club for the rest of his life, usually joining in games of croquet, billiards, cards, chess and, his personal favourite, snooker. His custom was to call into the Club for a couple of hours in the early evening before returning to the laboratory or his consulting room. He was also always invited to the Chelsea Arts Club Ball at the Albert Hall, which he attended dressed one year as a golliwog and the next as a small girl.[87] He continued to be an annual attendee at these events, though he was never considered a good dancer,[88] often inviting medical students or colleagues as his guests, where they could see him in a completely different light.[89]

Fleming grew closer to the Pegrams and their circle as his own family circumstances began to change. While the three youngest boys were still living with their mother, Robert had become engaged to Ida Tomkinson. Her first meeting with Alec had been disconcerting as his comment on her evening dress, worn to go to a ball with Robert, was an abrupt 'I suppose you think you look nice'. Robert explained it away as merely being his brother's way of saying that he thought that she looked nice. Her prospective brother-in-law's abrupt manner frightened her at first, until she came to realise that 'he would not willingly hurt anyone'.[90] With Robert's attentions focused on his forthcoming marriage, and pressure of work making holidays to Lochfield Farm impractical, Fleming would join the Pegrams and their friends on painting holidays at their cottage near Mildenhall in Suffolk. While his hosts sketched and painted, he would fish or swim. On these holidays began a lifelong love of the gentle Suffolk countryside that was such a contrast to the moorland of his boyhood.

There was another society that Fleming was to join at this time to which he was also to give lifelong commitment. He became a Freemason. It was said that in those days success in a London teaching hospital depended upon being a member of the right Masonic Lodges. This was perhaps an overstatement, as Almroth Wright never seems to have dabbled in Freemasonry and not all the consultants at St Mary's were members of the hospital Lodge, but the fraternity of Freemasonry did promote bonds of solidarity between its members, which aided and abetted their sense of professional cohesion. Fleming was initiated into the Sancta Maria Lodge in 1909. This Lodge was based at St Mary's Hospital and had been founded in 1897 by members of the honorary staff of the hospital and former students active in Freemasonry elsewhere. The first Worshipful Master of this Lodge, established in the year of Queen Victoria's Diamond Jubilee, was the Prince of Wales, uniting his close family connection with the hospital of which his son was President and the close royal links with Freemasonry. The new Lodge was open to all past and present students of the hospital 'to promote the union of Brethren connected with St Mary's Hospital and its Medical School and for their initiation into Freemasonry of those connected with that Institution'.[91] Many of these students were encouraged to join by Frank Nanfran, the medical school librarian who supplemented his meagre income from the school by playing the flute in West End theatres. Nanfran would identify possible members and whisper to them that there was no compulsion to join Sancta Maria and no penalty for failing to join but that it would not harm their careers to be initiated.[92]

Fleming did not join Sancta Maria until he had qualified, although many of his fellow masons had been recruited as students. There was a joining fee of 6 guineas and an initiation fee of 8 guineas, in addition to the annual subscription of 1 guinea for any aspirant Brother to consider, as well as the cost of the apron and other necessary regalia. This expense would have been a deterrent to any student on a tight budget, but by 1909 Fleming was becoming much more established. Once a member of the Lodge, he committed himself to Freemasonry, working his way through the various degrees of membership. He rose to the position of Master of the Lodge in 1928 and served as secretary from 1934 until 1949. As secretary, Fleming was characteristically to omit any mention of his various honours, which had duly been reported to the Lodge, causing R.M. Handfield-Jones, one of his fellow members, to annotate in 1960 the minutes of a meeting held in November 1947 with the comment, 'There is a serious omission in these minutes as I should know, because it was I who informed the Lodge of Fleming's elevation to the rank of Past Grand Warden, an honour which has never befallen Sancta Maria before. It is typical of Fleming's modesty as Secretary that he did not record the facts in the minutes.'[93] Other Masonic honours also came his way more in connection with his active role in Freemasonry than with his future eminence as the discoverer of penicillin.[94] Formal evening dress was worn to the quarterly Lodge meetings, which were followed by a banquet with speeches and music at the Imperial Restaurant in Regent Street. The attraction for Fleming, who liked games, lay partly in the rituals of the mason's craft but also in the conviviality of the Lodge and its social side. That it may have done no harm to his career was perhaps an added bonus.

There were many developing facets to Fleming's life, yet he kept them separate and private. At home he was known as Alec, at the laboratory as Flem and at the Chelsea Arts Club as Sandy. Very few people were admitted to all the sides of his life and were often surprised when they discovered something about him that was perhaps unexpected, though he did not deliberately go out of his way to cultivate any secrecy. Even an admirer such as G.W.B. James was surprised when he saw Fleming in his immaculate uniform as a private in the London Scottish Regiment in 1909. Even though Flem was well known as a crack shot in the St Mary's rifle team, his prowess on behalf of the London Scottish was not known at Mary's. The meeting changed some of James's preconceptions about military service; as he was later to recall, 'my upbringing was of the stern nonconformist, even puritan, outlook. Fighting and the taking of life were wicked. The realisation that one of my most highly esteemed seniors was prepared to risk his life as a soldier of the King made me revise my views. For the first time I was shaken in my firm belief that war with Germany was not inevitable.'[95]

By 1914, Fleming could feel confident that his professional career was progressing satisfactorily and that he was beginning to make his mark in the exciting and growing profession of bacteriology. Socially too his horizons were expanding. To some extent career and social opportunities were developing in tandem. It was important for anyone hoping to prosper in practice to develop social connections with prospective patients and also with medical colleagues who could direct private patients towards a specialist they knew as a friend. He was also building a reputation for specialist knowledge and expertise, although he remained very much under the wing of Almroth Wright. All too soon the outbreak of war on the day after the August Bank Holiday was to divert Fleming's career path, just as it so drastically changed the lives of so many of his contemporaries. Yet he had in those pre-war days laid the solid foundations on which his future was to be built.

FOUR

Into Battle

In April 1914, after fourteen years as a private in the London Scottish Regiment, Alexander Fleming resigned from the regiment, not long after his brother Lance-Corporal Robert Fleming had tendered his own resignation.[1] It had become increasingly difficult for him to attend regimental functions as the volume of his work had increased, while simultaneously his other social opportunities had expanded. Nevertheless it was a sad wrench after such a long and happy association. Captain G.C.K. Clowes, the officer commanding H Company, wrote in the *London Scottish Regimental Gazette* that Fleming had been an asset to the company as a marksman and that his retirement would be a great loss.[2] Four months later the First World War broke out and the London Scottish Regiment was mobilised and sent to France. There in October 1914 it suffered crippling losses at the Battle of Messines. Had Fleming still been a member of the London Scottish, bacteriology and medicine might have suffered a loss that could have changed the shape of the future. Instead, his wartime experiences studying and fighting disease were to be vastly different from those he would have experienced as a private at the front waging war directly against the Germans. He was also to find an interest in the search for the perfect antiseptic, and this was to influence much of his subsequent work in the fight against infection that absorbed his attention in both war and peace.

Immediately on the outbreak of war in August 1914, Almroth Wright was appointed a lieutenant-colonel in the Royal Army Medical Corps and was posted to France to establish a laboratory for the study of wound infections at the Casino at Boulogne. With him he took the team of young men who had formed the nucleus of his Inoculation Department at St Mary's, all of them issued with new temporary commissions: Captain Stewart Douglas, Lieutenant Parry Morgan and Lieutenant Alexander Fleming. It was a rapid promotion in military rank for the man who had risen no higher than private in his fourteen years as a territorial soldier. W. Clayden, a technician in the laboratories of the Inoculation Department, took on a new role as Wright's orderly with the new challenge of ensuring that Wright's uniform was not too disorderly, an almost impossible task with such a big, untidy man so negligent of appearance. Later, they were to be joined by John Freeman, fresh from preparing cholera vaccines in Russia, and by Leonard Colebrook. In effect the Inoculation Department had been relocated from Paddington to Boulogne.

Meanwhile, back at home, Wright mobilised the resources of his own department at St Mary's for the large-scale production of an anti-typhoid vaccine for the inoculation of the British forces. Throughout the war some ten million doses of vaccines were supplied to the Allied armed forces. In gratitude to St Mary's, King Albert of the Belgians extended his patronage to the hospital in 1934, the only non-British monarch or consort to hold that office.[3] St Mary's also capitalised on this by issuing a fundraising brochure in the early 1930s with the question *Who Won the Great War?*[4] It was at a time when there was much debate as to whether the victors had in actual fact been the defeated in the war to end all wars, and the startling answer was that St Mary's had some claim to having helped the Allied Nations to win. The official line was that the vaccines had been supplied to British, Belgian and Serbian armed forces free of charge throughout the entire war, whereas in fact government grants had been sought very rapidly to fund the project. Nevertheless, perhaps the greatest contribution Wright made during the war was to insist that the troops be vaccinated against typhoid. Using his usual tactic of a letter to *The Times* to appeal to the British public for support for inoculation, he was to be more successful than he had been at the time of the Boer War. Then the failure of the War Office to introduce his anti-typhoid vaccine had prompted his resignation from Netley. Now his ideas held their own. It has been argued that without vaccination there would have been closer to 120,000 deaths in the British Army from typhoid rather than the 1,200 actual deaths. Arguably this vaccine and its saving of lives during the war was to be the major achievement of Wright's long life.[5]

By the time Fleming and the team arrived at Boulogne in October 1914, it was already realised that wound infections would be a major problem in the days ahead, but that there had previously been little research into the subject. There had been no attempt at the bacteriological investigation of wound infections during the South African war, when indeed many of the injuries had been simple bullet wounds. In 1914 sepsis was rife, and the incidence of gas gangrene and tetanus led Sir Alfred Keogh, Director-General of the Army Medical Service, to pronounce in October 1914 that 'We have in this war gone straight back to all the septic infections of the Middle Ages'.[6] It was a daunting situation that confronted Wright and his colleagues.

The accommodation initially assigned to them at the Casino at Boulogne, now officially referred to as the Fourteenth General Hospital, was in a basement with a pipe leaking sewage from the once elegant wards above, where rows of camp beds filled the vast Salle de Baccarat and the other gaming rooms. Even copious use of the disinfectant lysol could not disguise the stench. Wright would have none of this and demanded to be rehoused. Eventually, after much argument, he obtained the top floor fencing club rooms. There was no water, gas or drainage in their new quarters. Fleming's flair for improvisation came into its own. Incubators were contrived and heated from paraffin stoves. Bunsen burners ran on alcohol. Fire bellows were used for glass-blowing burners. Water was supplied through a series of pumps and petrol cans. It was all makeshift, but Wright and his team thrived in such an environment of home-made apparatus and innovation. Fleming considered it to have been one of the best laboratories he had ever worked in.[7] At once they began on the study of wound infection at a time when gas gangrene and tetanus were responsible for 10 per cent of all deaths in the field hospitals, and septicaemia was rife.

The first challenge facing Fleming was to identify what was causing the infections. He took swabs from wounds before and during surgery and from the corpses piled up in the post-mortem room. He examined the bullets, shell fragments, shreds of uniforms, dead body tissue and fragments of bone. He then compared his findings with samples cut from uniforms that had been uncontaminated by the pus from wounds. His findings were a revelation: 90 per cent of the samples of uncontaminated clothing when cultured grew *Clostridium welchii*, the bacterium that caused gas gangrene, 30 per cent produced the tetanus bacilli, 40 per cent streptococci and 15 per cent staphylococci. The infection came from the soldiers' own clothing. The organisms that caused gas gangrene and tetanus flourished in the intestines of the horses whose manure fertilised the fields of Flanders, which explained their presence on the uniforms of men in the trenches, but there was something about them that could not be explained so easily. Both organisms are anaerobic and do not grow in the presence of oxygen, yet here they were multiplying in exposed wounds affecting tissues oxygenated by blood. Fleming investigated further and came to the conclusion that they could grow in porous tissue if aerobic organisms such as streptococci were growing in the surrounding fluid and consuming the oxygen. In the wounds most susceptible to gas gangrene or tetanus, the surface tissues were heavily infected with aerobic organisms, while in the depths of the wound was dead tissue and the oxygen-free conditions needed by the lethal anaerobic bacteria. His articles in 1915 in the *Lancet* describing his findings were the first comprehensive study of wound infections.[8]

He then went on to study under the microscope the behaviour of blood cells in the wounds and once again made some surprising observations. In fresh and untreated wounds, the phagocytes were actively devouring the bacteria. However, where antiseptics were being used, there were very few phagocytes that were not dying or dead. Effectively, the body's own defences, the phagocytes, were being killed off while the bacteria continued to flourish.

Wright felt that this vindicated his views that the phagocytes were more vulnerable to chemical antiseptics than infective bacteria, but most army surgeons found it difficult to accept that antiseptics not only might be useless but were potentially harmful. In order to answer such critics, Wright and Fleming then proceeded to find out why chemicals that could kill the bacteria in test tubes had no effect within the human body. The only viable approach was to look at the nature of the wound itself. The antiseptics could not reach the depths of the jagged wounds of modern warfare, with the result that the bacteria had an open road into the wound and could multiply unchecked in its irregular edges. Fleming demonstrated this with his usual ingenuity by constructing an artificial wound from a test tube which he heated before drawing out a number of spikes from its softened walls using the glass-blowing techniques at which he was so adept. He then filled his spiked tube with a liquid infected with bacteria, emptied it and replaced it with an antiseptic, which he incubated for twenty-four hours. This in turn he emptied out and replaced with a liquid culture medium in which any bacteria could grow. When he incubated this for one more time, the original bacteria were as virulent as ever. Obviously, they had remained in the hollow spikes untouched by the antiseptics. Fleming then went on to test his hypothesis that not only could the antiseptics not penetrate into the crevices of the wound but that they were also being removed by being absorbed by dressings and dead tissue. He filled a test tube with the coloured antiseptic gentian violet, pushed a plug of cotton wool through it with a glass rod so that the fluid was forced through the cotton wool, and found that the fluid on top of it was colourless because the plug had absorbed all the antiseptic.[9]

Fleming then took these findings one stage further and showed that the enzymes in blood serum were also being destroyed by the bacteria. Once again he called his vast ingenuity into play to illustrate that this was happening with the organisms causing gas gangrene. A series of test tubes was filled with blood serum to which he added differing concentrations of carbolic acid. He then inoculated them with the

bacteria and covered the surface of the liquid with a layer of melted
Vaseline. When these test tubes were incubated, any gas produced by
the growth of bacteria forced the Vaseline up the tube, showing that the
further it went the more bacteria had been produced. This experiment
showed that carbolic acid was actually encouraging the growth of
bacteria in the blood serum.[10]

With Wright, he argued that diseased and dying tissue be cut off. The
wounds could then be cleaned with a mild saline solution and the
wounds closed to sterilise them. The use of clean dressings would then
protect against further bacterial infection.[11] It was sensible advice for
the time, but, like most areas in which Wright was involved, this salt
method of treatment aroused controversy. Bitter argument was not
Fleming's style, but Wright relished becoming involved in an argument
with Sir William Cheyne, President of the Royal College of Surgeons
and a staunch Listerian supporter of the use of antiseptics to treat
wounds.[12] The debate became particularly acrimonious, but, to Wright's
chagrin and pain, antiseptics continued in use in the field medical
stations throughout the war. The prevailing view was that, if the
available antiseptics did not work, then stronger ones were needed. As
new and stronger antiseptics were tried, Fleming tested each one, but
found iodine, iodoform, eusol, gentian violet, flavine and acridine were
no better than carbolic acid.[13] The only antiseptic that he believed to be
any good was Carrel–Dakin solution, which soon lost its antiseptic
qualities when poured on a wound and actually turned into a simple
saline solution, which was what Wright and Fleming had advocated all
along. Sensible advice as this salt treatment may have been, it was not
until the Second World War that it was widely adopted; during the First
World War its rejection resulted from a lethal combination of military
and medical politics centred on Wright.[14] One thing that both doctors
and generals have in common is a dislike of being told what to do,
especially by a pontificating expert. However, his work did earn
Fleming a reputation as an expert on wound infection and gave him an
interest in the search for the perfect antiseptic, however sceptical he may
have been about finding it.

The political fallout from Wright's stormy relationship with the
military hierarchy and the medical profession continued, and it was
inevitable that the volatile and individualistic Wright should clash with
his army superiors and colleagues. He was opposed to the official policy
of evacuating all casualties back to England as soon as possible. Many
of the wounded were being moved just when they needed excision of
the wound or for it to be sutured, and by the time they arrived at the
military hospitals back in England their condition had deteriorated too

much for an operation to be viable. Lives were being lost and treatment delayed or hindered by this inflexible policy. During quiet periods on the Western front, many medical officers in France and Belgium were kept idle, while there was a shortage of doctors and beds at home. After the Battle of the Marne in 1915, he spoke out against this system, which he considered iniquitous: 'The surgeons are accumulated in France while the wounded are accumulated in England. It almost looks as if the problem proposed has been to keep the wolf, the sheep and the cabbage of the puzzle from ever finding themselves upon the same side of the water.'[15] Such trenchantly expressed views did not endear him to the military top brass.

An individualist himself, averse to taking orders, Wright found himself in the paradoxical position of arguing for greater standardisation of treatment and for control over medical officers attached to regiments at the front. Most of the medicine being practised in the trenches was by erstwhile civilian practitioners who, after enlisting in the Royal Army Medical Corps, had continued with their own pre-war methods of treatment in the very different conditions of total war. Jealous of their professional independence, they failed to coordinate their efforts. Wright's solution was for the War Office to set up a Medical Intelligence and Investigation Department to consider the issue of orders so that military medicine could be standardised. His memorandum advocating this proposal was presented through the usual military channels and also sent directly to the Prime Minister, Lloyd George, the Minister for War, Lord Derby, and Wright's old friend Lord Balfour.[16] In this paper, he praised the administrative achievements of the military organisation as regards the provision of hospitals, ambulances, medical staff and nurses, but castigated the failure of anyone to take responsibility for a uniform standard of medical treatment. Inevitably such views and the violation of military protocol in their presentation antagonised the authorities. Sir Arthur Sloggett, Director-General of Medical Services in France, urged that Wright be recalled from France in disgrace.[17] Wright had many powerful friends able to prevent his recall, but his proposals were shelved and Lord Derby took pains to disassociate himself from the politics of it all.[18]

While the First World War cut off contact with the scientific community in Germany and Austria with whom Wright had forged pre-war links, it now brought him and his disciples into greater contact with the Allied medical world. Wright actually enjoyed better relations with French surgeons than with the medical profession of his own country. They were generally more receptive to his ideas and took his intellectual pretensions much more seriously. Similarly his relationship was good

with the Americans, especially Harvey Cushing and Roger Lee, joint
heads of the Second Harvard University Unit, which took over control
of the military hospital in the Casino after 1917. Cushing even lived
with Wright for a time, although intellectually their stances were poles
apart. He also conspired with the British army authorities to ask
Fleming to ensure that the notoriously unkempt Wright went out
properly dressed according to military regulations every morning.
Fleming was to enjoy his contact with these Harvard men and, in
particular, became friendly with the physician Roger Lee, who later
said, 'I at once took a tremendous shine to Fleming who said practically
nothing.'[19] Whether communicative or not, Fleming was to maintain his
friendship with Lee for the rest of his life.

Fleming lived with Wright at Boulogne in a house on the Boulevard
Daunau, close to the River Liane and near to the Seaman's Institute that
Wright's clergyman father had set up forty-five years earlier. Leonard
Colebrook, Georges Dreyer, John Freeman and Parry Morgan also
made their homes there at various times during the war. Their simple
needs were catered for by their housemaid Lucienne, whose mother
cooked for them. In the middle of the house was an aviary, which was
subsequently destroyed by a bomb towards the end of the war. The
renowned Inoculation Department tea parties at St Mary's, at which
Wright had presided over discussions on a wide range of topics, were
replicated at Boulogne. There was also a constant stream of visitors
from the worlds of science, medicine, politics, arts and letters, much as
there had been back at St Mary's. At Boulogne, Wright and his young
men entertained Princess Marie Louise, whose openly risqué private life
had already relegated her to the fringes of the Royal Family, the
éminence grise of the medical profession, Sir William Osler, Dawson,
the Editor of *The Times*, the French surgeon Pierre Duval, the actor
Harley Granville-Barker and Wright's old sparring partner Bernard
Shaw, among many others. During one of Shaw's stimulating visits, he
and Wright became so engrossed in their heated discussion of
philosophical problems and medical science that they failed to notice
that they had set fire to a chimney and that black smoke was belching
into the room. It was left to John Freeman and the parlour maid
Lucienne to ensure that the house did not burn down.[20]

The pressures of war left little free time for Wright and his team, but
there were still some opportunities for relaxation and games. On one
occasion a group of high-ranking French medical officers was
scandalised when they walked in upon a wrestling match between
Fleming and one of his fellow officers.[21] Every Sunday, Fleming played
golf on a course on sand dunes at Wimereux, 2 miles along the coast

from Boulogne. Here he devised many of his own rules, sometimes even using his clubs like billiard cues. After a reprimand from a particularly waspish Staff Colonel, who told him to behave himself, he sought his revenge by picking up the Colonel's ball after one particularly long shot and dropping it in the hole so that the Colonel believed he had got a hole in one.[22] Later in the war, when based at a special hospital in Wimereux, for light relief he would play golf by candlelight on a putting green he set up in the hospital grounds.[23] Fleming's family back at home in the United Kingdom saw little of him during the war years and, as always, he continued to maintain the barriers between his working, social and family lives.[24]

On the surface, Wright's team enjoyed an easy wartime life with the opportunity for games of golf or the chance to go swimming denied to soldiers at the front. Yet, they were just as affected by what they saw of wounds as any medical officer at the front. For Almroth Wright, his abiding memory of the First World War was of the 'quiet, muffled tramp of the soldiers passing through the night' as he rested in his billet. This fuelled his resolve to work 'very hard because it makes me unhappy to see those wounded boys lose their limbs or their lives through infection, which could if we had the knowledge be cured'.[25] Fleming, characteristically, was less emotional and less forthcoming in articulating his feelings, yet he was also inspired by what he witnessed with the need for action. His old friend Dr James, serving as a battalion medical officer, visited him at the Casino on his return from leave and was at first irritated by what he saw as an easy life, the typical reaction of any frontline soldier to the top brass behind the lines. Then he noticed that Fleming was not really his usual self: 'I had caught him looking thin and grey and tired. . . . I saw that Flem was being driven by an intense desire to help the soldier.'[26]

Late in 1916, Fleming returned to England and to his old expertise in venereal diseases for a few months. A Royal Commission on Venereal Diseases, appointed in 1913 to look at the problem of effective national provision for the prevention, diagnosis and treatment of sexually transmitted diseases, had recommended that 'arrangements should be made for providing, free for the whole community, adequate laboratory facilities for diagnosis, combined with the provision of adequate and skilled free treatment, for all persons affected with Venereal Diseases'. County Councils and County Boroughs were given responsibility for making such arrangements and were encouraged to make agreements with the large general hospitals, many of them self-governing voluntary hospitals funded from charitable donations. Immorality in wartime was a major area of concern to politicians and public reformers and made the question even more pressing. In June 1916, St Mary's Hospital received a letter from Paddington Borough Council enquiring about the facilities at St Mary's for the diagnosis and treatment of venereal diseases. Perhaps the most cogent consideration for St Mary's, faced with financial pressures arising from the falling-off of income from charitable subscriptions and the increase in prices in wartime, was that there would be state funding for these services. It had also been made clear to the hospital that, although there would be regular visits of inspection from the medical inspectors of the Local Government Board, there would be no attempts at interference with the governance of the hospital. Much valued independence would be preserved and £1,500 gained. Thus, the Venereal Diseases Department opened on 1 January 1917. The new department was placed under the control of the surgeon Ernest Lane as medical officer in charge of the clinic, with surgical registrar Kenneth Lees and bacteriologist Alexander Fleming as his assistants. Fleming was also appointed pathologist under the scheme at an annual salary of £250.[27] The pathology laboratories now dealt not only with specimens sent for examination from patients at St Mary's but also with those sent by qualified medical practitioners working within the borough of Paddington. These medical practitioners were also given free instruction by staff of the department in the administration of anti-syphilitic remedies and how to collect material for pathological examination. The department also became the centre for the distribution of supplies of salvarsan to general practitioners throughout the borough of Paddington. The Local Government Board had been keen that women doctors should be appointed for the treatment of women patients, but St Mary's merely responded that, as women were now admitted as medical students, 'we should hope in time to appoint a Woman practitioner'. When Fleming returned to military service later in 1917, another male surgeon, Captain Russell Wilkinson, and a male pathologist, the wheelchair-bound Captain Hayden, were appointed in his place.[28]

In 1918, Fleming was appointed bacteriologist to a special hospital set up at Wimereux to deal with wounds involving bone fractures. Here his earlier observations on wound infections and the problems with using antiseptics finally bore fruit. A surgical regime was started there that considerably reduced the incidence of gas gangrene and directly followed from the work he had done previously.[29] With his colleague Dr A.B. Porteous, he now turned his attention to the new technique of blood transfusion and developed new practical methods.[30]

The influenza pandemic of 1918 brought further stresses and strains into the wards at the Casino, staffed by doctors and nurses by now inured to battlefield casualties. Influenza victims soon came to outnumber the war-wounded. Throughout the world, it was the seemingly young and healthy who were stricken, and there was nothing that the doctors could do against it. Fleming's new challenge was to investigate why influenza had become such a killer. His work showed that the high mortality was due to secondary infections from the streptococci and staphylococci that had been so important in his studies of war wounds, but he did not come up with any answers as to how to prevent the influenzal infection from damaging the air passages so that they became vulnerable to other more lethal infective agents.[31] It was his experience of this pandemic that interested Fleming in the bacterium *Haemophilus influenzae B*, also known as Pfeiffer's bacillus after its discoverer, which was at that time believed by many to be the cause of influenza. It was only in 1919 that the real cause of influenza was identified in Japan as a virus and many years before the viral nature of the infection became generally accepted.

Demobilization when it came in 1919 was welcome, and in January 1919 Fleming returned to the Inoculation Department at St Mary's. Some of the pre-war intellectual excitement had died as its members settled into middle age and a regular 9 to 5 job replaced the long hours worked before 1914. The war had been a watershed for the Inoculation Department, and, at the age of 58, Wright had lost much of his old energy. The war years had not been good ones for him. He saw many of his friends or their sons on the lists of missing or dead. His marriage finally came to an end after many years of disharmony, and Leonard Colebrook had commented on his loneliness during the war years. Despite his professed longing for peace and quiet, he did not yet feel that his work with vaccine therapy or immuno-transfusion had sufficiently advanced for him to rest from his labours. Yet vaccine therapy had had its day and Wright's faith in it had weakened to such an extent that he turned his attention to the study of a more perfect system of logic to replace the intellectual one that had let him down over his theories. It could not be his own ideas that were at fault, so it must be the conventional system of logic that had led him astray.[32]

Meanwhile the war years had further enhanced Fleming's already growing pre-war reputation and he was now the acknowledged expert on the bacteriology of wound infection. As such he was invited to deliver the Hunterian Lecture for 1919 to the Royal College of Surgeons. In it he lucidly summarised his wartime work on wound infections and his findings on the damage being done by over-liberal application of antiseptics.[33] The lecture, however clear and logical it may have been, lost much of its impact through Fleming's self-deprecating delivery and occasional inaudibility, and was soon forgotten by its audience. While this modest personal style was later to prove an asset to Fleming once he had achieved popular fame as the discoverer of penicillin, it was for many years to be perceived as a serious professional handicap.

The war years had also brought other changes to Fleming's life of even greater personal importance. While on leave on 23 December 1915, at the Roman Catholic church of St Charles Borromeo, Ogle Street, St Marylebone, he had quietly married Sarah McElroy, who with her twin sister Elizabeth ran a private nursing home in Baker Street.[34] The nursing home was not far from the Flemings' flat, but Fleming has left no record of how he first met his future wife. Ever reticent about his private life and with a reputation for shyness, Fleming had surprised all his friends by his marriage. In many ways it was the attraction of opposites. The daughter of Irish farmer Bernard McElroy of Leigherntain House, Kilfilian, County Mayo, Sally, as she was usually known, had been born on 28 May 1875 and so was almost seven years older than Fleming.[35] Embarrassed at the age gap, Sally declared herself to be 35 on her marriage certificate and this fiction was to be perpetuated when Fleming registered her death thirty-four years later.[36] She had trained as a nurse at the Richmond, Whitworth and Hardwicke Hospitals, Dublin, qualifying in 1907.[37] The nursing home that Sally established in London had soon acquired a good reputation and attracted many patients who swore that they would go nowhere else when in need of nursing care. She was described by those she had nursed as 'kind, good-hearted and generous'.[38] The McElroy twins brought different qualities to the success of Sally's nursing home. Sally was energetic, extrovert and maternal towards her patients, whereas Elizabeth was much quieter and more reserved. They were both to marry Fleming brothers. After the marriage of Sally to Alec, an attraction grew up between Elizabeth and John Fleming. Old Mrs Fleming fell ill and Elizabeth went to nurse her at the Clarence Gate Gardens flat, where John was still living. Much more extrovert than his brother Alec, John was attracted to the shy and retiring Elizabeth, the widow of an Australian, and they were soon married, allowing Grace Fleming to return home to Scotland happy in the knowledge that her children were now settled.

In many ways, for Alec and Sally, as indeed for John and Elizabeth, it was the differences in their personalities that brought them together. Where Alec was quiet, Sally was vivacious and lively, with a love of conversation and argument, which made her a convivial and popular hostess.[39] At the dinner parties she arranged, sometimes thinking nothing of walking home to Chelsea from a West End theatre matinée to cook dinner for her guests, she would often throw out provocative statements to begin a discussion, 'relying on scorn rather than reason to win her case'. She was also a very capable and thrifty housewife and an excellent cook well able to provide her husband with a comfortable home life, though she had some difficulties in keeping a maid as, despite her generosity to her employees and the devotion to her of those who did live up to her exacting standards, she was intolerant of slackness in any form.[40] Fleming in turn was oblivious of how his home was run and always took his domestic comfort for granted in his undemonstrative way. If they ever quarrelled, it was never in front of anyone else, despite Sally's natural love of argument.[41]

At first the newly married couple set up home in a flat in Bicknell Mansions convenient for Sally Fleming's nursing home. With Fleming's return from the war in 1919, they were able to settle down to married life. Sally sold her nursing home and devoted herself to her husband. They now moved to a flat at 20 Danvers Street, Chelsea, which they rented from the firm of James Gray and Son, heating engineers, whose business premises were behind the house. The company was owned by the family of Ronald Gray, the artist with whom Fleming had formed a firm friendship before the war. They rented at a reasonable rate a maisonette, consisting of a ground floor and basement. It was a twenty-minute drive by car from St Mary's and also close to the Chelsea Arts Club, which suited Fleming perfectly.[42] It was to remain his London home for the rest of his life.

However, they both loved the countryside and wanted a home in the country for weekends and holidays. When they did find a house that suited them, the decision to buy it was made very much on the spur of the moment. While visiting Fred Pegram, another member of the Chelsea Arts Club and the brother-in-law of Ronald Gray, at his cottage at Mildenhall, Suffolk in 1921, they heard that The Dhoon, a house at nearby Barton Mills, was for sale and decided to buy it using part of the capital from the sale of Sally's nursing home, although they had only set out to buy a fender for the fire.[43] Here they were to spend most of their weekends and summer holidays for the rest of their lives together. Sally made the house comfortable with the antiques she enjoyed collecting, while her husband found simple pleasure in a spacious garden with a paddock and a river at the bottom, a garden he created himself from a bare field.[44] The garden was also the scene of a variety of games on improvised putting courses, using such obstacles as flower beds, cold frames and the river to make the games more difficult. Sally was fond of company, and The Dhoon soon became the centre of hospitable weekend house parties for family members and friends. John and Elizabeth Fleming, who remained childless, were frequent visitors, as were Tom and his wife Florence and their children Rosamund and Donald. Robert and Ida Fleming, now living at Radlett, perhaps saw less of Alec and his wife than they had done, but their visits to The Dhoon with their children Angus, John and May were always welcomed.

The Flemings were both fond of children, organising parties for the village children at Barton Mills,[45] and were particularly indulgent towards their nephews and nieces. Sally, not liking to be referred to as 'Aunt Sally' and also wishing to emphasise her Irish origins, adopted the name Sareen, by which she was to be known for the rest of her life. Family life, though, was not to be complete until the birth of their own son Robert on 17 March 1924 after nine years of marriage. Over the next few years Sareen, a mother at nearly 50, began to spend more time at The Dhoon with her infant son over the summer, often accompanied by nephews and nieces and always joined by her husband at weekends and usually for a month in August. Fleming always enjoyed his time at The Dhoon, which truly became the focus of a contented family life. As a proud and doting father, Fleming had a remarkably relaxed attitude to his parental responsibilities. On one occasion he took the 5-year-old Robert and a weekend visitor, Gerald Willcox, fishing. Excited at seeing his father land a pike, Robert fell into the river. He was fished out of the water by Willcox, while his father, only too used to his son falling in, calmly and unconcernedly continued to land the fish.[46]

Life now followed a regular routine for Fleming in his early middle age. He arrived at work at nine each morning and worked in the laboratory until five in the afternoon, a great contrast to the frenzied and feverish atmosphere of the pre-war Inoculation Department of his younger days. After work, he went to the Chelsea Arts Club for a game of billiards, snooker, cards or chess, often playing with the artist Vivian Pitchforth, whose deafness made idle conversation unnecessary. After enjoying a drink, he would set off for dinner at home at eight o'clock. Although the Chelsea Arts Club was important for him as a social centre rather than for artistic reasons, he retained an informed interest in art and took a keen and tasteful interest in art and antique auctions. He owned a collection of pictures by Wilson Steer, Philip Connard, Ronald Gray and his other artist friends. On one occasion he took his colleague V.D. Allison to Sothebys to an auction of etchings by Whistler. At over £30, they were too expensive for him to bid for, but he encouraged Allison to bid for three sketches by Pablo Picasso, which he obtained for £3.[47] Weekends were spent at The Dhoon. It was on the surface a calm and unruffled life.

The postwar years, which saw his life settle down to a comfortable domestic routine, also marked a period of professional consolidation for

Fleming. Following Wright's example, he had not resumed his private practice on his return from the war but had decided to concentrate on research and teaching at St Mary's. His income was now totally derived from his salary of under £1,000 a year from the Inoculation Department, augmented by payment from the medical school for undergraduate teaching, investments from savings from his time in private practice and, in the early days, income from Sally's nursing home.[48] However, there were opportunities for promotion for Fleming, especially since there was a degree of unrest among the returning staff of the Inoculation Department, unsure of their future in the postwar world with an ageing and increasing intractable Wright. Stewart Douglas left St Mary's in 1919 to become Director of Bacteriology at the Medical Research Committee Central Institute at Mount Vernon, a post that should have been Wright's had he not resigned amidst disagreements with the Medical Research Council.[49] Colonel Douglas had been responsible for the production and sale of the vaccines vital for the success of the Inoculation Department, and Wright now placed Fleming in charge of this crucial area of activity.

Promotion brought its own problems, coming as it did against a background of unrest and rivalries within the Inoculation Department, centring on the eventual succession to Wright as director. As early as 1919, Leonard Colebrook had noted that the once friendly and cooperative atmosphere of the pre-war days had gone for ever and that he feared that 'the Old Man is going to have a poor house and an unhappy one to work in for his latter days'.[50] Wright himself was responsible for this atmosphere. It was expected that he would retire by the age of 67 in 1928, but because of the anomalous position of his department he was able to remain in post for as long as he wished, and he had no desire to relinquish the reins. Yet the reputation of his department depended on his retaining able subordinates. The loss of Douglas and Colebrook to Mount Vernon in 1919 had been a blow. The two longest-serving men in his department were now John Freeman and Alexander Fleming. Both men were promised the eventual succession by Wright, employing a tactic of divide and rule to keep them loyal to him personally. Freeman, whom Wright referred to as his 'son in science',[51] was unhappy when Fleming was made Assistant Director. Wright placated him with promises for the future, promises that were also made to Fleming, but the once amicable relationship between Freeman and Fleming was now at an end. Over the next quarter of a century, Wright continued to tantalise them with his imminent retirement before he finally gave up the role in 1946 at the age of 86. Freeman continued to run the routine bacteriology services of the hospital and build on his reputation as an allergist in charge of the Allergy Department he had begun with Leonard Noon before the First World War. Fleming's responsibilities focused on the production of vaccines and the general administration of the laboratory, taking on many of the practical management roles that Wright would not bother himself with.

A further promotion came Fleming's way in 1921 when he was made Assistant Director of the Inoculation Department and Director of the Department of Systematic Bacteriology in the Pathological Institute of St Mary's Hospital.[52] It was a title that meant more on paper than it ever did in reality. The semi-autonomous nature of the Inoculation Department within St Mary's was administratively untidy, but it had brought with it considerable prestige, money in the form of rent and the funding of a research ward, and reasonably cheap and effective pathology teaching. However, Wright's position represented a challenge for the new Dean of the Medical School, Dr Charles McMoran Wilson,[53] appointed in 1920 at a time when the school faced possible extinction. As Dean, Wilson built St Mary's from a small, poorly endowed school to one of the country's leading medical schools over the next twenty-five years by a careful selection of students and staff and by adopting Wright's tactic of cultivating benefactors. Although the two men shared a desire to make St Mary's into a centre of research and teaching, Wright and Wilson were to jostle for supremacy throughout the 1920s. The Pathological Institute was an early outcome of the power struggle and superficially seemed to represent a compromise. Clinical and laboratory research in the Inoculation Department and medical school were to be integrated and given formal recognition within the new institute. The Departments of Anatomy, Experimental Pathology, Special and General Pathology and Chemical Pathology from the school, and Systematic Bacteriology, Clinical Bacteriology and Immunology and Vaccines from the Inoculation Department were brought together with Wright as director.

The idea behind the new organisation was that the heads of the four departments from the medical school would counterbalance the influence of Wright and his henchmen Freeman and Fleming on the council of the new institute. In practice, the Pathological Institute worked to the advantage of Wright, perhaps because it remained largely funded by £1,000 a year from the Inoculation Department, £400 of which was used to support research scholarships. Such scholarships allowed Wright to recruit able new researchers to the Inoculation Department at a time when it was no longer such a mecca for talented visitors from overseas. One of the early beneficiaries was Ronald Hare, who commented that 'without the benefit of even an internship and still less a postgraduate qualification, but far, far more important, when only twenty-five years old and still possessing the youthful enthusiasm the modern system of training so effectively dissipates before a man starts his life's work, I entered the laboratory that was to be my scientific home for the next six years'.[54] The institute also began a lecture series on applied research that attracted distinguished line-ups of guest speakers, many of them friends of the Old Man himself.[55] What was left from the meagre resources of the institute went towards departmental research projects, but was inadequate if St Mary's was to compete in the modern world. Wright considered applying to the Rockefeller Foundation for a research grant in October 1925, but was more used to presenting himself as the scientific expert soliciting funds from the scientifically illiterate and medically deferential wealthy patron than to appealing before the peer review system of modern grant-giving bodies. As a consequence of this attitude, his grant application was little more than an unsupported request for money and simply stated that the hospital had a tradition 'from the very outset of the modern movement in medicine' of fostering 'Medical Research and the more modern methods of treatment that have sprung from it', but that money was now needed to develop research facilities which would give 'a powerful impetus . . . to the development of scientific medicine and higher education'. Wright did not get his funding.[56] With scant money available, the institute council met only twice a year to do scarcely more than allocate research funds and scholarships. Wright had little need to try to absorb the four departments independent of the Inoculation Department into his empire – he could merely ignore them and continue to rule the Inoculation Department as he had always done.

Although still powerful, Wright no longer dominated the research interests of his staff in the way he had once done. It was now even possible for a researcher to disagree with Wright in print.[57] This growing tendency to leave researchers to their own devices resulted in studies coming from the Inoculation Department of such subjects unrelated to Wright's interests as the bacterial factors in the aetiology of dental caries, the structure of salivary gland tumours and the bactericidal action of streptococcal toxin. Fleming himself was able to develop a research interest in bactericides that did not originate with Wright's guidance. In his earlier years as a bacteriologist, he had very much worked along the lines laid out by his chief, often in collaboration with him, as in the wartime work on wound infection, and even where he had diverged, as in his work on salvarsan, it had been at Wright's direction. Now he enjoyed more intellectual freedom to pursue areas that interested or appeared important to him.

The early 1920s saw a shift in Fleming's attitude away from his initial scepticism towards antiseptics. Wright, of course, had no time for antiseptics or any form of chemotherapy. Moreover, Fleming had trained as a medical student at a time when Listerian ideas on operating-theatre hygiene were considered outdated and aseptic techniques had superseded the use of strong antiseptics to control infection during surgery. In his 1944 Lister Memorial Lecture to the Society of Chemical Industry, Fleming freely admitted that 'When I was a student people talked of Lister as a back number'.[58] It had been with Lister that the search for the elusive perfect antiseptic had indeed begun. Pasteur's demonstration that specific diseases in animals were caused by specific germs and that germs could cause the putrefaction of wounds had inspired Lister in 1865 to begin the quest for a chemical that could kill the bacteria that caused hospital gangrene without harming the patient.[59] Carbolic acid was found to be the best available antiseptic for such purposes, provided it was strong enough to kill the bacteria but dilute enough not to harm too much the tissue of the patient. Lister believed that most harmful bacteria were airborne and after 1872 introduced steam-powered sprays of carbolic acid into the operating theatre. The hands and instruments of the surgeon were invariably soaked by the carbolic acid, which effectively but unintentionally produced an aseptic operating area by means of a chemical antiseptic. However, for many surgeons it felt as if they were operating in a Turkish bath under a fine mist, which irritated them, never mind being dangerous to the patient. As a result, there was a move towards aseptic techniques in surgery by which the theatre became a sterile environment before the operation began. Instruments, gloves, caps and masks were now sterilised by steam and the use of carbolic sprays was found to be unnecessary and had gone out of general use by the early 1900s. Fleming himself came to realise that aseptic surgery was 'merely the substitution of one antiseptic for another, heat for carbolic acid' and that sterilisation was the key to both techniques, but for a long time most doctors saw antisepsis and asepsis as sharply defined alternatives.[60] Fleming's prejudice against antiseptics had been further reinforced by his work with Wright on wound infection during the war. However, he remained interested in the idea of a search for a perfect antiseptic and, with his experience with salvarsan behind him, was not as unsympathetic as Wright to chemotherapy. Nor was his mind closed to new ideas that might overturn the old.

As with penicillin, it was Fleming's remarkable ability to be receptive to interesting if accidental phenomena that led him to make the first of his great discoveries, lysozyme, the body's own antiseptic. In November 1921, he was suffering from a cold and on a whim cultured some of his nasal mucus on agar jelly in a petri dish. A few weeks later, he picked up the culture plate and showed it to his research student V.D. Allison with the comment 'This is interesting'. Allison could see that the culture plate was covered with golden-yellow colonies of bacteria. Had that been all, there would have been nothing very noteworthy about the plate, but closer examination showed that there were no bacteria growing close to the blob of nasal mucus. Beyond this zone of inhibition was another zone where the bacteria had become translucent, glassy and lifeless in appearance. Further towards the edges of the plate and well away from the mucus were normal, fully grown, opaque bacteria. Clearly something had spread out from the nasal mucus to prevent the bacteria from growing close to it and to kill or dissolve the bacteria already grown beyond this initial zone. Fleming was quick to investigate further and to test some fresh nasal mucus on the bacteria. However, this time he prepared an opaque, yellow suspension of the contaminant in saline and added a further sample of his nasal mucus to it. The result was astonishing, as within two minutes the saline solution was completely clear. The mucus had dissolved the bacteria. It was a thrilling moment as both Fleming and Allison realised that they were on to something exciting, though Fleming remained as phlegmatic as ever.[61]

At first Fleming did not know what he had discovered, and his initial experiments were concerned with establishing whether or not all types of bacteria were dissolved by his own nasal mucus. At this stage, he may have wondered whether he was dealing with a bacteriophage, a viral parasite affecting certain bacteria, which kills them and which it was believed might function in natural immunity, since he used this heading in his notebook for his first experiments.[62] Once again he took some of his own nasal mucus dissolved in saline, centrifuged it and then placed a drop of the resultant clear fluid onto three different bacterial cultures streaked across a blood–agar culture plate. The plate was next incubated for three hours and then examined. Only in the case of one of the culture streaks labelled 'Staphyloid coccus from AF's nose' was there no bacterial growth near to the drop of mucus. The other two streak cultures of the bacteria *Staphylococcus albus* and *Pneumococcus* remained unaffected by the mucus. In a similar experiment using different bacteria, only the 'AF coccus' was affected by the mucus.[63] A few days later, Fleming grew the 'AF coccus' in a bacterial broth to which he added a drop of the diluted mucus. Once again, the fluid became clear after five minutes. He then repeated this experiment with other organisms, but only *Staphylococcus albus* and the cholera bacillus showed any signs of 'slight clearing'.[64] He had established that his nasal mucus did not affect all bacteria.

There remained the possibility that there may have been something particular about his own nasal mucus that had dissolved the bacteria. Accordingly, he collected samples of nasal mucus from his colleagues and friends, including Ronald Gray, and repeated his tests. The results were the same as for his own mucus and told him that the ability to dissolve certain bacteria was a normal property of nasal mucus and not just the result of a common cold infection. At this stage he realised that the substance he had discovered was not a bacteriophage, but something different. It was also important to establish whether other body fluids had similar effects, especially those related to nasal mucus such as tears draining into the nose, which were shown to be highly active. Saliva, sputum, blood serum, plasma and peritoneal and pleural fluid also all showed lytic activity. Tissues obtained from the operating theatre and post-mortem room were next examined and Fleming found signs of this lytic agent in skin, mucus membranes, most of the internal organs and even in hair and nails. He widened his research to cover animals and found it present in rabbits, guinea pigs and dogs, though it was stronger in some animals than in others. The conclusion was inescapable that most of the normal body fluids must contain a bacteriolytic substance.[65]

Compared with the rapid advance they made in understanding the scope of the action of this agent, Fleming and Allison, neither of whom made any pretence of being a chemist, were able to make little headway with any knowledge of the nature of the substance. Their work showed that it was destroyed when it was heated to 70°C and that it was precipitated by alcohol, acetone and picric acid, the chemicals that precipitate proteins. These qualities, together with the fact that the lytic agent dissolved bacteria, suggested to Fleming that it was a ferment or enzyme, a protein that acts as a catalyst for chemical change without being changed itself. A name was needed for this ferment and Almroth Wright suggested lysozyme, meaning an enzyme that lyses or dissolves bacteria.[66]

Throughout all this work, Fleming continued to use the so-called AF coccus as an indicator of the degree of lytic activity. A test fluid or tissue extract would be added to a suspension of the coccus to see if it cleared, in which case it was dissolving the bacteria. It was also used as part of a second technique involving a 'well plate'. Holes would be cut into the solid agar or gelatine in a petri dish. Discs of paper soaked in the fluid being tested would then be placed into these holes and the surface of the culture plate covered with a layer of melted agar until the holes had been filled smoothly. The 'AF coccus' would next be added and the plate placed in an incubator. Once incubated, the coccus would have grown everywhere except in those areas to which the lytic agent had diffused out from the wells. This indicated the lytic activity of different body fluids and organs. Fleming continued to use this bacterium, which had first brought the lytic agent to his attention, because he found it to be the most sensitive of all the bacteria he tested. It was also a bacterium that he himself had discovered, although this discovery tends to be forgotten when set against the more important discovery of the agent in his nasal mucus. Fleming's notebook entries labelling it 'Staphyloid coccus from AF's nose' suggest that he thought it came from his own nose and the cold he was suffering from when he made the discovery, but his own observation that it was destroyed by his own nasal mucus within minutes makes this unlikely and Allison's supposition that it was an airborne contaminant the most reasonable explanation.[67] It was a micro-organism Fleming had never seen before, and he named it at Almroth Wright's suggestion first *Micrococcus lyticus* and later *Micrococcus lysodeikticus*, a term derived from Greek that means a member of the *Micrococcus* group of bacteria that exhibits signs of lysis.[68] It was a rare bacterium and neither he nor Allison was able to find it again.

The results of all these bacteriological tests were disappointing if Fleming had hoped to have discovered an effective antiseptic. While the 'AF coccus' or *Micrococcus lysodeikticus* was the most sensitive, other non-pathogenic airborne organisms were also susceptible, but the most virulent forms of staphylocci, streptococci, pneumococci and coli-typhoid were not affected by the lytic agent. This limited any practical, therapeutic value it may have had. Nevertheless it remained an important contribution to the academic understanding of the immune system and its workings.

Fleming first presented his findings at a meeting of the Medical Research Club in December 1921. Founded in 1891, this provided a forum for medical researchers to present papers on work in progress to a group of like-minded colleagues. Almroth Wright had been a founder member of this exclusive club and had proposed Fleming for membership. The rules of the club restricted all papers to no more than 15 minutes.[69] It was an impossibly short time in which to describe, explain and indicate the importance of Fleming's novel observation and he failed miserably to arouse any interest. His flat and often inaudible presentation of what seemed to be no more than a rare and harmless germ that was soluble in tears, saliva or nasal mucus was met with silence and total lack of interest. No one asked a question or made any comment at all. Sir Henry Dale later commented that 'we all said "oh, is that not charming, that is the sort of naturalist's observation which Fleming makes"'.[70]

Such a response did not discourage Fleming, who often took a lack of questions to be a sign that his lucid and comprehensive exposition merely needed no further clarification,[71] and he continued with his work on lysozyme as wholeheartedly as ever. One aspect of his work caught the popular attention, however much it had failed to excite the elite of the medical world. Human tears were a good source of lysozyme, and an accessible one. Fleming and Allison pressed their colleagues and even unwary visitors to the Inoculation Development into producing them. When the patience of their colleagues and thus this supply dried up, the laboratory boys were each paid 3*d* a time to have lemon juice squeezed into their eyes to make them cry. Fleming told his technician Dan Stratful that 'if you cry enough, you will soon be able to retire'.[72] The satirical magazine *Punch* picked up on these strange goings on and published a cartoon by J.H. Dowd showing children queuing up to be paid a penny a time to be thrashed to produce this tear antiseptic.[73]

As well as investigating human and animal tissue, Fleming extended his search for sources of lysozyme to the realm of vegetables, plants and flowers. Once again the enzyme seemed to be ubiquitous; turnips, in particular, proved to be a good source of it, although not as productive as human tears. However, a better one was soon identified in egg-white and was destined to become the best source.[74] Later, a fishing trip at The Dhoon uncovered a particularly valuable source of lysozyme in pike's eggs and gave Fleming the opportunity to combine his work and sporting interests in the investigation of other fish as sources. Country walks and gardening sessions uncovered birds' eggs and plants for examination. Allison was sent to the Ministry of Agriculture laboratories at Weybridge, Surrey, to collect tears from horses, cows, hens, ducks and geese, though pigs proved remarkably uncooperative, and to London Zoo, where he collected them from over fifty different species.[75] There could be no doubt about the wide distribution of this anti-lytic substance in nature.

Fleming's initial work on lysozyme was published in the *Proceedings of the Royal Society* in 1922. Wright was a Fellow of the Royal Society and entitled to communicate to the society the work of his colleagues, even if they were not themselves Fellows, if he considered it to be of sufficient scientific importance. He had no doubts about the value of the work done by his colleagues over the previous two months and on 13 February submitted the paper by Fleming, which was accepted for publication. In it, Fleming wasted little time on discussing the origins of the discovery, but preferred to present his findings on its chemical and physical properties and to list those organisms susceptible to its effects.

He dismissed the previously held assumption that the function of tears, saliva, sputum and mucus was merely to wash away bacteria from the surface of the body and instead suggested that they contained an active antibacterial property that, by inference, acted as a first line of defence against bacteria.[76]

The communication of this paper was a mark of Wright's high regard for Fleming's work and it was soon followed by Wright proposing Fleming for election to the Royal Society, one of the highest honours available to a British scientist. In favour of Fleming's candidature was his latest work on lysozyme and previous research on the bacteriology of wound infection and his technical ingenuity. It was enough to get him considered for election, but it failed to secure for him the much coveted fellowship. Each candidate was eligible for consideration every year over a five-year period before the proposal was deemed to have lapsed for unsuccessful candidatures. A candidate had then to wait for three years before he could be proposed again. Fleming's name came up for consideration by the election committee every year, apart from the statutory three-year gaps, over the next twenty years. Not until the success of penicillin had been more than proven was his candidature successful.[77] It was not in his nature to comment on how he felt about this continued lack of recognition.

Work continued on lysozyme over the next five years. Allison was awarded a Beit Fellowship to continue his work in Fleming's laboratory on lysozyme, work that formed the basis of an MD thesis.[78] In the next decade, Fleming published eight papers on lysozyme, five of them as a co-author with Allison. Perhaps one of the most significant of their further findings on lysozyme was that normally susceptible bacteria could acquire resistance to it. They demonstrated this by repeatedly culturing the bacteria in concentrations of lysozyme that were only partially lethal, then by selecting the survivors and subculturing them.[79] They were joined in this work in 1926 by Frederick Ridley, a young ophthalmologist brought in to study the effects of lysozyme on eye infections. Ridley showed that when a non-virulent form of staphylococcus was made resistant to lysozyme it regained the ability to cause conjunctivitis.[80] Ridley's work showing that undiluted tears could kill some virulent organisms also reinforced the observation made by Fleming and Allison that in a strong enough concentration lysozyme could even inhibit such pathogenic bacteria as staphylococci, streptococci, meningococci, typhoid and anthrax bacilli, thus affording a natural protection to otherwise vulnerable parts of the body.[81]

Fleming's further study of the body's own natural antiseptic confirmed his earlier views on the uselessness of chemical antiseptics.

He had observed that the leucocytes contained lysozyme and was able to pursue this line of investigation using a new technique involving 'slide cells' devised by Almroth Wright.[82] It involved the preparation of a slide cell from two microscopic slides separated by five strips of Vaseline-smeared paper, which divided the space between the two slides into four very thin cells that were open at each end. A drop of fluid could then be placed into each cell, which would then be sealed with wax and incubated, and then observed under the microscope. It allowed for easy comparison between the contents of each compartment or cell. Using these slide cells filled with mixtures of serum, phagocytes, staphylococci and dilutions of twenty different antiseptics in common medical use, Fleming showed that in those cells containing weak antiseptics the phagoctyes were killed, allowing the bacteria to flourish unchecked, while in those cells without any added antiseptics the staphylococcus had been inhibited by the phagocytes. So far, it was confirmation of his work during the war and it led him on to conclude that his *in vitro* observations would be repeated in the human body and that 'these experiments show that there is little hope that any of the antiseptics in common use could be successfully introduced into the blood stream to destroy the bacteria in cases of septicaemia'.[83] Fleming wondered whether the ability of the phagocytes to digest the infective bacteria might be linked to their containing lysozyme. Together with Allison, he compared the phagocytosis of lysozyme-sensitive and lysozyme-resistant organisms using slide cells. The results showed that sensitive strains were digested but that resistant strains survived.[84] Ridley added the observation that most leucocytes contained enough lysozyme to digest most pathogenic organisms.[85]

The link having been made between leucocyte lysozyme and phagocytosis, there remained the question as to whether this natural antiseptic might have any benefits for the treatment of patients. Egg-white lysozyme was not destroyed by stomach acid, so Fleming and Allison decided to see what effects it might have in cases of intestinal infection. They did find through tests that the number of streptococci in the stomach of one patient was reduced after being given egg-white lysozyme orally, but it did not seem to make any difference to the overall course of the infection. Intravenous injections into rabbits showed that the injected lysozyme seemed to be rapidly eliminated from the bloodstream. In human therapy, repeated injections would be necessary, but there was a danger of an allergic reaction.[86] Fleming hoped that the elimination of the egg-white proteins might overcome this problem, but the purification of lysozyme was beyond the expertise of Ridley, the only person available with any biochemical knowledge.

The limitations of lysozyme against the most harmful bacteria to mankind resulted in the clinicians taking little interest in it.

Nevertheless, Fleming himself always considered that his best work as a scientist had been his work on lysozyme and remained proud of both his discovery and his study of the enzyme. He described himself as having 'a fatherly interest' in this enzyme, which had an 'importance in connection with natural immunity . . . not generally appreciated'.[87] Like all proud fathers, he was eager to display his offspring to all comers. It was lysozyme that he chose to demonstrate to the Duchess of York when she visited St Mary's after her election as President of St Mary's Hospital in 1930. Sixty-five years later she still retained vivid memories of the kindly Fleming having given her an onion to make her cry and of the contrast he made to the more terrifying figure of Almroth Wright.[88] Fleming's pride in his work was understandable. It was his first truly independent line of investigation and as a scientist he was able to take it further than he ever did with penicillin. Yet, as with penicillin a few years later, his lack of deep chemical knowledge and the absence of any suitable collaborator prevented him from taking it as far as he might have done.[89] However, it did make him more receptive than he might otherwise have been when he noticed the effect of a fungal contamination on a culture plate of bacteria in the autumn of 1928. The work on antiseptics and lysozyme was the essential prelude to the discovery of penicillin.

FIVE

'Purge me with hyssop'

It was one thing to observe something new and interesting, but it was another matter to establish just what it was and whether or not it was of any importance. Fleming discovered penicillin in September 1928 and took pains to preserve it for further investigation, but it was not until the end of October 1928 that there is any surviving record in Fleming's notebooks of work on the chance contaminant. His care in preserving the mould and, even more, the contaminated culture plate indicates all too clearly the importance he gave to it, yet there were other matters that demanded his immediate attention before he could turn to his fascinating mould, including work on his paper on staphylococci as well as a myriad of administrative matters.

Before he could begin work, it was necessary for Fleming to secure a supply of his 'mould juice', which was essentially little more than a filtrate of the broth in which he had grown the fungus. As such, it was a very impure substance, but adequate for his early experiments. He tried various growth media to establish what would give him the best yields and found that an ordinary bacteriological meat nutrient broth was as good as anything, the digest broth from the heart of a bullock proving the best. His next step was to find out what was the optimum temperature and period of incubation for growing the mould. When growing it on a culture plate, he found that the best method was to grow the mould colonies for about five days at room temperature before sowing the micro-organisms he wished to test. Using a method he had earlier developed for testing the activity of lysozyme, he would cut a gutter across the agar jelly in a culture plate. This gutter was then filled with a mixture of molten agar and mould extract. When this had solidified, he used a platinum loop to streak cultures of the bacteria he wished to test across the plate at right angles from the gutter to the edge of the petri dish. The plate was then incubated at 37°C, close to body temperature, the preferred temperature at which most of the bacteria he tested would grow. The substance capable of inhibiting bacteria in the gutter would diffuse rapidly through the growth medium until within a couple of hours it had formed a clear zone of inhibition on either side of the gutter. In this zone, any organism sensitive to penicillin would not grow, while the length of the streak of bacteria would be a very rough indicator of how sensitive that particular organism might be to it.

Using this method, Fleming tested a number of bacteria. The first experiment recorded in his notebook on 30 October 1928 under the heading 'Staph. inhibiting mould' showed him that staphylococci were inhibited by the substance diffusing through the plate but that there was no effect on organisms that he labelled 'coli'[1] or 'hay'.[2] The result of this experiment showed Fleming that he was dealing with a selective inhibitor, acting against very specific bacteria but not against all germs. Another experiment recorded on the same date in which he incubated mixtures of his mould extract and staphylococci in a test tube at different temperatures showed him that most of the bacteria were dissolved at 45°C but none of them at 56°C. He concluded that the 'mould culture contains a bacteriolytic substance for staphylococci'.[3] Further experiments showed that his mould juice prevented the growth of virulent members of the group of bacteria known as Gram-positive[4] pathogens, which could be stained by a purple dye. These types of bacteria not only included staphylococcus, but also the microbes that caused scarlet fever, pneumonia, gonorrhoea, meningitis, diphtheria and the acute throat infection known in North America as 'strep throat'. However, it had little or no effect on the bacilli that cause typhoid, paratyphoid or enteritis, nor on the bacterium Haemophilus influenzae, commonly if erroneously believed to be the cause of influenza.[5]

Fleming followed up this work with some experiments using the slide-cell technique he had previously used in his studies of lysozyme. He was now interested in seeing what effect his mould juice had on leucocytes and their ability to swallow bacteria. He soon found that it had no ill-effects on the leucocytes, yet even when diluted to 1 in 800 it remained lethal to the virulent bacteria. It was far more powerful than the carbolic acid he was so disdainful of, yet it did not harm the sensitive blood cells. This might have suggested that here was an end to the search for the perfect antiseptic, except for one thing. While most antiseptics killed microbes within a few minutes, mould filtrate was slow-acting and did not take effect for several hours. This would have been a serious limitation to any therapeutic use, especially when further work demonstrated that in mixtures containing blood serum the mould filtrate seemed to lose most of its power. This suggested that in any wounds or septic infection where blood serum might be exuded, the filtrate would lose its activity long before it could begin to work against the infection.[6]

While he could investigate the phenomenon of the action of his mould juice, it was plainly desirable for Fleming to know exactly what fungus he was dealing with. He made no pretence at being a specialist on moulds and sought advice where he could most conveniently obtain it. Working in the laboratory immediately beneath his own was just the person he needed, C.J. La Touche, who was conducting a study of the effects of fungi on asthmatics for John Freeman's Allergy Department. La Touche, then aged 25, quickly narrowed down the search to the penicillium family of moulds and then attempted to identify which particular member of this genus it was. By February 1929, using the standard work on penicillia by the Belgian Biourge,[7] he had identified it as *Penicillium rubrum*. Fleming was not so sure and thought it might be *Penicillium crysogenum*.[8] While he made no pretence to be a student of the classical languages, he did have enough knowledge of Latin to wonder why a yellow-coloured mould should be called *rubrum* or red. However, he deferred to the superior knowledge of the expert on moulds and it was as *Penicillium rubrum* that it appeared in his first published papers on penicillin. In fact it was *Penicillium notatum*, closely related to *Penicillium crysogenum*.[9] This fungus had been identified and classified by the Swedish naturalist Westling in 1912, having been found on decaying hyssop. Although not a classicist, Fleming knew the Scriptures and, on learning about how the fungus had been found, was said to have quoted a relevant verse from the Psalms, 'Purge me with hyssop and I shall be clean'.[10]

With the identification of the mould, however mistakenly, came the time to christen the product of that fungus. Fleming's favourite name for it was 'mould juice'. It was hardly the most scientific nomenclature and certainly not a name that would have been popular with patients when it eventually came into clinical use. The full description of the substance, 'mould broth filtrate', was a cumbersome phrase. For once Almroth Wright did not come up with a suggestion based on classical Greek, and Fleming was free to choose his own name for his discovery.[11] His choice of the short, easily memorable name penicillin, the product of a penicillium mould, though he did not know it, was to become a worldwide household word.

Fleming also concerned himself with the question of whether this mould was unique and whether other fungi produced similar effects. Although he would not have described it as such himself, he was conducting an antibiotic screening programme.[12] Moulds were collected from mouldy cheese, jam, shoes, boots and wherever else he could obtain them, much to the amusement of his fellow members of the Chelsea Arts Club who were pressed into the search.[13] Only one of the eight strains of six species he collected and identified[14] showed any evidence of antibacterial activity and that fungus, obtained from La

Touche, seemed to be identical to the original mould.[15] Just over a year after his discovery of penicillin he described a 'new inhibitory mould', which produced a 'port wine colour under white felt', which inhibited staphylococci and streptococci, and which he named 'red mould'.[16] It was the first of a number of fungi antagonistic to pathogenic bacteria that he now examined. Not being a mycologist, he gave all these descriptive names, such as 'red mould' and 'green mould', since he had no idea what they actually were. In most cases they appeared to be airborne contaminants.[17] In 1932, he actually seemed to have discovered a yellow mould colony similar to *Penicillium notatum* and effective against a similar range of organisms.[18] However, he pursued this new mould no further, perhaps suspecting it to be the same one he had discovered four years earlier.

Another area that Fleming needed to investigate but for which he also required help was an analysis of its chemical properties, combined with work on the most effective means of producing enough active penicillin for his own experiments. He turned to two young research scholars working in the Inoculation Department for assistance in this area. Frederick Ridley had earlier worked with Fleming on lysozyme in relation to eye infections in 1926. He had also reinforced Fleming's view that organisms normally susceptible to lysozyme could acquire resistance by showing that when a non-virulent staphylococcus was made resistant to lysozyme it also regained its ability to cause conjunctivitis.[19] Ridley, who had taken a biochemistry course for B.Sc. students at the University of Birmingham where he was studying for his University of London medical qualifications, had failed to prepare the purer and more concentrated lysozyme for which Fleming had hoped, but they were old collaborators. However, they were never close and were never to have 'a personal chat'. Ridley found Fleming, with his 'rather penetrating, rather quizzical blue-eyed glance', a difficult person to get to know.[20]

The other research scholar involved in the work on penicillin was to have a much warmer and closer relationship with Fleming from the start, lasting for many years and maturing to a deep friendship. Stuart Craddock had qualified at the age of 24 as a doctor at St Mary's Hospital Medical School the previous year and after working as house surgeon in both the Outpatients Department and Surgical Unit, had recently been appointed research scholar in succession to Merlin Pryce. Before being set to work on penicillin, he had started off studying the antiseptic effect of mercuric chloride on microbes. Soon he was on good enough terms with his mentor for Fleming to tease him mercilessly and 'derive a mischievous pleasure from slightly overstating a fact about one that required a blushing and stammering denial or toning down by the victim'. He once told Wright, who despised any sports as a distraction from the important work at hand, that Craddock was a well-known footballer who might get a trial to play professionally if he could only practise enough, and on another occasion called out, 'Did you know, Old Man, that Giles is courting?' Giles, as Craddock was known, was acutely embarrassed, but took it all in the spirit of fun that Fleming had intended.[21]

The two young men were given woefully inadequate facilities, a draughty corridor 11ft long by 4ft wide and containing a bedpan sluice for a nearby ward, a couple of taps and a giant centrifuge. Close to the rising water main, the sluice had sufficient water pressure for their distillation work, and this was not available elsewhere on the second floor of the Clarence Memorial Wing. The draining board was the only surface on which they could place their apparatus. Gas for heating had to be brought to them in a long tube run through from the main laboratory of the Inoculation Department. The passage in which they worked led to the lavatory used by their colleagues in the main laboratory, who had to squeeze past two big burly rugby players working in a confined space whenever they felt the need to answer a call of nature.[22] It was also inconvenient for the two hard-working researchers to be interrupted so often in their work in conditions that were far from ideal.

However, they set to work with a will and made good progress despite all the difficulties with which they had to contend. The mould was grown at room temperature in large 5-litre flat-sided bottles and after about four days formed a white fluffy mass on the surface of the nutrient broth, which changed to a dark-green felted mass after a few days, while the broth gradually changed to a deeper yellow colour the more active it became against bacteria. After about ten days this reached its peak and the liquid was poured off from below the mould and filtered through cheesecloth, paper and the asbestos pads of a Seitz filter with the aid of compressed air produced using a bicycle pump. A clear yellow liquid was the result of all this activity, but it still contained impurities from both the mould and the broth. The next stage was to concentrate this filtrate in an airtight distillation flask. The flask was heated to evaporate the water while the air was removed using a vacuum pump at the neck of the flask. This vacuum distillation method produced a 'sticky mass' in which most of the impurities were still present, but very little of the active penicillin was lost.[23]

Fleming's initial thoughts on the nature of penicillin up to this time had been that it might be an enzyme similar to lysozyme, but Ridley and

Craddock now produced evidence that they were dealing not with an enzyme at all but with something very different. If it had been an enzyme, it would have been a protein and soluble in water though not in alcohol. They decided to add 90 per cent alcohol to a watery solution of vacuum-distilled filtrate, which remained active against staphylococci even when diluted to 1 in 3,000, which should have had the effect of separating the proteins from the non-proteins. A heavy precipitate formed, which they separated out from a clear fluid. They then found to their surprise that all the penicillin activity was in the fluid, not in the precipitate, which meant that penicillin was soluble in alcohol. It was not a protein and thus unlikely to be an enzyme.[24] However, while changing their thoughts on what Fleming's discovery might be, the very solubility of penicillin opened up a new possibility for concentrating and partly purifying the substance, since solutions in alcohol were much easier to evaporate at low temperatures. This means of separating the penicillin from the protein in the broth was a step closer to the removal of the impurities that was essential for any clinical use of the substance. However, the resultant crude filtrates of penicillin were extremely unstable and soon lost most signs of activity within a few days of being left at room temperature. It quickly became apparent that the stability of this crude penicillin was affected by just how acidic or alkaline it might be. The mould became more alkaline as it grew in the broth and at the resultant pH 8.5 to pH 9 its activity would be destroyed by vacuum distillation. By acidifying the fluid to maintain a pH value of 6.5, they could keep the penicillin preparations active for a few weeks.[25]

All of this work on the extraction of penicillin was done by young doctors with only a basic grasp of the chemical processes necessary. Craddock considered that Ridley had 'sound and pretty advanced ideas on chemistry', but neither of them had any practical experience of extraction methods and were driven to consulting basic textbooks, learning as they went along with the work: 'We knew very little when we began; we knew just a little more when we had finished.' Fleming, who was perhaps less up to date on chemistry than his assistants, who enjoyed the advantage of reading up on the subject as they proceeded, adopted a hands-off approach. Craddock stressed that 'Flem was in on all we did but I don't think that you can say he directed us in all our efforts to concentrate and extract', while making it plain that 'in all the work I did, Flem was behind it all'. Each day Craddock would leave notes of the results of the day's work on a loose sheet of paper for his mentor to examine and all the titrations he did were done on Fleming's instructions.[26] Ridley was more critical than Craddock of Fleming's understanding of chemistry.[27] This may be linked to Fleming having misquoted the results of the extraction work, stating that 'Mr Ridley has found that if penicillin is evaporated at low temperature to a sticky mass the active principle can be completely extracted by absolute alcohol. It is insoluble in ether or chloroform.'[28] However, Ridley's work had shown that it was soluble in ether and acetone, as well as alcohol, whereas he had not yet tried it out in chloroform when Fleming wrote the work up.[29]

Fleming was on surer and more familiar territory, just as he had been with the bacteriological aspects, when he turned his attention to an examination of the possible clinical value of his find. It was important to establish just how toxic or otherwise penicillin might be, since any systemic use of it, given by injection so that it would reach all parts of the body, depended on it being safe to administer. Intravenous injections into a rabbit and a mouse produced no toxic symptoms and indicated that this powerful antibacterial mould filtrate was relatively safe to use on animals. So far this was encouraging and suggested the possibility of injection, as with salvarsan.[30] Craddock performed a further experiment in which mould juice was injected into the ear vein of another rabbit. The activity of penicillin in the blood serum was tested after a minute and found to be as active as expected, but when a further blood sample was tested half an hour later almost all the activity of the penicillin had gone.[31] The implication of this was that penicillin soon lost any power to do any good in the presence of blood serum, which could severely limit any systemic action.

However, Fleming did continue with Craddock's help to follow up the suggestion that penicillin might have potential as an antiseptic. Craddock foolhardily acted as a guinea pig to test its toxicity to human beings. He grew the mould in milk in a cool incubator and 'ate the product, which in the curdled milk after a week or so was very like stilton cheese. It did me no harm.'[32] Reassured that Craddock was unaffected, Fleming used penicillin on a suitable patient in the nearby Annie Zunz ward. This man had a streptococcal infection in his gut, suffered from arthritis and ran a temperature at night. The mould juice in milk had no effect on controlling his temperature. Craddock was now selected as a suitable patient. He had suffered from sinusitis for some months and his nasal antrum had been so chronically infected that an operation had proved necessary. Fleming offered to take swabs from his nose to test the antiseptic power of the mould filtrate and also suggested irrigating the antrum with penicillin. It had very little effect, although Craddock continued to wash out his open antrum twice a day a few more times.[33]

A much more severe case now presented itself. A patient in one of the surgical wards of the hospital was seriously ill with an infected

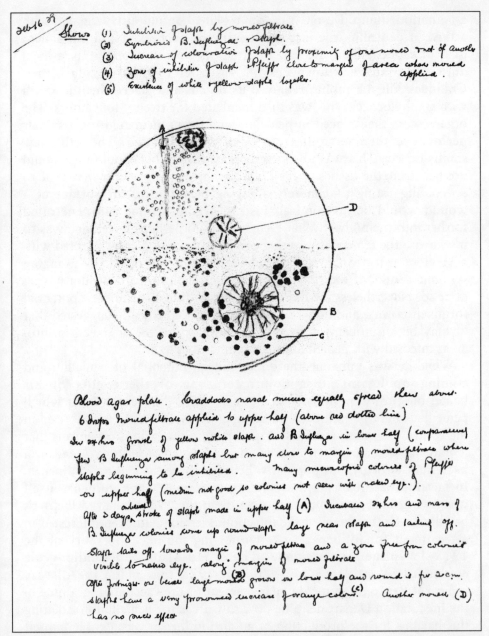

Investigating the properties of the mould: Fleming's notebook for 16 February 1929 in which he tests the effects of penicillin on Stuart Craddock's nasal mucus. *(Alexander Fleming Laboratory Museum, St Mary's NHS Trust)*

amputation stump. Despite the stump being continuously irrigated with a flow of penicillin, the infection continued unchecked and the patient died of septicaemia.[34] So far all attempts to use penicillin as a local antiseptic had been unsuccessful. In order to try to explain this, Craddock killed a rabbit, removed its organs and placed them in broth with staphylococci. This was then incubated for twenty-four hours. The organs were then placed in penicillin and again incubated for a similar period and then sections from them were cultured. They all grew staphylococci. This was taken as demonstrating that mould juice could not penetrate the tissues of the organs whereas the bacteria were able to do so, suggesting that merely applying penicillin to the surface of a wound would be no good against an organism that had penetrated further into the body.[35] What Fleming should perhaps have done was to investigate the effects of injecting penicillin into an animal infected with a virulent infection, which would have demonstrated the amazing systemic results of the substance, but there is no record of him having done so. Nevertheless, he did not lose his faith in a therapeutic potential for his discovery, and in his first publication on penicillin suggested that 'it may be an efficient antiseptic for application to, or injection into, areas infected with penicillin-sensitive microbes'.[36]

While he was pursuing the direct clinical potential of penicillin and coming up against disappointment, one of the results of his bacteriological experiments suggested a very different way in which penicillin might be indirectly of therapeutic use. Fleming had noticed in the course of assessing the effect of penicillin on various organisms that it had no effect on Pfeiffer's bacillus or *Haemophilus influenzae*, a bacterium wrongly, but popularly, believed to be the cause of influenza. In fact the bacillus caused secondary infections while influenza itself was a viral infection, but many doctors in the 1920s believed Pfeiffer's bacillus to be the origin of the infection. Fleming had been interested in a treatment for influenza since witnessing the high mortality of the 1918–19 influenza pandemic. There had also been smaller-scale epidemics of influenza in 1926 and 1928 that made the disease topical.[37] Responsible for the management of the vaccine programme in the Inoculation Department, he now saw a use for penicillin in isolating this bacillus for the production of an anti-influenza vaccine. He himself described the use of penicillin in this context as a 'bacterial weed killer', destroying the common or garden resistant bacteria that were susceptible to penicillin in order to isolate the desirable flowers or resistant bacteria. Penicillin plates soon became a standard medium in his laboratory for investigating throat and chest infections. By isolating Pfeiffer's bacillus, Fleming hoped to develop a potentially life-saving vaccine and may have done so had *Haemophilus influenzae* actually been the cause of influenza.[38]

By 13 February 1929, Fleming felt ready to present his findings to the Medical Research Club. His reception was almost identical to his experience when presenting lysozyme to the club in 1922.[39] His presentation on 'A Medium for the Isolation of Pfeiffer's Bacillus' was greeted with silence and followed by neither questions nor discussion. H.J. Parish of the Wellcome Research Laboratories was unimpressed by what he heard, which seemed likely to be an interesting phenomenon like lysozyme but without much practical therapeutic significance, and 'did not think an epoch-making discovery had been made, mainly because penicillin in those days was very weak and also because a number of other substances of interest to bacteriologists, including bacteriophage and mercury compounds, had not fulfilled the early claims made for them'.[40]

Undiscouraged as ever, Fleming then began to write up his findings for the *British Journal of Experimental Pathology*. His paper was submitted on 10 May 1929 and it appeared a month later. Now acknowledged as a classic of medical literature and a collector's item, the paper 'On the Antibacterial Action of Cultures of a Penicillium, with Special Reference to their Use in the Isolation of *B. influenzae*' aroused as little interest as the talk to the Medical Research Club had done. It was concise and precise in its presentation of the findings on penicillin and its use in the isolation of the organism believed to be the cause of influenza. It has been criticised for this very quality of brevity and clarity and its lack of a review of previous literature on antibacterial substances,[41] but Fleming was just conforming to the editorial style of the journal for which he was writing.[42] Apart from its comments on the as yet unrealised therapeutic potential of penicillin, it made no extravagant claims but confined itself to the work done on it over the previous few months.[43]

The emphasis in the paper on the role of penicillin in isolating *B. influenzae* reflected the importance Fleming gave to the development of vaccines against a disease such as influenza that had been so devastating within recent years. Selective culture of resistant strains of bacteria was also an area in which penicillin was demonstrably effective, compared with a therapeutic potential that could be realised only if the problems of purification and stability could be overcome. It was little wonder that, in a scientific paper on his early work, Fleming should emphasise laboratory use. It was this laboratory use that led a number of bacteriologists around the world to request samples of the mould for use in their own laboratories, including the Lister Institute, the Sir

William Dunn School of Pathology at the University of Oxford and
Sheffield University Medical School, which were all to be important in
the dissemination of penicillin and its later development. In his own
department, his colleague I.H. Maclean used penicillin to isolate the
whooping cough bacillus.[44] Not only was Fleming keeping the mould
alive in his own laboratory for the isolation of Pfeiffer's bacillus, but
other research laboratories were doing the same. When the time came
for further work, it had been preserved in a number of places, and
without its preservation Fleming's mould would have been an
interesting phenomenon without much further significance.

There have been many claims made since penicillin first came into
clinical use that penicillin had been discovered before Fleming, but in
the absence of the moulds themselves it is very difficult to substantiate
such boasts. Fleming was not the first to notice the inhibition of
bacteria by moulds or by other bacteria. There are many old wives' tales
about the use of moulds in folk remedies. In Serbia and Greece, mouldy
bread was a traditional treatment for wounds and infection, while the
attachment of the Russian peasant to Mother Earth was reflected in the
use of warm soil as a treatment for infected wounds.[45] This idea of
using moulds as a form of treatment was recorded by apothecaries such
as John Parkington, King's Herbarian, who advocated the use of moulds
in his 1640 book on pharmacology.[46] It was only in the nineteenth
century that such observations were put onto a more scientific basis.
The term antibiosis had been coined by Vuillemin in 1889,[47] but the
scientific observation of the inhibition of bacteria by other micro-
organisms had begun earlier. One of the earliest examinations of the
effects of moulds on bacteria had been undertaken by Sir John Burdon-
Sanderson, whose early professional career had begun as Medical
Superintendent of St Mary's Hospital from 1852 to 1858 and as a
lecturer in the newly founded St Mary's Hospital Medical School from
1854 to 1862. In 1870 he observed that culture fluids exposed to the air
were soon filled with growing bacteria but that if the surface of the fluid
was contaminated by moulds of the penicillium group there would be
no bacterial growth.[48] This observation by Burdon-Sanderson was
followed up by John Tyndall, who demonstrated to the Royal Society
the antibacterial effects of a penicillium mould.[49] It also prompted
Joseph Lister to investigate the action on human tissue of a mould he
described as *Penicillium glaucum*, which caused bacterial colonies to
disappear from liquid cultures.[50] It is possible that Lister may have used
a mould preparation in 1884 to treat a nurse at King's College Hospital
with a wound that would not respond to any antiseptics until Lister
tried another substance on it. The nurse had asked his registrar to write

down for her the name of this miraculous substance, which turned out to be 'Penicillium'.[51] Fleming was interested in the claim that Lister had possibly discovered penicillin and commented, 'What a pity that his experiment of 28 November 1871 did not come off. He had the idea of penicillin, but he had the wrong mould, or the wrong bacteria, or both. If Fate had been kind to him, medical history might have been changed and Lister might have lived to see what he was always looking for – a non-poisonous antiseptic.'[52]

In the years between Lister's inconclusive work and Fleming's discovery there were further observations along similar lines.[53] Pasteur and Joubert in 1877 mentioned the therapeutic possibilities of bacterial antagonism as a by-product of their work on the prevention of anthrax.[54] Ten years later Garré recorded further examples of such antagonism.[55] In Naples in 1895, Vicenzo Tiberio made extracts of penicillium moulds and injected them into animals infected with virulent bacteria, but the results were inconclusive.[56] Meanwhile at the École du Service de Santé Militaire in Lyons, a 23-year-old army doctor, Ernest Augustin Duchesne, studied the ways in which *Penicillium glaucum* could protect animals injected with normally lethal doses of bacteria. In his 1897 thesis 'Contribution a l'étude de la concurrence vitale chez les microorganismes: antagonisme entre les moissures et les microbes', he commented on these observations but made no claims to have actually demonstrated a substance with antibacterial properties.[57] Nevertheless, this has not prevented assertions that Duchesne, who died of tuberculosis in 1912, rather than Fleming had priority in claims to having discovered penicillin.[58] The problem in assessing many of these claims is that *Penicillium glaucum* was a catch-all term often used by nineteenth-century scientists to describe their active isolates of moulds; it was a term often used to refer to *Penicillium expansum*, a fungus that does not produce penicillin. None of Fleming's predecessors retained their moulds and it is now impossible to know whether these cultures actually produced penicillin or another antibacterial substance such as the toxic patulin.[59]

Once penicillin had come into clinical use, there was a suggestion that it might have been discovered in Belgium three years before Fleming's discovery by one of his friends, the bacteriologist André D. Gratia at the University of Liège. In 1925 Gratia, then aged 32, had observed the antibacterial action of a green mould, which he tentatively identified as the omnipresent *Penicillium glaucum*, which had cleared cultures of the actinomyces family of bacteria from broth. He had transplanted this interesting mould to an agar culture plate that he had seeded with a diluted culture of the anthrax bacillus. After a few days, Gratia had 'observed a picture which was almost exactly the same as the now historical original plate of your work of 1929'. However, before he could investigate further, he had fallen ill, and when he recovered his health he had lost his cultures of active penicillium and of the actinomyces he had actually been studying. In telling Fleming of this, Gratia stressed, 'I never tried to make any claim about the discovery of penicillin and its bacteriostatic action and I am certainly not contesting your paternity; it would be simply foolish and ridiculous.'[60] Gratia was especially keen to be given recognition that he had realised the general significance of his observation, as this could have been helpful to his attempts to build up a research centre for antibiotics at Liège and would have helped to consolidate his position. It is conceivable that Gratia had discovered Fleming's penicillin, but, without greater knowledge of the fungus, it is impossible to know whether his discovery was toxic to mankind or not. The friendship between the two men was long standing and Fleming was not offended by his colleague's plea for recognition. Gratia had also discovered another bacteriolytic substance, *Streptothrix*, and in the early 1930s Fleming repeated and extended Gratia's work on this phenomenon.[61] The two bacteriologists remained friends and in contact with each other until war and the German occupation of Belgium cut off lines of communication. Immediately after liberation, Fleming and Gratia, who was fresh from five months with the Maquis, re-established contact and Gratia congratulated him on his 'glorious success' with penicillin.[62] Fleming in turn was ready to assert, in supporting his friend's nomination for the 1949 Nobel Prize, that, 'had he elected to pursue the antibiotics produced by moulds, he would probably have found penicillin, but he worked at those produced by bacteria which have not produced as yet any startling antibiotic agent'.[63]

The work on penicillin by Craddock and Ridley slowed down and came to an end after some four months of intense work. Ridley developed boils and went off on a sea voyage for the sake of his health.[64] His annual research scholarship of £275 also came to an end in 1929, and, after briefly resuming his work on lysozyme, he now firmly directed his career path to his real love, ophthalmology, with a move to Moorfields Eye Hospital. Craddock continued to work with Fleming, concentrating on the use of penicillin in the isolation of the acne bacillus for the preparation of vaccines.[65] However, he too left St Mary's in 1930 to take up an appointment at the Wellcome Research Laboratories at Beckenham, which he had obtained with Fleming's patronage. He had contracted tuberculosis while working with Fleming, which had been a factor in the decision not to continue with administration of penicillin to cure his infected antrum, since penicillin had no effect on the tubercle bacillus. After an operation to remove a lung, he left the field of medical research for the quieter life of a country general practitioner in Devon.[66]

Fleming's interest in the clinical application of penicillin did not end with the departure of the two research scholars and he continued to be on the lookout for suitable cases for treatment. Its use on cases of sinusitis was slightly more successful than with Craddock, but 'there was nothing miraculous'.[67] He also used it as a dressing for septic wounds, where it proved more effective than dressings containing stronger chemicals, but 'septic wounds are uncommon in hospital and as the potency of penicillin rapidly disappears on keeping, the therapeutic aspect of this substance was dropped'.[68] It was only in 1932 or 1933 that Fleming could point to a clinical success with penicillin on another of his research students. Keith Rogers had an attack of pneumococcal conjunctivitis days before he was due to represent St Mary's in an inter-hospital rifle club match. He mentioned his problem to Fleming, whose first appointment in the Inoculation Department was due to his own shooting skills, and was reassured that he would be able to treat it by Saturday, when the competition was scheduled to take place: 'he put in some yellow fluid, which he assured me was safe and which I imagine was penicillin, that was made in the lab then.' Rogers's eye infection had cleared up by the time of the match and he was able to compete. He was also able to lay claim to having been the first successful case to be treated with penicillin, although it was used as a local antiseptic rather than injected systemically.[69]

Fleming himself believed that the main problem in gathering together any clinical data for assessing the true potential of penicillin lay in the mismatch between the availability of suitable cases and the availability of batches of penicillin: 'when we asked the surgeons if they had any septic cases, they never had any, and then perhaps a septic case would turn up and we had no penicillin, for it was an unstable substance and if left at room temperature for a week its activity had disappeared. When we had penicillin, we could not find any suitable cases, and when a suitable case presented itself, we had no penicillin.'[70] Although this situation was frustrating and led to the end of any attempts at clinical studies, Fleming remained convinced that his latest discovery was of more value than as a mere laboratory tool, noting in a paper on antiseptics for the *British Dental Journal* that 'Penicillin is valuable for us at present in the isolation of certain microbes, but it is quite likely that it, or a chemical of a similar nature, will be used in the treatment of septic wounds'.[71]

Fleming was not the only one to take an interest in the therapeutic application of penicillin. Cecil George Paine, a 24-year-old graduate of St Mary's Hospital Medical School and a junior assistant in the Bacteriology Department in 1928, had been shown the penicillin plate by Fleming and had been given a culture of the mould before he moved to Sheffield in January 1929 to take up an appointment as clinical pathologist at Sheffield Royal Infirmary and demonstrator in pathology at Sheffield University. His first attempts to use the crude filtrate of mould juice on three men with sychosis barbae, a staphylococcal infection of the beard follicles, proved 'uniformly disappointing'. However, a second series of trials involving eye infections proved much more successful, including three cases of conjunctivitis in new-born babies. However, the most spectacular result was in clearing up a severe pneumococcal eye infection in a local colliery manager as the result of a piece of stone penetrating his right eye. After the eye had been irrigated with penicillin, the infection cleared up within 48 hours and the stone could be removed, allowing the man to recover his vision. Paine failed to publish his results and very soon moved from the Royal Infirmary to the Jessop Hospital, Sheffield, where he concentrated on the study of infections in childbirth but abandoned his work on penicillin. Ironically, penicillin was later to prove a life-saver for women who would once have died of puerperal sepsis. However, Paine did discuss his work with Howard Florey, Professor of Pathology at Sheffield, who 'showed not the slightest interest at the time', although later, like Fleming, was to owe his lasting fame to penicillin.[72]

Without compelling evidence of the clinical potential of penicillin, Fleming had little hope of convincing any biochemists that purification of his penicillin might have any medical benefits. He insisted that 'I was a bacteriologist working in a laboratory where there was no skilled chemist'.[73] Lacking any suitable biochemists as collaborators at St Mary's, Fleming turned elsewhere for help but without any success. He approached H. Berry, Dean of the School of Pharmacy, and urged him to take up the problem of the isolation of penicillin in the mid-1930s. Berry was impressed that 'he seemed so convinced that the discovery had a great value', but such conviction did not prove persuasive enough either to Berry or to Harold King of the Medical Research Council, whom he also approached.[74] Fleming's answer to later questions about why he had failed to develop penicillin to the practical stage was to retort to fellow scientists, 'Why didn't you? All the information was in the literature.'[75]

Meanwhile, the biochemistry of penicillin was being studied independently of Fleming a few miles away at the London School of

Hygiene and Tropical Medicine. There Harold Raistrick, recently appointed Professor of Biochemistry, had his attention drawn to Fleming's 1929 paper at the beginning of a research project into chemically active mould pigments by his colleague W.W.C. Topley, the Professor of Bacteriology. Topley even seconded one of his own researchers, the bacteriologist Reginald Lovell, to work with Raistrick, the biochemist P.W. Clutterbuck and the mycologist J.H.V. Charles. Doubtful of the classification of the mould as *Penicillium rubrum*, Clutterbuck sent a strain to the mycologist Charles Thom at the United States Department of Agriculture, who was very quickly to reclassify it as a strain of *Penicillium notatum* Westling in the *Penicillium crysogenum* Thom series of fungi.[76] The identity of the mould was academic for the work at hand. Although Fleming had not instituted this work and did not even know Raistrick until later, he was constantly telephoned by Lovell for advice on the best media for growing the mould and was happy to give what little help he could.[77] Lovell was to consider that the main contribution made by his co-workers was to demonstrate that penicillin could be grown successfully on a semi-synthetic medium containing salts and glucose known as Czapek–Dox medium, which was later used by others to produce penicillin, and that it could be kept a long time if it was slightly acidic.[78] As Frederick Ridley had done before them, they also extracted the active substance with ether, but then found that it lost most of its activity when they tried to re-extract it from the ether through evaporation. Perhaps of most significance to their own research interests was their success in isolating the pigment that gave the mould filtrates their golden colour.[79] However, the failure to recover the active penicillin from ether discouraged them from any further attempts at purification, which had indeed never been their aim. Raistrick said, 'we could do nothing in the face of it, so we dropped it and went on with our other investigations and experiments'.[80]

With another failure to overcome the problems of purity and stability, the lesson was not lost on Fleming, who later said that 'I had failed to advance further for the want of adequate chemical help. Raistrick and his associates had lacked bacteriological cooperation so the problem of the effective concentration of penicillin remained unresolved.'[81] The obvious thing would have been for Fleming and Raistrick to have combined forces, but Raistrick and his colleagues were not trying to purify penicillin for clinical use when they studied it, so such an undertaking would have been a major deflection from their primary research. Fleming later admitted to Howard Florey, 'It now seems rather a pity that we did not collaborate. In those days I was working in an immunological laboratory with a Chief whose sole interest was immunology. Antibiotics for me was rather a sideline and when Raistrick published his paper showing that the concentration of penicillin was not quite successful even in the hands of a successful chemist, I am afraid I got quite discouraged about the problem.'[82]

Fleming's own professional life in the decade following the discovery of penicillin was very active. His biographer André Maurois has depicted this period as one of frustration, describing Fleming as 'suffering from some secret sorrow'.[83] On the contrary, it was a fruitful period with much to interest him and he was not one to brood. In 1932 he was elected President of the Section of Pathology in the Royal Society of Medicine and chose lysozyme as the subject of his presidential address.[84] Meanwhile, at St Mary's he continued to be responsible for vaccine production and was heavily involved in the planning of new laboratories, an opportunity offered by plans for the major rebuilding of both the hospital and its medical school.

St Mary's had always suffered from its confined site in a heavily built-up area. Nevertheless a constant theme in the history of the hospital has been the desire to rebuild on a grand scale. The construction of the Clarence Wing had almost brought disaster, but by 1928 there was a need for more space if only to keep up with the demand for the services of the hospital and the need to accommodate the growing specialisation of medicine and the latest advances. In 1928, when new operating theatres and additional wards were needed, the only way to expand was upwards, with a new floor built above the attics of the Albert Edward Wing.[85] In the same year, the opportunity arose to buy for £65,000 a triangular 'island site' bounded by Cambridge Place facing the hospital, Praed Street and South Wharf Road and occupied by slum housing. Charles Wilson, the Dean of the Medical School, saw this as the ideal opportunity to build a new school worthy of his ambitions for St Mary's as one of the premier medical schools of the British Empire. Almroth Wright was not to be left behind, and it was agreed that attached to the new medical school buildings would be a new Institute of Pathology.

Money for this grandiose scheme was obtained through appeals, flag days and applications to the University Grants Committee and benefactors of the hospital and school. The students and nurses were enthusiastic in assisting with fundraising, but the most important source of funds came from patronage. Wilson successfully solicited £25,000 from the merchant banker Lord Revelstoke and £63,000 from his patient, the newspaper magnate Lord Beaverbrook, against which £10,000 from the University Grants Committee seemed small beer.[86]

Beaverbrook had been especially impressed during an incognito visit to the Outpatients Department when a volunteer from the Ladies' Association working in a canteen for patients had replied to his enquiry about the cost of tea and a bun that he could have it for nothing if he was unable to afford it.[87] Wright also had few problems in mobilising support and funds for his part of the scheme. Lord Iveagh, Chairman of the Inoculation Department Committee, personally donated £40,000 while other benefactors contributed a further £22,000, and £43,000 came from the surplus funds of the department itself, deriving from vaccine production and the fees of private patients.[88]

The foundation stones of both Wilson's and Wright's new buildings were laid by the Duchess of York, President of the Hospital, on 30 June 1931, with a speech by Stanley Baldwin, Conservative leader of the Opposition and soon to be Lord President in the National Government, broadcast by the BBC to the Empire.[89] In it he stressed the importance of medical research, a sentiment close to the hearts of both Wright and Fleming. Progress on the new buildings was swift and by 1933 the move to the spacious new quarters could begin, though it was disruptive to research and routine work. The Inoculation Department now occupied a five-storey brick building designed by the architect Sir Edwin Cooper. The ground floor offered an imposing entrance hall to the institute, which was connected to the medical school at all levels, but the ground floor of the wing occupied by the institute was leased out as shops opening onto Praed Street, their rent providing a new source of income. As well as access to the wood-panelled medical school library, which doubled as a speech hall, the Inoculation Department also had its own library where the famous tea parties presided over by Wright could be held in more spacious surroundings. There was a lecture theatre and adequate laboratory space for teaching and research. Wright and Fleming occupied laboratories on the second floor of the new building, with a public telephone box in between them.[90] Vaccine production was hidden away on the third floor and in the basement. A bridge connected the new laboratories with the research ward in the Clarence Memorial Wing.

The new buildings were prestigious enough to be opened by George V and Queen Mary on 12 December 1933. As part of the celebrations, Wright had decided that the Inoculation Department should demonstrate its work through impressive displays. Fleming thought that the King and Queen might appreciate a lighter touch and prepared for them some of his germ paintings, created using differently pigmented bacteria. He had made a collection of chromogenic bacteria, which he then grew on agar plates in such a way that the colours would as if by magic produce designs, pictures and miniature rock gardens.

Competently executed sketches on absorbent card or on blotting paper would be placed face down onto nutrient agar to absorb some of this culture medium. The sketch was next coloured in with differently pigmented bacteria, incubated and then fixed by exposure to methanol vapour. Examples of his work included landscapes, dancing ballerinas, nursing mothers, The Dhoon, guardsmen, the fleur-de-lis in St Mary's blue and the red, white and blue of the Union Jack.[91] Queen Mary, whose acquisitive eye had been caught by carpets borrowed for the occasion through Fleming's contacts, was not at all amused and commented, 'Yes – but what good is it?' Her daughter-in-law, the Duchess of York, was more appreciative and tactful. Fleming quite enjoyed telling the story against himself.[92]

Some of the medical students of that time, affectionately rather than maliciously, were to consider 'old Flem' to be something of a joke, though once his role as the discoverer of penicillin had been acknowledged he overnight became the 'great man'.[93] He was a poor lecturer, often inaudible, and he failed to convey his enthusiasm for his subject to his students, perhaps because of 'a fundamental mental honesty in presenting the case as undramatically and as fairly and scientifically as he could'.[94] One problem, apart from inaudibility, according to Philip Wilcox, was that 'in teaching students and others with very limited knowledge of his subject he was not well able to grasp the limited mental capacity of his hearers or their capacity to absorb the details of his quickly described experiments'.[95] Despite his limitations as a lecturer, he had a mastery of his subject and was 'always extremely helpful to students individually'.[96] It was on that individual level that 'he was always able to put you on to something that you had not thought about and open up a completely fresh series of experiments for you'.[97] The brightest students and those working closely with him were to rate his qualities as a teacher more highly than those who merely attended his rather dull undergraduate lectures.

As well as his teaching, Fleming's administrative responsibilities within the Inoculation Department were increasing as Wright became more remote from the day-to-day concerns of his institute. Slow to anger except in cases of palpable injustice or unjustified scientific claims, Fleming found his talents as a peacemaker were needed with an ever more irascible chief.[98] Fleming himself was put out when he thought himself slighted by a throwaway comment from Wright that everyone in the department just did as they liked. Fleming, who indeed was the only one to attend to the business of the laboratory and to ensure that research reports were produced, was piqued, but contented himself with the retort, 'Thank you, Old Man, thank you!'[99] He could be more forceful in defending staff who fell foul of Wright's short temper, such as Dyson, who had made the cardinal mistake of criticising Wright's methods of estimating the bactericidal power of blood, however justifiably. In challenging the Old Man, Fleming always remained his usual calm and equable self.[100]

Fleming, despite his many duties, returned to the problem of penicillin in 1934. Lewis Holt, a chemist, had been appointed to work with Almroth Wright on scurvy and with Fleming on the production of a staphylococcal toxoid, a vaccine prepared from a toxin made harmless by chemical means. He had recently graduated and was newly married. The month before he started working at St Mary's had been an anxious one for him as so haphazard was the administration of the Inoculation Department that he was kept waiting for four weeks before his appointment was confirmed. When he did eventually start work, Fleming, one of his few new colleagues not to consider him beyond the pale because he was not medically qualified,[101] showed him the effect penicillin had on staphylococcus. Intrigued by it, he responded to Fleming's suggestion that he should try to extend the work of Raistrick and his colleagues, but Fleming had failed to mention the work done by Ridley and Craddock. Holt started at the point where Raistrick had stopped with the problem of extracting the active penicillin from ether, but instead of ether to extract the active penicillin from the mould filtrate he used slightly acidic amyl acetate. He then found that the active substance could be recovered from the amyl acetate by extraction back into a slightly alkaline aqueous solution of sodium bicarbonate. In doing this he had removed many of the impurities and was well on his way to success with a procedure that researchers at Oxford would utilise triumphantly a few years later. However, failing to recognise the significance of his own achievement, he considered the results of this work too unsatisfactory to be worth doing much more and abandoned the project after a few weeks.[102]

The following year Roger Reid, a graduate student at Pennsylvania State Agricultural College, published the results of a study of moulds undertaken to establish which of them were capable of producing Fleming's antibacterial substance. Inspired by Fleming's paper, he had obtained a sample of the mould from Charles Thom in November 1930. After examining twenty-three species of mould without finding any antibacterial activity, he had tried to extend the extraction process followed by Raistrick, but made very little headway other than to confirm the results of previous attempts at isolation and purification.[103] Later saluted by Fleming as 'the first penicillin pioneer in America', Reid had been directed to another topic for his doctoral thesis, since his supervisor's view was that penicillin was obviously 'no better than chlorine for sterilising milk cans'.[104]

Fleming has been charged with having lost interest in penicillin, other than its use in the laboratory, after 1929 and his failure to isolate it. While it may have been only one of a number of strands he was working on, he actually continued to take an interest in it until the end of 1939. In 1934 he showed that it was ineffective against anaerobic bacteria, which thrive in the absence of oxygen.[105] In 1935 he undertook a series of experiments to establish the effects of acidity on the shelf-life of penicillin and tried to improve its longevity by storing it under a layer of Vaseline.[106] He was interested in the means of production, demonstrating in 1935 that when grown on paper his original penicillium mould produced penicillin[107] and examining in December 1939 various growth media including ox heart.[108] He also turned his attention to the effects of penicillin on various strains of staphylococci.[109] Next he looked at the question of the development of resistance to penicillin, noting in 1936 that certain 'prawn variants' of staphylococci showed signs of resistance[110] but concluding after further experiments in 1938 that 'there was no increased resistance to penicillin on those staphs. which had previously been in contact with penicillin'.[111] None of this work was published at the time and had all been superseded by the publication of a report in 1940 on work being done from 1938 onwards by a team at the Sir William Dunn School of Pathology at the University of Oxford. Had Fleming felt ready to publish this work, he would have written it up.[112] He did occasionally mention the potential of penicillin in lectures to students, none of whom were in a position to further the work.[113]

Fleming's failure to gain extra resources from the Inoculation Department to pursue the further development of penicillin has been blamed on Sir Almroth Wright's hostility to chemotherapy in any form.[114] Indeed it has been suggested that Fleming defied him in including reference to the therapeutic potential of penicillin in the conclusion to his 1929 paper.[115] According to this interpretation, Wright was the villain of the piece. It was the picture painted by Maurois, acting under the influence of Fleming's second wife, herself a bacteriologist repelled by the Old Man's attitude to women scientists and by his dominance in his relationship with her husband. However, Wright was taking less interest in the work of his department by the early 1930s and did not impede any of the research actually being done into chemotherapy, just as he had not blocked work on salvarsan before the First World War though it did not interest him personally. There is no evidence that Wright ever attempted to stop Fleming from working on penicillin and it was that very work which he cited in again proposing Fleming for membership of the Royal Society in 1930.[116] Indeed he even encouraged some of his younger colleagues in their researches into the detested chemotherapy by returning from a visit to the Pasteur Institute in Paris carrying a large wicker basket containing a rabbit infected with syphilis of the scrotum so that they could assess the effects of arsenical compounds.[117]

Fleming himself turned his attention to the study of a new chemotherapeutic agent in the mid-1930s. In 1936, his former colleague Leonard Colebrook, now honorary Director of the Research Laboratories at Queen Charlotte's Lying-in Hospital, announced the successful use of a new drug sulphanilamide in the treatment of puerperal fever, slashing mortality rates from 20 per cent to 4.7 per cent.[118] Sulphanilamide, developed by the chemist Gerhard Domagk at the I.G. Farbenindustrie Bayer plant near Düsseldorf, was the first new effective drug since salvarsan back in 1909. Searching for chemical remedies, Domagk had found that one of the azo dyes manufactured by his firm, the brilliant red dye prontosil, used for colouring textiles, cured mice injected with lethal haemolytic streptococci, an infection that dissolved the red blood cells. He had then used it successfully to treat his own small daughter. Scientists at the Pasteur Institute were able to split the compound into its components and established that it was not the dye that stopped the growth of the bacteria but its other part, the sulphonamide molecule. This molecule had been synthesized as early as 1907 so it could not be patented, with the result that other firms could produce the new drug and also develop comparable compounds. These new sulpha drugs transformed medicine, offering for the first time treatment for such infections as pneumonia, meningitis, erysipelas, scarlet fever and puerperal fever. Domagk was awarded the 1939 Nobel Prize for Medicine, but was forbidden by the Nazi government to accept it and was detained by the Gestapo to prevent him from going to Stockholm.[119]

Despite the success of the sulpha drugs, they did have some serious disadvantages. They were not effective against all bacteria and did not work well on localized infections where pus had formed. They also had side effects, including skin rashes and vomiting. Some patients turned blue as a result of the drug's effect on blood pigments. More alarming, though rare, they could also suppress the production of the white blood cells, impairing natural resistance to infection. Ronald Hare, who had moved from St Mary's to work with Colebrook at Queen Charlotte's Hospital, soon had first-hand experience of treatment with prontosil. In January 1936 he developed an infection after pricking his finger on a sliver of glass infected with streptococci. There was a danger that he would lose his arm, so Colebrook decided to administer prontosil by mouth and by injection. Hare turned bright pink and did not know whether he was dying from the infection or the drug. Fleming visited him during his treatment at St Mary's and asked Hare's wife 'Hae ye said your prayers?'[120] Happily the new drug worked its wonders on Hare without the need for divine intervention.

Despite Wright's expressed disdain for chemotherapy, this exciting new area of research set the stage for the investigation of possible new killers of bacteria and attracted Fleming's attention. Using his tried and tested routines for testing new antiseptics, he began his research on the sulphonamides in October 1936.[121] Very soon he found a way of reconciling the dramatic effects of the sulpha drugs with Wright's system of vaccine therapy. A simple compound, para-aminobenzoic acid, which was very similar chemically to sulphanilamide, was an essential nutrient for those bacteria sensitive to the sulpha drugs. It seemed that the sulphonamide molecule was being taken up by the bacteria in mistake for para-aminobenzoic acid, with the result that the bacteria were starved of the nutrients essential for their growth. Fleming proposed that what then happened was that the leucocytes and antibodies in the blood killed the microbes weakened by the action of the drug. If this were the case, the stimulation of the phagocytes by vaccines would improve the success rate of chemotherapy. Experiments with rabbits and mice supported his thesis.[122] This combined therapy, which Fleming continued to advocate until penicillin had proved its worth, gave a renewed validity to the ideas that had underpinned the work of the Inoculation Department for over thirty years and gave a boost to the vaccine production, which funded that work but which the increased use of the sulphonamides had threatened.

Unfortunately the sulphonamides came too late to save the life of Fleming's brother John in 1937. A staunch supporter of all the St Mary's sports teams, Fleming attended as many sporting fixtures as he could. The day after cheering on the St Mary's rugby team with his brother, John went down with a bout of pneumonia. Two years previously, he had recovered from a similar illness after being injected with an anti-pneumococcal serum prepared by his younger brother. This time he failed to respond to the serum and prontosil was equally ineffective. Sulphapyridine, better known as M and B 693, developed by the firm of May and Baker, which was to prove effective in cases of pneumonia, was not available for another year. John, the most outgoing and affectionate in manner of the Fleming brothers, died. His widow Elizabeth moved into the flat above her sister and brother-in-law in Danvers Street, but never fully got over her loss.[123]

Family life continued to be centred on weekends at The Dhoon, which formed a second home for his nieces and nephews, but parenthood had brought some changes. Fleming, 'happier with children than he was with grown-ups', gave up playing golf in order to spend more time every weekend with his son Robert.[124] The boy and his friends were even allowed to play ping-pong in his father's shed, originally built for the Pegrams as a studio and transported to The Dhoon, where it housed fishing rods and a half-size billiard table,[125] as long as they did not touch any of 'Dad's things', which included such curiosities as 'jars of gruesome orange peel and a stuffed owl', prompting Phyllis Norton, one of the village children, to consider Robert's father to be 'slightly dotty'.[126] Weekends were too short, even when driving down to Suffolk on Friday evenings and returning to London on Monday mornings. Fleming would enliven such drives by racing his car against the local train, which ran on a line close to the road, giving himself a handicap so that he would not win too easily.[127] One weekend, he took Robert with him to his laboratory and the boy, finding himself the centre of attention, became as shy and silent as his father, prompting Maclean to remark that 'Robert has so little to say because Mrs F. has so much'.[128] Fleming himself made a joke of Sareen's vivacity compared to his own silences and often remarked that at The Dhoon 'she did all the work and I all the talking'.[129]

Robert's upbringing could have been a source of tension between husband and wife, as Fleming came from a Presbyterian background and Sareen was a Roman Catholic. However, religion was never a source of conflict. Fleming makes mention of the role of a divinity in shaping men's ends in his lectures on penicillin,[130] but makes no deeper confession of faith, although he reputedly once commented in his usual deadpan fashion that God had obviously created Alexander Fleming because he wanted penicillin, in response to a suggestion that he might be the tool of God's purpose.[131] Merlin Pryce believed that Fleming was a rationalist, oblivious to religious differences, though he did once remark that he believed 'a convent education very suitable for girls'. He remained tolerant of his wife's Irish Catholic background, with the result that she lapsed.[132] Robert, in turn, was given freedom of choice by both his parents and chose the broad church of Anglicanism, although, like his father, he was actually 'nothing much' in religious adherence.[133] Robert's preferences were also taken into account when it came to his education. He had been entered for Eton, causing Dorothy Wilson, wife of the Dean of St Mary's, to comment that 'Fleming – who had the education of the very poor – is sending his son to Eton as he says that nothing matters except to be a good mixer'.[134] Robert himself had other ideas and started at Stowe School in January 1938.[135]

Financial security for his family was important to Fleming but never at the expense of quality of life. Helen Buckley, Ronald Gray's niece, who was to become Fleming's first ever secretary in 1939, thought that 'he was a man who was not indifferent to money, because he could see the fun of having money, but never would money come first with him'.[136] His salary had been raised from the £1,200 he had earned since 1924 to £1,600 in 1936, allowing him to enjoy a comfortable lifestyle.[137] It enabled him to indulge in his generous hospitality at The Dhoon and towards medical students, whom he invited to the Chelsea Arts Club Ball and other functions. Generosity did not stop him from keeping an eye on his investments, and his stockbroker, Tony Ritchie, considered that in financial matters 'he was not conventionally informed, but using his uncanny power of pure reasoning he could sometimes make my propositions about the disposition of his securities look ridiculous'.[138]

By the mid-1930s, modern communications were making contact with the rest of the world and travel easier. This enabled more personal and swifter communication with fellow bacteriologists and also the opportunity to travel further afield than Suffolk and Ayrshire. In January 1935, Fleming went to Iraq as a guest of the Iraqi government to attend the opening of a new oil pipeline, an invitation obtained for him by his friend Dr M.Y. Young, who was medical adviser to King Feisal. On his first trip by air, he began his practice of keeping diaries of his travels and noted how beautiful the Swiss Alps were from the air. He broke his journey at Rome to attend a medical congress and a papal reception with his fellow delegates. On his way to Baghdad from Rome, he stopped off in Jerusalem and returned via Damascus, Beirut, Haifa and Alexandria, from where he sailed home.[139] He had taken a sample of water from the Jordan for use in the christening of the newborn son of the Allisons, but, characteristically, he took the precaution of sterilizing it before it was placed in the font.[140]

There was also the opportunity to meet on an international basis fellow workers throughout the world. At the Second International Congress of Microbiology held in London in 1936, he demonstrated his selective culture techniques and spoke of penicillin, but once again this aroused little interest.[141] At the Third International Congress of Microbiology held in New York in the troubled summer of 1939, he chose to lecture on the advantages of combining vaccine and chemotherapy, concluding that 'the advent of sulphapyridine increases the importance of vaccines and serums, especially in the case of organisms not extremely sensitive to sulphapyridine'.[142] The last ten years had been dominated by work on penicillin, the sulphonamides and vaccines and it seemed by 1939 that penicillin would merely be an interest on the sidelines while the thrust of Fleming's work would be to further the combination of sulphonamides and vaccines. Very soon the advent of penicillin would sweep aside this combined therapy and the discovery that had initially aroused very little excitement in the medical world would triumph.

The Flemings were still in New York when news of the outbreak of war reached them on 3 September. The European delegates made hurried plans for a premature return home. On board the blacked-out liner *Manhattan*, the normally reserved and taciturn Fleming proved a very agreeable companion, with rounds of drinks and anecdotes stretching far in to the night.[143] Ahead of them across the Atlantic lay the new challenges brought by unfamiliar wartime conditions, but aboard the *Manhattan* that world still seemed very remote. It would be six long years before Fleming would return to America in very different circumstances. In the intervening years contact would be lost with many of his colleagues from that Third International Congress, as some faced loss of homes, laboratories and freedom in war-torn Europe. As they had said farewell to the many friends they had made at the Congress, Sareen Fleming had said to André Gratia, 'It will be tough, it will be long, but we will win.'[144] They were defiant words that held true for penicillin as much as for the war that was to see the triumph of the drug as well as of the Allies.

SIX

Oxford Breakthrough

The previous night had been a long and hard one. An all-night bombing raid on London marked the beginning of the Blitz. There was little to suggest that the issue of the *Lancet* published that Saturday morning, 24 August 1940, would offer anyone a distraction from the bombs that had fallen for the first time in this war on Central London. Yet, when Alexander Fleming opened his copy, he was surprised to see a paper entitled 'Penicillin as a Chemotherapeutic Agent' written by seven scientists working at the Sir William Dunn School of Pathology at Oxford. After reading its account of tests of penicillin on mice infected with virulent bacteria, *Streptococcus pyogenes*, *Staphylococcus aureus* and *Clostridium septique*, he came to the short two-page paper's conclusion that 'penicillin is active *in vivo* against at least three of the organisms inhibited *in vitro*. It would seem a reasonable hope that all organisms inhibited in high dilution *in vitro* will be found to be dealt with *in vivo*.'[1] The significance of this suggestion that there was a demonstrable therapeutic potential for penicillin was not lost on Fleming, although it was to be another two years before most other people picked up on it. He immediately decided to go to Oxford to see for himself what was being done with his discovery.

Many years later Ernst Chain, one of the co-authors of the paper that had interested Fleming so much, remembered that Fleming had turned up unannounced the very next day. It had been quite a surprise for him in particular, since he had not been aware that Fleming was still alive.[2] In fact it was actually a week later that Fleming, accompanied by his colleague Dr Young, arrived at Oxford, on Monday 2 September, having first telephoned Howard Florey, Professor of Bacteriology, to make an appointment the previous evening. He told Florey, 'I have come to see what you've been doing with my old penicillin.' During this, his first and only visit, Fleming hardly spoke, but he paid close attention to everything he was shown and listened carefully although he had very few questions for his hosts. Later Fleming's proprietorial attitude to his discovery and his failure to offer any congratulations to the Oxford researchers was to be the cause of some resentment, though in after years he never failed to pay tribute to their work. For the moment, the atmosphere between Fleming and Florey, Chain and Norman Heatley was cordial and they gave him a sample of their precious brown powder to take back to St Mary's.[3]

Howard Florey at 42 was a superficially genial and direct but fundamentally reserved Australian pathologist with a flair for choosing productive lines of research. After qualifying as a doctor in his native Adelaide, he had won a Rhodes scholarship to study medicine and physiology at Oxford in 1922. There he rapidly came to the attention of Sir Charles Sherrington, Professor of Physiology, impressed by the young Australian's academic brilliance, capacity for hard work and intense drive to succeed. This consuming ambition was fuelled perhaps by the failure of his father's once prosperous shoe-manufacturing business while Florey was still a medical student in Adelaide. Sherrington, an expert on the nervous system, became a mentor to Florey and encouraged him to study the function and reactions of the capillaries of the brain. His brilliance was also recognised outside Oxford and in 1924 he accepted the offer of a post as John Lucas Walker Student in the Department of Pathology at Cambridge, where he was able to continue his study of blood-flow changes in inflammation and thrombosis. The following year he was awarded a Rockefeller Fellowship to study micro-surgical techniques in the United States. There he spent three months working with the pharmacologist A.N. Richards in Philadelphia, little realising that the resulting friendship was to have significance in the development of penicillin many years later. He then went on to Chicago to study mucus secretion, a subject that had interested him ever since he had begun to suffer from indigestion during the summer vacation he had spent as medical officer to the Oxford University Arctic Expedition in 1924. A post as pathologist at the London Hospital in Whitechapel proved disappointing, as the emphasis was on routine diagnostic work rather than on the experimental research that appealed to him, and in 1927 he returned to Cambridge as lecturer in pathology, Fellow of Gonville and Caius College and Director of Medical Studies at the college. There was also time for research and he continued to study blood flow and a new interest, lysozyme, which he continued to study after being appointed Joseph Hunter Professor of Pathology at Sheffield University in 1932.[4]

Florey did not remain at Sheffield for long. In 1935 he was appointed to the Chair of Pathology at Oxford University. There he inherited the Sir William Dunn School of Pathology, created by his predecessor Georges Dreyer and housed in palatial purpose-built laboratories only opened in 1927 but moribund by the time of Dreyer's death in 1934. It had not attracted the calibre of researcher anticipated when the Sir

William Dunn Trustees had made a grant of £100,000 to build a new Pathology Department and even undergraduate lectures were poorly attended. Perhaps its most thriving section was its Standards Laboratory, set up by Dreyer as a reference collection of pathogenic bacteria useful for checking the organisms used as antisera in other laboratories for identifying unknown organisms and to provide known organisms to help to identify antibodies in the patient's blood. Funded by the Medical Research Council, this was headed by A.D. Gardner. Elsewhere, the school resembled a mausoleum to Dreyer rather than a thriving research institute when Florey arrived.[5]

His first task was to galvanise his new department into action in the fields of teaching, research and technical assistance. His reputation for outspoken toughness had preceded him and staff at the Sir William Dunn School were apprehensive. However, the expected cull of staff left over from Dreyer's time never materialised. Instead, Florey directed them towards the areas most suited to their abilities. Gardner had been a disappointed candidate for the Chair of Pathology and had expected that the new professor would get rid of both him and his Standards Laboratory. Florey, however, needed a good senior bacteriologist and an ally experienced in the ramifications of university politics and kept him on as reader in bacteriology. He also brought with him allies from Sheffield, Dr Beatrice Pullinger, who as demonstrator in bacteriology became one of the mainstays of the department, and his technician Jim Kent, who had been with him since joining him as a 14-year-old boy in 1927. Although hampered by the pressing need to raise funds, Florey managed to attract young postgraduates working on grants. Success bred further success and the quality of work produced by the school attracted more recruits. His method was to form project teams in which these new recruits could contribute their own expertise under the general control of the professor.[6] It was a far cry from the way in which research was organised by Fleming, who preferred to work alone or with a few chosen collaborators.

One of the research projects that Florey initiated was on lysozyme, which he had been interested in since 1929. The presence of lysozyme in mucus and its antibacterial action prompted him to attempt to discover its true nature and how it actually worked. This research marked the beginnings of his interest in antibiosis, the inhibition of one micro-organism by another, and also brought his first contact with Fleming when he asked for, and was given, help in making assays of lysozyme.[7] Fleming had also supplied Florey and his collaborator in this work, Neil Goldsworthy, with cultures of *Micrococcus lysodeikticus*, the most sensitive indicator of the activity of lysozyme. The results of this work proved inconclusive in supporting Florey's idea that the presence of lysozyme in mucus was necessary for natural immunity, since different animals had varying amounts of the substance in different tissues yet still remained healthy regardless of its presence or absence.[8] Fleming referred to the work of Florey and Goldsworthy as the most complete study of the differential distribution of lysozyme in species of animals in his presidential address to the section of pathology of the Royal Society of Medicine in 1932, commenting that 'the explanation of these variations is quite obscure'.[9] Fleming still believed that lysozyme had a role to play in natural immunity.

Florey was able to resume his own interest in lysozyme at Oxford in collaboration with an Australian Rhodes scholar, B.G. Maegrith, working as a demonstrator in bacteriology, and a chemist, E.A.H. Roberts, seconded by Sir Robert Robinson, Professor of Chemistry. With research grants from the Medical Research Council and Rockefeller Foundation obtained by Florey, the biochemical expertise was in place for the purification of lysozyme. By 1937, they had purified it to such a degree that Sir Robert Robinson and his research student Edward Abraham could crystallize the enzyme.[10] This provided the starting point for Ernst Chain to begin to study how lysozyme acts on bacteria.

Ernst Chain was a contrast to the calm, rather reserved, bespectacled Florey. A Jewish refugee from Nazi Germany, Chain was mercurial and excitable. With his wild jet-black hair, he bore a striking physical resemblance to Albert Einstein and corresponded to the popular image of the mad scientist. He was also a brilliant and imaginative biochemist with an artistic approach to science that reflected his origins in a cultured and sophisticated Mittel-European milieu. A skilled musician, he could have chosen a career as a concert pianist. Instead he brought the artistic temperament of the prima donna to all he did as a scientist. Born in Berlin in 1906, the son of a Russian chemist who had settled in Germany and married a relation of the Social Democratic politician Kurt Eisner, Chain was a graduate in chemistry and physiology at the Friedrich Wilhelm University in Berlin. Interested in biological approaches to chemistry, he had obtained a job as demonstrator in chemistry at the Institute of Pathology at the Charité Hospital, Berlin, in 1930, where he began to study the action of enzymes. It was not the most propitious of times for a Jewish scientist with left-wing political ideas and family connections to launch his career in the increasingly anti-Semitic hothouse of the German Republic. When Hitler assumed power in January 1933, Chain decided to leave Germany for a more promising environment. He claimed to have been one of the first scientists to leave Nazi Germany and arrived in England in early April

1933, leaving behind his mother and sister, who were both to perish in the Theresienstadt concentration camp.[11]

After working with Gowland Hopkins at Cambridge on the paralysis-inducing role of an enzyme in snake venom, Chain was recommended in 1935 to Florey, who was on the lookout for a biochemist with knowledge of enzymes. While a job in a pathology department where he had to fight to establish a biochemistry laboratory may not have been the first choice for an ambitious chemist, Chain, as a refugee, gladly took up the appointment. It was to be another two years before he could begin work on the research project on lysozyme that Florey had had him in mind for from the start, but he had the opportunity to establish his laboratory and finish his work on snake venom. Working with an American Rhodes scholar, Leslie Epstein,[12] Chain began his investigation of the nature and mode of action of lysozyme in 1937. They confirmed Fleming's hunch that lysozyme was actually an enzyme and that its action was primarily against a polysaccharide, a particular chemical component in the cell wall of susceptible bacteria. In order to identify the vulnerable polysaccharide, Chain and Epstein grew large quantities of *Micrococcus lysodeikticus* in large Roux bottles and then separated the cell walls of this particular bacterium. Having done this, they were able to identify the component of the cell wall as a simple derivative of the chemical glucose-N-acetylglutonasamine. Lysozyme destroyed this chemical, causing the disintegration and lysis of the cell wall first observed by Fleming back in 1921.[13]

It was a great advance in knowledge of lysozyme but as a line of research it offered nowhere else to go. A new research subject was needed. Most evenings, Florey and Chain would walk to their homes though the University Parks and discuss any research problems that may have cropped up during the day. It was during one of these evening walks that the two men found that they shared an interest in the wide but largely untapped field of bacterial antagonism and decided to investigate further antibacterial substances.[14] It was a logical progression from the work on lysozyme, which had indicated the possibilities of natural substances capable of destroying bacteria yet non-toxic to mankind. The indefatigable Chain began an exhaustive survey of the scientific literature of antibacterial substances in a search for suitable substances for his next research project. Having looked at more than two hundred papers on antibiosis, he narrowed his interest to three micro-organisms, *Bacillus subtilis*, discovered by Maurice Nichol in 1907, *Bacillus pyocyaneus*, discovered by R. Emmerich and O. Löw in 1889, and *Penicillium notatum*. All three of them were reported as having a bacteriolytic action like that of lysozyme. Fleming's

1929 paper on penicillin struck Chain in particular. Both Fleming's description of his discovery and his photograph of the petri dish showing a clear zone of inhibition around the fungus attracted Chain's interest in the same way that Fleming's had been aroused. Chain commented that in Fleming's paper 'penicillin was described as a bacteriolytic substance and was described as being very active against a whole series of pathogenic organisms which was an interesting contrast to the action of lysozyme which was active only against non-pathogenic organisms'.[15] It was the essential similarities with lysozyme and the possibility that penicillin might be a more potent enzyme that initially intrigued both men.[16]

Before he could do anything with penicillin, Chain needed a culture with which he could work. As it happened, there was actually a specimen of it at the Sir William Dunn School. Working in the laboratory next to Chain was Miss Campbell-Renton, one of the staff left over from Dreyer's time, who was continuing with her former boss's work on bacteriophage. Dreyer had obtained a sample of Fleming's mould soon after the publication of the 1929 paper and had established that penicillin was not a carrier of bacteriophage, as he had first suspected. However, the mould had proved useful in isolating penicillin-resistant strains of bacteria for laboratory work in connection with the research into bacteriophage and had been grown for this purpose. After Dreyer's death, Miss Campbell-Renton had not only gone on with the work he had begun but she had also kept the mould. Chain had often seen her in the corridor carrying this culture in large Roux bottles. He asked her for a sample for his own new project and was promptly given a subculture.[17]

Nevertheless, it was pyocyanase, derived from *Bacillus pyocyaneus*, that Chain first began work on with one of his graduate assistants, Regine Schoental, a Polish biochemist. Miss Schoental was successful in extracting active substances but soon found that they were extremely toxic. Meanwhile, Chain had already turned his attention to penicillin. Florey seemed at first to have no particular preference as to which antibacterial substance they should concentrate on and rarely mentioned penicillin in any discussion of the matter, although it soon became obvious to Chain that he already knew as much about penicillin as Chain had gleaned from his more recent extensive literature searches. There was no mention of Cecil Paine's work at Sheffield, but Florey was able to direct Chain to the paper on the biochemistry of penicillin by Raistrick and his colleagues at the London School of Hygiene and Tropical Medicine. His interest in penicillin was only increased by what he read, especially the observation that penicillin, like lysozyme, disappeared when shaken in ether, seemingly further confirmation that penicillin was an enzyme.[18] Yet Chain could have saved himself a lot of work if he had believed Fleming's comments in his original 1929 paper that penicillin was not an enzyme.

Chain began to work tentatively on penicillin with Epstein in 1938. In his later accounts of his work, Chain was often cavalier with chronology, and his notebooks have not survived to corroborate the sequence of events as he remembered them. However, he seems to have begun minor work on penicillin in the summer of 1938 only to discontinue it under the pressure of other research commitments, not resuming the work until June 1939.[19] The early work was largely a repetition of that done by Raistrick and his colleagues. Once again it was confirmed that penicillin was not an enzyme. In many ways this could have been a drawback, as Chain's expertise was with enzymes. On the more positive side, its not being an enzyme raised new biochemical research possibilities for him and offered a challenge. There were problems of producing enough of the mould juice, overcoming its instability and dealing with what he found to be a relatively small molecule, even before a full investigation of its properties could begin.

There was another problem that had to be faced before the research project could begin to progress: the perennial one of funding. Florey had mentioned the start of the work on antibacterial substances in a grant application to the Medical Research Council in January 1939. He now followed it up with a specific application on 6 September 1939 for £100 to pay for the special equipment and chemicals needed for the project, which would include preparation of the antibacterial substances selected for study in a purified form suitable for study *in vitro* and for intravenous injections. A few days after the outbreak of the Second World War was perhaps not the most propitious moment to make such an application, but Sir Edward Mellanby, Secretary of the Medical Research Council, responded with a grant of a mere £25 to get the project started. Florey then made an application to the Rockefeller Foundation in November 1939 for a three-year grant to work on bacterial antagonism. In this application, much of it drafted by Chain,[20] he requested a minimum of £782 start-up costs for equipment, which he thought might need to be increased to a maximum of £1,000 because of wartime inflation, and £1,670 p.a. to cover recurrent expenses and the salary costs of employing an additional biochemist and two technicians.[21] The Rockefeller Foundation approved a grant of no more than $5,000 for one year from 1 March 1940. It had decided that in the prevailing unsettled wartime conditions it would not give aid to any European applicant for more than twelve months at a time, although it was acknowledged that under normal circumstances the reputation of

Florey and his group, coupled with the importance of the work, would have secured for them the requested funding for three years. Florey received his bid in full, despite the Trustees of the Foundation later considering that to advance funds for the undertaking was very much an 'act of faith, particularly so in the winter of 1939–1940, as England was moving deeper into the orbit of war'.[22]

Despite the almost throwaway references in funding bids to the possibility of purifying antibacterial substances, of which penicillin appeared the most promising of the organisms under investigation, for systemic use by intravenous injection, Florey and Chain were at this stage not thinking in terms of research of immense therapeutic benefit. Their interest was purely academic, with no significant clinical usage in mind. Neither of them was ever to claim otherwise and Chain, in particular, was adamant that 'the possibility that penicillin could have practical use in clinical medicine did not enter our minds when we started our work'.[23] Even had penicillin turned out 'to be as toxic as prussic acid, it would still have been of considerable chemical interest', at least to Chain.[24]

The funding was in place and a loosely organised group had already been assembled from the existing staff of the School of Pathology to work on the project. Chain was later to claim that Florey had only invented the idea of a team under his leadership to justify his role in the penicillin development, and the team had not been formed until after the crucial breakthrough had been made.[25] Yet it was actually multi-disciplinary teamwork and cooperation that had made that breakthrough possible. It was a small team by modern standards, with only eight or so people working together at any one time.[26] Howard Florey led the team and, with the aid of his faithful technician Jim Kent and Margaret Jennings, later to become the second Lady Florey, undertook the study of the biological effects of penicillin. Chain and Edward Abraham worked together on the purification process and the study of the biochemistry of penicillin. The task of assessing the bactericidal power of penicillin was assigned to A.D. Gardner and Jean Orr-Ewing, a former medical student of St Mary's Hospital Medical School during the brief period from 1916 to 1924 when it had admitted women, and a colleague of Georges Dreyer. The production of penicillin fell to Norman Heatley, a 28-year-old Cambridge-educated biochemist.

Norman Heatley, a small and slightly built man, hid great scientific ability under a modest and unassuming manner. He knew the worth of his work but did not push his ideas forward in the forceful manner that was perhaps necessary when dealing with Ernst Chain, who was in many ways his antithesis.[27] Chain may have been better qualified than Heatley, whose strength lay in sound, imaginative practical research, but his arrogance in expecting unquestioning agreement with his views had made him a difficult colleague for Heatley when they had worked together for a few months in 1936 on tumours in mice. Heatley had been awarded a Rockefeller fellowship to work in Copenhagen with the biochemist Lindestrøm Lang and had been due to leave Oxford in mid-September 1939. The outbreak of war changed his plans, and Florey recruited him to the penicillin project and ensured that his fellowship could be held at Oxford instead of Copenhagen in the changed circumstances. Chain assumed that Heatley would report to him, but, mild-mannered as he was, Heatley insisted that if he were to be involved it was on condition that he was accountable only to Florey, who listened, gave credit to his colleagues and directed his subordinates with a 'light and responsive touch'.[28] This condition was readily granted, but Chain continued to think that Heatley was answerable to him and this misunderstanding was to create continued tension between the two men as a backcloth to the great project to which they were both indispensable.[29]

Essential to the success of the study of penicillin was the development of an accurate method of assay for the measurement of its activity. One of the first tasks for Heatley was to devise a suitable standard of assay for use in the William Dunn School. He was so successful that he was to establish the Oxford unit as the international standard for measuring the strength of any penicillin preparation. With great ingenuity, he developed a method for measurement using what he was to call the cylinder plate. Petri dishes were sowed with staphylococci in the usual way. Six or eight short lengths of glass tubing were then pressed into the agar and each cylinder filled with the penicillin solutions being tested for strength. The plate was then incubated while the penicillin diffused into the agar in a widening circle. It was then possible to measure the diameter of the resultant zone of inhibition, which gave an indication of the strength of penicillin in any particular solution. The amount of penicillin contained in $1cm^3$ of a buffer solution was adopted as a purely arbitrary penicillin standard for the convenience of the workers in the laboratory and was later adopted as the international standard of measuring penicillin.[30]

Heatley next turned to the task of isolating the penicillin from the mould juice. Chain had found the same problem as Raistrick in that he could extract penicillin from a slightly acid solution in water by shaking it with ether, but had lost the active penicillin when he tried to retrieve it from the ether. Heatley decided to use back-extraction techniques to overcome these problems. Using the same principles that, unknown to him, Lewis Holt had used six years previously at St Mary's, he decided to extract the penicillin from ether into slightly alkaline water. The acidified mould extract flowed down a long glass tube while a stream of ether flowed up the same tube, allowing contact between the two liquids. This enabled the penicillin to pass from the water to the ether, which was collected at the top of the tube. It was then recovered from the ether by reversing the process and passing it into a flow of slightly alkaline water. Unwanted impurities were removed at each stage of the process. The resultant penicillin was stable enough to be kept for several months at 0°C. However, use of the process of freeze-drying, developed during the 1930s, meant that its activity could be preserved for even longer. Freeze-drying was not essential for stabilising the penicillin, but it was useful.[31]

By March 1940 Chain now had a stock of 100mg of brown powder with an activity of two Oxford units per milligram, compared to the activity of two units per millilitre of the crude mould filtrate they had started off with. A year later Chain and Abraham were working with material with an activity of 30–50 units per milligram. Only in 1943 was it realised that one milligram of purified penicillin actually had an activity of 1,800 units. The penicillin of 1940 was very impure and even when first used on patients in 1941 was still estimated to be 97 per cent impure.[32] Impure or not, it was time for testing for toxicity on animals. Florey was away from Oxford at the time, but Chain was too impatient to await his return. Instead he asked John Barnes, who had a licence for animal experiments, to inject penicillin into two mice with the result that the mice experienced no ill-effects. Florey, unhappy at having been bypassed, insisted on repeating the experiment before beginning a more extensive study of toxicity with Margaret Jennings.[33] They established that penicillin was virtually harmless, but that it was easily destroyed by gastric acid and readily excreted in urine. So far, the research had consolidated Fleming's work of eleven years earlier and confirmed his findings.

There was one important test Fleming had left no record of having performed: the effect of penicillin on infection in animals. Its effects on bacteria in laboratory conditions having been studied by Fleming and once more confirmed by Gardner and Orr-Ewing, it was now time for Florey to test its effects *in vivo*. The date chosen for this crucial test was nationally an anxious one. The German advance on Dunkirk was sweeping the British Expeditionary Force to the sea on Saturday 25 May as Florey instructed Jim Kent to prepare eight white mice for injection with a potentially lethal dose of 100,000,000 virulent streptococci. Two of these mice were injected with 10 milligrams of penicillin but received no further treatment. Another two mice were given a first injection of 5 milligrams followed by four further injections spread out over the next ten hours. The four untreated control mice died by the early hours of Sunday morning, but the four mice treated with penicillin still seemed healthy. Heatley cycled home at a quarter to four in the morning only to be stopped by the Home Guard. Despite having been delayed on his way home, he considered it to be a lucky omen when he realised that he had put his underpants on the wrong way the previous morning. This luck continued on the Sunday afternoon when Florey, Chain and Heatley reconvened to find the four treated mice alive and well.[34] Florey contented himself with a comment that would have been worthy of Fleming at his most laconic – 'it looks quite promising' – before proceeding to devise a series of experiments to confirm the findings and assess the effects of different dosages. For Chain, almost dancing with excitement, this was perhaps the most exciting moment of the entire project and 'we knew now that we had stumbled upon one of those very rare drugs which would not only kill bacteria in a test tube, but also in the living animal without harming it. We realised at once that penicillin could play a vital role in war medicine.'[35]

It was the turning point of work for the Oxford team. At this critical stage of the war, with the Dunkirk evacuation in full flow and the threat of invasion a reality, penicillin now appeared to be of practical importance in treating war wounds. So important was it that Florey, Chain, Heatley and the pathologist A.G. Sanders smeared spores of *Penicillium notatum* into the linings of their suits so that in the event of an invasion they could attempt to escape with the mould and continue their work overseas out of Nazi hands.[36] In the meantime, they continued with the laborious work of producing and testing penicillin while France fell and then the Battle of Britain raged in the skies to the south of them. Four members of the laboratory staff now kept nightly watch, and by June the army were keeping guard overnight.[37] Florey attempted to interest the Wellcome Laboratories at Beckenham in producing penicillin, but, despite a visit in July 1940 from the Director, J.W. Trevan, and Chief Biochemist, Dr Pope, there was no take-up of the proposal. The Wellcome Laboratories were already overextended in producing vaccines, antitoxins and blood plasma for the war effort without taking on cultivation of a temperamental mould to produce something whose clinical value remained as yet unproved.[38]

It was at this juncture that the publication of the preliminary findings of the Oxford group in the *Lancet* prompted Fleming to interest himself in the work being done on his discovery. During his first and only visit to the Oxford laboratories, he noticed that the cultures of *Penicillium notatum* they were working with produced a good deal of yellow pigment and impurities. He believed that he had cultures that produced relatively little pigment and promised to send them. He also returned to London with a sample of the best penicillin that the Sir William Dunn School could produce. He tested this and found it produced a higher activity than the penicillin he had used previously. He praised the work being done at Oxford in a lecture on 'Antiseptics in Wartime Surgery' given at the Pharmaceutical Society on 14 November 1940 and said that it was a stronger antiseptic than the sulphonamides. However, at this stage, like many others over the next few years, he put his faith in its future in it being synthesized by a manufacturer.[39] He said as much to Florey when he sent him the long-promised eight cultures of mould, which he claimed produced a good yield of penicillin with very little pigment: 'It only remains for your chemical colleagues to purify the active principle, and then synthesize it, and the sulphonamides will be completely beaten.'[40] Unfortunately, the strains he sent them contained plenty of pigment and proved hardly worth waiting for.[41]

In the meantime, Florey had decided that the only way of obtaining enough penicillin for clinical trials was to turn the Sir William Dunn School of Pathology into what virtually amounted to a penicillin production plant. Ever the brilliant improviser, Heatley had cultured the mould in whatever containers he could find, as wartime shortages of materials made his task ever more difficult. Flasks, flat-sided bottles, biscuit tins, petrol cans and hospital bedpans were all pressed into service.[42] The bedpans had proved the most productive, so Heatley designed a ceramic vessel based on their design and Florey found a manufacturer who would make them. Heatley collected the first batch himself from J. Macintyre and Company of Burslem in a borrowed van two days before Christmas 1940.[43] The students' classroom became the inoculation department, the preparation room was turned into an incubator where racks of culture vessels were kept at a constant temperature for two weeks before being harvested, some laboratories were turned into extraction and purification rooms and others were used as the base for the bacteriological, chemical and biological control sections. Makeshift equipment was contrived from oil cans, food tins, bathtubs, dustbins, milk churns, refrigerator coolants, library book racks and centrifuges. Large quantities of ether and amyl acetate posed a fire risk. It was a Heath Robinson-type vision, but wartime shortages brought Heatley's ingenuity to a peak, though Chain's somewhat unfair view was that 'a little less improvisation and more professionalism would have profited our work'.[44]

Production, however improvised, on such a scale was labour-intensive. A grant from the Medical Research Council was obtained to enable Florey to employ six 'penicillin girls' to maintain production. Dressed in sterile caps, gowns and masks to prevent contamination of the mould, they worked in unpleasant conditions for £2 a week. It was less than they could have earned doing other war work. In 1943 Florey applied for further funds to raise their wages to £2 10s, pointing out that they could have earned £3 10s by simply serving in a canteen and more doing war work in a factory in nearby Cowley.[45]

While the penicillin girls used paint sprays to distribute the spores of penicillin, Chain and Abraham made great strides in improving the purification process with the use of column chromatography. The penicillin solution would be passed through a column of adsorbent alumina. The different components of the solution would be separated out and adsorbed into different layers of the column. It was easy to distinguish the reddish-orange band of active penicillin, which could be extracted using a suitable solvent.[46]

With increased supplies of purer penicillin, the time was approaching for clinical trials. In January 1941 Florey approached Charles Fletcher, a Nuffield Research Fellow at the Radcliffe Infirmary, for help in finding suitable patients. First of all he needed to test it to see whether or not it was toxic and asked Fletcher to find him a dying patient who, having nothing to lose, would willingly receive an injection of penicillin that might prove toxic. Unlike the perhaps foolhardy Stuart Craddock, who had tested for toxicity by eating some of the mould, Florey was reluctant to try it out systemically on a healthy young adult among his team. Fletcher found a suitable volunteer in a 50-year-old woman, Elva Akers, dying of breast cancer. She reported that she had a musty taste in her mouth, but the only other ill-effects were shivering and a raised temperature because of a reaction to impurities in the drug. It was now safe enough to use it on healthy volunteers. At first it was excreted from the body in urine so rapidly that Florey described it as being like trying to fill a bath with the plug out. Trial and error showed that the best way of maintaining penicillin levels in the bloodstream was by hourly injections into a slow-running, citrate saline intravenous drip. With this knowledge it was possible to move on to the first treatment of a patient with a serious septic infection.[47]

Albert Alexander, a 43-year-old Oxford policeman, had scratched the side of his face on a rose bush when gardening. The resulting staphylococcal and streptococcal septicaemia had spread through his body over the next four months. His face was covered with multiple abscesses. He lost an eye. Osteomyelitis had developed in his right leg and there were abscesses in his lung. Here was a patient who had everything to gain and nothing to lose from treatment with penicillin.

On 12 February 1941 he was injected with 200 milligrams containing 10,000 Oxford units of penicillin and then a further 300 milligrams every three hours. Penicillin was in such short supply that his urine was collected and rushed by Fletcher on his bicycle from the Radcliffe Infirmary to the School of Pathology so that the excreted penicillin could be extracted and reused. Florey later said that 'penicillin was discovered at St Mary's Hospital, extracted at Oxford and purified by passing through the Oxford constabulary'.[48] After five days, Alexander was much better, but as the supply of penicillin was exhausted he began to deteriorate and died a month later. The total dose of penicillin given to him over five days was only 220,000 units, much too small to overcome such a severe infection.[49]

It was then decided that further trials should concentrate on children and more localised infections, where less penicillin would be needed. Fletcher most clearly remembered a 4-year-old boy with a septic spot on his left eyelid that had caused septic cavernous thrombosis. He had only a few hours to live when he was given an injection of penicillin. A week later he was sitting up and playing with his toys. Unfortunately, he later died of an aneurysm of a carotid artery, ruptured by his infection.[50] The other cases were more successful. A 48-year-old labourer was cured of a large carbuncle on his back. A 15-year-old boy with streptococcal septicaemia following a hip operation and a 14-year-old boy with a staphylococcal septic arthritis of the left hip, complicated by septicaemia, were both successfully cured. A six-month-old baby with a urinary tract infection was also cured with penicillin administered by mouth together with enough alkali to neutralise the stomach acids. Four patients with acute eye infections were also successfully treated.[51] There could be little doubt about the remarkable therapeutic potential of penicillin after its use in cases that had been given up as hopeless by the surgeons and that had seen recoveries that Chain described as 'nothing short of miraculous'.[52]

A full account of the early clinical trials and of the work on purification was published in the *Lancet* in August 1941. It proclaimed the potential of penicillin and was praised in the medical press. An editorial in the *British Medical Journal* on these promising results from Oxford suggested that Fleming had failed to recognise any clinical potential in his discovery.[53] Fleming reacted with a letter to the Editor in which he refuted any suggestion that he had not seen the therapeutic value of penicillin, quoting from papers in which he had referred to exactly that and in which he stated that the Oxford group had made a great advance in producing dry penicillin, which 'enabled a clinical trial to be made which has more than justified the suggestions I made ten or more years ago'.[54] There were a few newspaper articles following this exchange, most of which gave prominence to Fleming's role, but nothing on the scale of the press coverage that was to come the following year.[55]

Neither Florey nor Heatley had been in Oxford when the second paper on penicillin had been published. Unable to get the cooperation from the British pharmaceutical industry to produce the penicillin he needed for more extensive trials, despite approaches to both the Wellcome Laboratories and Kemball Bishop, Florey had turned to the United States for help, just as he had turned to the Rockefeller Foundation for a grant in 1939 when the Medical Research Council had proved less than generous. It was again the Rockefeller Foundation that came to his aid with a grant of $6,000 to cover the travel and subsistence costs of Florey and Heatley during a visit to the United States in the summer and fall of 1941 'to make arrangements for its mass production in this country and to present these important findings to American physicians'. The mission to North America had been discussed with Warren Weaver of the Rockefeller Foundation during his visit to England that April and he had done much to develop the planned visit. Sir Edward Mellanby and Sir Henry Dale of the Medical Research Council had supported the American project, ensuring that the two men had priority for flights out of England on 27 June, while the United States Surgeon General had ensured they would have priority for flights to New York.[56]

Florey returned to Oxford at the end of September, leaving Heatley behind to help with the beginnings of production in North America. He found that production at home had suffered during his absence when Chain had been left in charge. Gordon Sanders, who had worked closely with Heatley over the last year, was promoted to take charge of production and given the task of scaling up the facilities.[57] In a large and up to then underused animal house, Sanders constructed what was to be for the next two years the largest penicillin extraction plant in the United Kingdom.

While frustrated that 'after telling the Yanks every single thing we knew on the understanding that they would give us some penicillin to do some more cases . . . they have kept the lot for themselves',[58] Florey was encouraged to receive some penicillin from British commercial sources at last. In January 1942, ICI began to send small consignments from a pilot plant it had set up at Trafford Park, Manchester.[59] In September 1942, Kemball Bishop, based in the East End of London, sent the first batch in two milk churns of what was later to become a regular weekly consignment of 200 gallons of crude mould filtrate.[60] Sir Robert Robinson was a consultant to the company and had acted as an intermediary for Florey in his approach for help. Kemball Bishop had responded to this request by sending a biologist, V.J. Ward, and an organic chemist, John Gray Barnes, an Oxford athletics blue and consequently the acceptable face of commerce for the university, to Oxford to learn about production methods and obtain samples of the mould.[61] Back at the Kemball Bishop factory at Bromley-by-Bow, they had installed air filtration equipment to achieve a sterile environment and maintain a constant temperature of 24°C in two basement rooms set aside for the cultivation of the mould in open trays. Despite the regular night raids on the heavily bombed East End, the factory never suffered a direct hit, though contaminants ruined many batches and the staff on firewatching duties sometimes saw their own homes burning from the roof of the works they were protecting.[62]

With guaranteed supplies of penicillin, Florey could begin the second clinical trial he had vainly hoped to obtain from American production. Charles Fletcher had now left Oxford and Florey's wife Ethel took on the task of selecting, treating and recording suitable cases. Fifteen patients were studied and in fourteen of them what would previously have been considered to be hopeless cases were cured. In the one exception the patient, suffering from bacterial endocarditis affecting the heart, died when the microbe became resistant to the penicillin. In order to make the most of limited supplies, the Floreys then turned their attention to studying its value as a local antiseptic. Once again the results were amazing and proved the clinical value of the new drug beyond the shadow of a doubt. However, when publishing the results in a total of 189 cases, the Floreys were determined not to make themselves hostages of their own success, warning readers that 'penicillin is as yet available in only the smallest quantities – no applications should be made for it to the authors or to ICI (Dyestuffs) Ltd for supplies'.[63] One application they had been unable to refuse had come from Fleming in August 1942, but in other cases they had no choice but reluctantly to refuse requests. The Oxford team, bringing different approaches to a common problem, had made the breakthrough that enabled the full realisation of the clinical potential of penicillin, though they had not set out with this in mind, and the means of producing it so that it could be injected safely into patients. They were not prepared for the great demand for penicillin that was about to be unleashed.

SEVEN

Disputed Laurels

There was no doubt that 52-year-old Harry Lambert was dying. He had been feverish for seven weeks but had dismissed it as influenza at first. After a month it became obvious that he was actually suffering from meningitis. Luckily for him he worked for the optical firm of J. and R. Fleming and his employer Robert Fleming had called on his brother, himself a director of the firm, for help in getting him admitted to St Mary's Hospital. He had been treated with sulphonamides for three weeks but his condition had rapidly worsened. On 1 August 1942 Alexander Fleming was recalled from a short holiday to attend to the dying patient, in whose condition he had shown a personal interest. Using a hollow needle and syringe, he drew off some of the cerebro-spinal fluid surrounding the spinal cord and isolated the virulent streptococcus that had caused the infection. It was obviously resistant to the action of the sulpha drugs, so he tested it with penicillin and found that it was penicillin-sensitive. However, up to this time he had never used penicillin as anything more than a local antiseptic and knew little more about its systematic use than he had read in the medical press. Moreover, he had only very crude filtrates of penicillin to hand and these were far too impure and unstable for use against such a severe infection. The only available source was at the Sir William Dunn School of Pathology in Oxford.

On 5 August Fleming telephoned Florey with a request for penicillin. Florey's immediate response was to place all his supplies of penicillin at Fleming's disposal and to deliver it himself, so he could advise on how it should be administered. On the evening of 6 August Fleming injected penicillin into a human being for the first time and saw for himself the therapeutic effects of the substance he had discovered fourteen years earlier. Penicillin was injected every two hours and within a day Lambert's temperature had fallen to near normal and his fever had abated. However, the signs of meningitis persisted and further tests convinced Fleming that the penicillin was not passing from the blood into the cerebro-spinal spaces where the streptococci were still lurking. Once more he telephoned Florey to ask him whether penicillin had ever been injected into the spinal fluid. Florey at once cautioned him against the risks of such an intrathecal injection. He advised him to wait to see what happened on an animal first, if he wanted to try out this as yet untested means of administration on his dying patient. Florey immediately gave an intrathecal injection of penicillin to a rabbit, which promptly died.[1]

On this occasion the usually cautious Fleming did not wait for the results of Florey's animal testing before deciding to inject penicillin into Lambert's spinal canal. There was little to lose anyway. With such drastic action, there was a chance that the result might be fatal. Without it, Lambert would certainly die. He appeared moribund when Fleming injected the first dose of penicillin on 13 August. The results were dramatic. His temperature fell once more, his delirious ramblings stopped and his recovery began. For the next fourteen days he was treated with intramuscular injections of penicillin every two hours and a daily intrathecal injection. Fleming wrote to Florey, 'I am rather a pessimist, but it really seems to me that Lambert (the penicillin patient) is going to recover. When you saw him, he was a dying man. When you see him on Tuesday you will see an enormous difference.'[2] Although penicillin therapy had been shown to be so effective, Fleming also dissolved penicillin into the patient's serum for one injection into the body to provide opsonins in another attempt to combine the new therapy with the orthodoxy of Wright's methods, which had already been superseded. A month after the injection that might have killed him, Lambert was discharged, fully recovered.[3] Yet, had Fleming waited for the results of Florey's animal tests, he might never have given the treatment that was to save this man's life. It took great personal courage to take such a life-or-death decision and Fleming was not wanting in this quality.

It was a time when life was precarious and so doubly precious. Fleming's own career had changed since his hurried return from the United States in September 1939. On his return to St Mary's, he had taken up his duties as sector pathologist for Sector Six of the Emergency Medical Services. In preparation for the coming war London had been divided up into sectors stretching out into the Home Counties with a teaching hospital at its apex. The idea was that each teaching hospital should serve as a casualty clearing station and patients would then be bussed out to base hospitals in the sector. Sector Six extended out westwards as far as Buckinghamshire and Hampshire with its main base at Harefield Hospital near Uxbridge. Sir Charles Wilson, the Dean of the medical school who had chaired the Wilson Committee, which had recommended the organisation of London into sectors, was the group officer for Sector Six until his responsibilities as personal physician to the Prime Minister made this role impossible, and the Matron of

St Mary's was appointed as sector matron.[4] As sector pathologist, Fleming was expected to move his base to Harefield. He never did so but shillied and shallied. He found excuses to continue to work in his laboratory at St Mary's throughout the war, visiting the base laboratory at Harefield only once a week, despite St Mary's being located in a prime target area next to Paddington Station. He prided himself on being the only sector pathologist never to leave London during both the Blitz and the later V-bomb attacks.[5]

St Mary's, almost uniquely among the London teaching hospitals, did not suffer a direct hit during the heavy bombardment of London, though it suffered from fire-bomb attacks. Fleming's own home was not so lucky. In November 1940 the Flemings had returned home from dining with friends to find that their house in Danvers Street had been hit by incendiaries. The Dhoon had been requisitioned for the use of RAF officers stationed at East Anglian air bases, but anyway would have been too remote for them to have commuted to London in war conditions, though its garden did provide them with regular supplies of vegetables for the next five years.[6] They were offered shelter by Merlin Pryce at Rickmansworth. In March 1941 they returned to Danvers Street, but a month later were bombed out again. They were actually in bed when their house was hit and the bedroom door was blown in.[7] Dan Stratful, Fleming's laboratory technician, helped him to clear up and was astounded that his only comment on the whole incident was, 'When I saw the entire window frame moving towards me, I decided to get out of bed.'[8] The typical understatement was reflected in his views on Hitler, 'he's a bad man – I'd like to twist his tail'.[9]

Lucky not to be injured by the collapsing ceilings and blown-in windows, the Flemings went to stay with Robert and Ida Fleming at Radlett, Hertfordshire. While her husband continued with his duties as sector pathologist, Sareen, in addition to dealing with the stresses of wartime housekeeping and the loss of her home, worked as a volunteer at the Shamrock Club, a canteen in the West End for Irish soldiers, and the Scottish and Irish Officers' Club. For the first time ever, she began to look tired.[10] Wartime shortages of building materials meant that she was unable to return to her own home for the duration of the war. However, after a few months at Radlett, the Flemings were offered the use of a house in Highgate by V.D. Allison, who had been posted as a Home Office scientist to Cardiff. On official visits to London, Allison was able to stay with the Flemings. While Sareen dealt with the problems of wartime rationing with such improvisations as a generally acknowledged unappetising but nourishing artichoke soup, Fleming found relaxation in gardening.[11]

The bombing of London left Fleming unmoved. He had no fear of loud bangs and his only reaction some years before the war when a child had put a firework under him at a fireworks party had been 'squib gone off'.[12] This calm attitude stood him in good stead as the war progressed, and he refused to allow the bombing to affect his work. During the flying bomb attacks on London of 1944 he was to dictate letters calmly to his secretary as the bombs screeched overhead. It was only when the all-clear sounded that he actually said 'duck' to her, having been so intent on his work that he had blocked out the raid.[13] During nights on duty at St Mary's, he shared the firewatchers' temporary dormitory in an underground passage linking the hospital with the medical school and new nurses' home. He also happily joined the students for a couple of pints of beer at the Fountains Abbey in Praed Street, the closest pub to the hospital. There, in a convivial atmosphere reminiscent of Boulogne during the First World War, he would invariably order a pint of Mild and Bitter by asking for a pint of 'M and B', humorously referring to the sulphonamide of that name.[14]

It was not the sulphonamides that he now placed most faith in. The dramatic results of his treatment of Harry Lambert in the summer of 1942 convinced him of the importance of penicillin in the battle against infection. Even before Lambert had been discharged from hospital, Fleming had taken action to get official support for increased penicillin production. An old friend from the Ayrshire Society was Sir Andrew Duncan, Minister of Supply and Member of Parliament for the constituency in which St Mary's lay. Fleming went to see him and told him of the immense possibilities offered by penicillin for the treatment of wounds, a subject on which Fleming was an acknowledged expert. Duncan, impressed by his friend's arguments, gave Sir Cecil Weir, Director-General of Equipment at the Ministry of Supply, the task of organising a project to get mass production under way. Fleming was always proud of his intervention with Sir Andrew Duncan and his own small part in mobilising the resources to make penicillin production a reality.[15]

Fleming had been involved at the request of Duncan in some microbiological investigations for the Ministry of Supply earlier that year. In March 1942 he had been asked by Duncan personally to look into some work on antibacterial substances produced by moulds that Duncan and Fleming both suspected to be a waste of public money.[16] He had then been told that these substances that he had been asked to test were 'merely a smokescreen for other activities and that if these other activities were unsuccessful you would not further subsidise work on a smokescreen'. In these circumstances he informed Davidson Pratt, Controller of Chemical Defence at the Ministry of Supply, that he was prepared to undertake the necessary investigations if they were of help to the war effort, but was otherwise afraid that he might be wasting his time 'on something in which the Ministry has no interest and which does not seem to have such value in medicine as other well authenticated substances produced by moulds such as penicillin'.[17] Reassured that he was making a contribution to the national effort, Fleming went ahead and tested these substances produced by the mould *Aspergillus clavatus*, only to find them of very little value or interest.[18] The result of Fleming's work, and also of a report he made indicating the failure of some associated but independent lines of work, was the suspension of the project. Fleming felt that his time had been well spent if it had led to the closing-down of 'an undesirable activity'.[19] Following this rather mysterious incident, Fleming continued to do bacteriological investigations for the government, including testing the activity of sulphonamide preparations captured in North Africa that confirmed German claims about the superiority of the drugs Marfanil and Marfanil-Prontalbin.[20]

It was, consequently, not surprising that Fleming's voice was respected at the Ministry of Supply when he urged that something be done about penicillin production. A conference, chaired by Sir Cecil Weir, was held on 25 September 1942 at Portland House. It was attended by representatives of the main pharmaceutical and chemical producers and of the Ministry of Supply and the Army Medical Directorate. Fleming and Florey were both present, as was Harold Raistrick, who had been involved in early studies of the biochemistry of penicillin. The message of the meeting was that urgent steps should be taken to 'ensure that all the available knowledge of this drug be pooled and concentration and extension of production facilitated, even to the extent of Government assistance if required'.[21] As a result of the conference, the General Penicillin Committee was set up to coordinate the commercial production of penicillin in Britain and control its distribution.

Cooperation was already a feature of the wartime pharmaceutical industry. The Therapeutic Research Corporation had been formed in 1941 by Boots, May and Baker, British Drug Houses, Glaxo Laboratories and Burroughs Wellcome to coordinate and extend British pharmaceutical research. Research and manufacturing facilities were to be pooled in fields of common interest to all the member companies, and the corporation could act as a unified voice in representing the views of the pharmaceutical industry to government and the medical profession. Old commercial rivalries between members and a conflict of loyalties for scientists and businessmen involved in joint projects made for tensions within the Therapeutic Research Corporation, which made it less effective than it might have been. It did little to interest the British government in coordinating and financing work on penicillin in the way that the Office of Scientific Research and Development and War Production Board were to forge cooperation between some twenty-five rival companies in the United States. Nevertheless, despite problems of air raids, shortages of manpower, accommodation and raw materials and the pressure to produce other necessary drugs, the Therapeutic Research Corporation had responded to the challenge posed by penicillin, however tardy and tentative their response may have seemed. In 1942, Lord McGowan, Chairman of ICI, was approached with a proposal that Imperial Chemical Industries should collaborate in penicillin research.[22] By September 1942, the Therapeutic Research Corporation was already collaborating with companies in America and British universities.[23] In November 1942, ICI joined the Therapeutic Research Corporation, and, at the request of the Ministry of Supply, a committee was formed to coordinate work on the purification and production of penicillin. Both Fleming and Florey, together with Dr Harrington, a representative of the Lister Institute, were invited to sit on the committee.[24]

Even before the formation of the General Penicillin Committee, the British pharmaceutical industry had begun to dabble in penicillin production. At the Wellcome Laboratories at Beckenham, a few small-scale experiments in 1940 had failed to produce even a reliable assay method. Parke Davis expressed an interest in penicillin production towards the end of November 1940 and asked Fleming if he could supply them with mould cultures and penicillin preparations for their Detroit headquarters. Fleming had referred the company to the work of the Oxford group and said that 'penicillin offers considerable promise, particularly from the standpoint of chemical analysis to determine the structure, with the ultimate possibility of synthesizing the active principle'.[25] Using a mould culture supplied by Fleming, Parke Davis set up a production process at their Hounslow laboratories but abandoned the project in the face of technical difficulties. ICI, meanwhile, opened a pilot plant at its Trafford Works in 1941 with an initial weekly capacity of five 100-litre batches of fermentation liquor, and was able to send small amounts of penicillin to Florey at Oxford from January 1942.[26] Kemball Bishop too began to send regular consignments of crude mould filtrate to Oxford in September 1942.[27]

With official encouragement, penicillin production now began its slow progress towards meeting the wartime need for the new drug. In February 1943 Glaxo, which had already begun production at its Greenford works in December 1942, opened a penicillin plant in a disused cheese factory in Aylesbury, sharing the costs with Burroughs Wellcome, and with financial support from the Ministry of Supply. The production of surface cultures in milk churns and their subsequent processing used much of the same equipment and processes already used by Glaxo in its processed cheese and dairy food business, although there were major technological differences in the two production processes. Using penicillium cultures he had obtained from Harold Raistrick, Dr R.D. Andrews of Glaxo investigated production and in September 1942 Glaxo Laboratories took out its first patent on the production process, which it assigned to the Therapeutic Research Corporation. Further plants were later opened by Glaxo on the upper storey of a rubber vulcanising plant in Watford, which by 1946 produced 90 per cent of British penicillin, and in a converted cattlefeed factory in Stratford, East London.[28] Essentially all these early penicillin plants were merely using scaled-up versions of the laboratory production techniques developed by Norman Heatley and Gordon Sanders at Oxford.

A myth has grown up that penicillin was also being produced at St Mary's. Howard Hughes, who was a member of the staff of the Inoculation Department, later claimed that Fleming had the means of growing larger amounts of mould than Oxford and that crude penicillin was poured into large churns and put on the passenger trains at Paddington to be collected an hour later at Oxford. He also ascribed the first systemic use of penicillin on the dying policeman to Fleming rather than to Charles Fletcher at Oxford.[29] With regard to production, he was obviously thinking of the factory producing vaccines where penicillin had been grown weekly by the technicians for use in the selective culture of resistant bacteria used in vaccine production. This factory was hidden away since too great a commercial orientation was not conducive to the raising of other funds. It was really only when Parke Davis officials visited that most of the staff in the department became aware of the existence of the factory.[30] With such secrecy, false rumours could easily arise.

There were also rumours that Germany might begin penicillin production. Copies of the *Lancet* and other medical and scientific publications were available in neutral countries and from there could easily find their way to the Axis powers. In spring 1941 Florey heard that the Swiss pharmaceutical company CIBA was interested in penicillin research and that there was a possibility that the Germans might get their hands on it. He warned Fleming against responding to any requests for the culture.[31] Fleming replied that he was in agreement with ensuring that 'we should not pass on cultures of the penicillium to the enemy'.[32] He also said that he could not remember having sent cultures to Germany before the war. However, R.J.V. Pulvertaft thought that Fleming had told him that he had. Pulvertaft also admitted that he himself had given the culture of the mould to Turkish officers during the war because of his personal belief that 'there should be no limitation of medical services between nations, even if they were at war' and wrongly assumed that Fleming might have done the same.[33] However, Fleming's views in wartime were firmly against any aid to the enemy, but it is possible that he had sent samples of the culture before the Nazi takeover. Certainly the Schering Company were working on an 'old strain of penicillium' originally obtained from Fleming, but were unable to obtain any penicillin from it.[34] German failure to develop penicillin production from the mould and a continued reliance on the sulphonamides did not prevent Hitler from awarding the Iron Cross for the discovery of penicillin to his personal physician Theodore Morell in 1944. Morell had treated the German Führer with penicillin after the assassination attempt on him by his own officers that year. Fleming's comment was that 'the Germans try on most things and it was only to be expected that they would claim to have discovered penicillin'.[35] It was fortunate that with so much published information available on penicillin there had not been more concentration on research and production in Germany.

The General Penicillin Committee back in Britain had considered and rejected at its first meeting the possibility of centralising research and production in one place. The danger from such concentration of resources was that one bombing raid could set back research and wipe out production in one blow. Commercial rivalries in the guise of cooperation also ruled out any such measures that eroded the independence of firms. It was resolved that 'not only would the vulnerability of a single unit make the proposal undesirable, but it was thought that until more knowledge of the properties, use and manufacture of penicillin has been gained, all the available resources should be kept in being'.[36] As a result, production remained dispersed. As some factories were in heavily bombed areas such as East London, this was a sensible decision. At an experimental plant established in late 1943 by Kemball Bishop at its works in Bromley-by-Bow to produce penicillin for Florey, heavy air raids destroyed the homes of thirty to forty of the workmen with the result that twenty-four members of staff were absent on 15 August 1944. It was only because the experimental plant was 'mainly worked by members of our Research Staff, all university trained', that 'the flying bomb has in no way interfered with our limited output', though had the V-bomb raids continued uninterrupted production could not have been guaranteed.[37]

Schemes were put in place for an interchange of visits between workers in various laboratories and the disclosure of experimental results at an early stage to avoid duplication of work and in the hope that any problems in one research programme might be resolved elsewhere: 'the essence of speed, in arriving at the desired result, was frequent communication between workers, and it might be better to disclose the minutiae of experimental work than wait until definite and complete pieces of work could be reported.'[38]

Despite official efforts, the pooling of information and expertise did not proceed as smoothly as might have been hoped. Not all production companies were willing to collaborate in the penicillin project. Kemball Bishop, the firm that Florey had considered the 'most likely to be able to produce penicillin in considerable quantities',[39] was reluctant to join in the collaborative project and release information in instalments as research progressed. J.E. Whitehall, the Managing Director of Kemball Bishop, bluntly told Sir Arthur Mortimer of the Ministry of Supply that, while ready to 'put into it all that we have' to further the expensive and as yet unprofitable pioneering work on penicillin for the national good, he did not consider such a way of sharing every scrap of information with other companies to be 'fair to those young men who are investigating this penicillin problem nor do I want their thoughts divided between what they are doing here and what others are doing'.[40] Mortimer replied that no one wanted to interfere with the work of the young scientists at Kemball Bishop, but pointed out that, 'if they are up against a difficulty which someone else has encountered and overcome, I would have thought it would have been to their advantage to meet their co-workers and get the best information that others could provide'.[41] As a result of Kemball Bishop's intransigence, the firm was denied access to reports on the chemistry of penicillin and it was only because of Florey's intervention with the Minister of Supply that the scientific team at the Crown Chemical works at Bromley-by-Bow was not deprived of information valuable for their work, though there were further attempts to deprive them of access to the work of others.[42]

One of the reasons that the Ministry of Supply and other pharmaceutical companies were so wary of Kemball Bishop and its refusal to share fully in all scientific information was a suspicion that the firm was holding back something of great importance. At the very first meeting of the General Penicillin Committee, the representatives of Kemball Bishop had felt unable to promise full cooperation because of their work on fermentation processes in conjunction with their American associates Pfizer, who had insisted that nothing be disclosed.[43] Since 1936, Kemball Bishop had had an agreement with Pfizer for the use of its surface fermentation techniques for the production of citric acid for the European market. Despite having six 20-gallon stainless steel fermenters at their works for citric acid production, which were later to be erroneously referred to as the 'old penicillin fermenters', the management of Kemball Bishop was convinced that its technique of growing the mould by surface culture on open trays was superior to the closed bottles used by other firms and never investigated production by submerged culture.[44] Pfizer, however, was successful in building the first submerged culture plant in the United States. It was suspected that Kemball Bishop knew more about these techniques being used by Pfizer than the firm was prepared to admit and that it was these processes that were being protected rather than the fermentation methods for the production of citric acid. In actual fact, Kemball Bishop was using the methods developed at Oxford and communicated to its scientific team by Florey, not the much sought after Pfizer process for penicillin.[45]

Lack of collaboration and a feeling that firms in the United States were not as ready to release information to their British counterparts as they claimed to be were not the only problems facing the scaling-up of penicillin production. Producers had to compete for scarce resources in wartime and even the obvious importance of the drug could not always guarantee priority access to supplies of lactose and corn-steep liquor, labour and permits and raw materials for the construction of buildings and plant. In December 1943, the General Penicillin Committee warned that 'the production of penicillin in this country for the essential requirements of the Services and for Civil needs will fall below what is expected and what can be achieved by the producers here, unless the importance of the designation of penicillin as an A1 priority ranking for labour and materials, equally with the munitions of war, is recognised by all ministries concerned'.[46] The Ministry of Labour had to be asked by the Ministry of Supply to issue specific instructions to the Labour Exchanges at Watford and Aylesbury that they needed to give priority to the direction of unskilled labour to the production of penicillin.[47] The manpower problem remained such a difficulty in terms of both quantity and quality that Sir Henry Dale suggested that it might be desirable to draft servicewomen from non-combatant units into penicillin production.[48] Dale's proposal was not taken seriously, but competing needs in wartime led to many discussions about the best use of scarce resources, whether of people or of raw materials. Rival demands for the allocation of lactose raised even greater ethical issues. While there was no question that the use of lactose in milk stout should be stopped, it was not so easy to decide between allocating it to the production of penicillin and using it in the manufacture of baby foods. The Ministry of Food had already drastically cut the use of lactose in baby foods to redirect it towards penicillin production, but the Ministry of Health insisted that it was essential that there should be an allocation for the manufacture of infant food. However, it was prepared to compromise by making lactose available only to babies under three months with digestive problems if it was indeed absolutely essential for penicillin.[49]

Yet, despite all the problems, more factories were set up by all the pharmaceutical companies represented on the General Penicillin Committee and by other companies such as Distillers and Allen and Hanbury. Production figures rose dramatically. In 1942, the only penicillin available for clinical use in Britain was being produced in Florey's laboratories at Oxford, supplemented by 5 grams from ICI in March and 5 grams from Merck in April, the only supply Florey was to receive as a result of his American mission. In 1943, the average monthly production of penicillin was 300 mega units.[50] There was now enough penicillin being produced for further and more extensive clinical trials. Not only was there enough material for the treatment of one hundred systemic cases in a Medical Research Council trial; there was also enough for Florey and Hugh Cairns, Consulting Neurosurgeon to the Army, to begin a clinical trial of penicillin in North Africa.[51] A year earlier, in July 1942, Florey had supplied some penicillin for clinical trials by Lieutenant Colonel R.J. Pulvertaft, Officer Commanding the Central Pathological Laboratory of the Middle East Forces, in Egypt. Although supplies were small and the potency of the penicillin was low, Pulvertaft was able to report satisfactory results.[52] Among the wounded soldiers successfully treated was W.J. McGowan, son of the Chairman of ICI, who had been shot by a German sniper at El Alamein in October 1942. Lord McGowan later wrote identical letters to both Fleming and Florey thanking them because penicillin had saved his son's life.[53] When more penicillin was available by May 1943, the War Office had sent a penicillin team to Algiers to study the effects of penicillin on war wounds. Florey borrowed a movie camera from Professor Liddell, Professor of Physiology at Oxford, to film the results of the trials for subsequent use in instruction on the application of penicillin.[54]

The results of the trials on war wounds were astounding. Men who would once have lost limbs as a result of infection were able to recover the use of them. Even the largest wounds healed completely when treated with penicillin.[55] Yet the most impressive aspect so far as the War Office was concerned was its miraculous effects in curing cases of gonorrhoea within twelve hours of injection. Gonorrhoea was causing more casualties in North Africa than the enemy forces, and penicillin offered the possibility of combating this infectious foe at least. However, such a use was bound to cause controversy. Florey and Cairns believed that penicillin should be reserved for wounds where the infection needed further research. The issue was simpler for the military authorities. Treatment of gonorrhoea with penicillin allowed them to get soldiers back into action much more quickly, in more ways than one. If wounds were to be treated, it would still take longer for the wound to heal even once the infection had cleared. Yet, there was still awareness of the political reaction if it got out that penicillin was being given to treat sexually acquired infections rather than the wounds of war heroes. The matter was referred to the Prime Minister, Winston Churchill, by General Poole, Director of Pathology at the Army Medical Department. Churchill scrawled across the memorandum in green ink that 'this valuable drug must on no account be wasted. It must be used to the best military advantage.'[56] It was an ambiguous comment and was interpreted as official sanction for the use of penicillin to treat venereal diseases in the armed forces.

The Allied invasion of Sicily in July 1943, the forerunner of the long-awaited opening of the Second Front in Europe, intensified the need for penicillin. The depletion of active troops by the scourge of gonorrhoea was checked and the availability of American supplies of penicillin made up for the deficit in penicillin available for the treatment of war wounds as casualties mounted in the Italian theatre of war.[57] The demand for penicillin simply increased the more successful it seemed to be, and the armed forces were prepared to take all supplies produced in Britain and any additional supplies from the United States. It was accepted by the General Penicillin Committee that it 'would be a mistake for the country to rely on getting penicillin in any quantity from the USA before the end of 1944 and that the product was of such vital importance for the war effort that this country must take urgent steps to meet its own needs'.[58] The pace was stepped up and progress was impressive, even if it lagged behind what was being achieved with the greater resources of North America, with British monthly production rising to 3,166 mega units in 1944 and to 26,000 mega units in 1945.[59]

With increased production, penicillin could be made available for selective civilian use in cases that might extend knowledge of the therapeutic use of the drug. Fleming was appointed to a subcommittee of the Penicillin Clinical Trials Committee, which allocated penicillin to civilian centres.[60] Inevitably demand exceeded supplies and Fleming found himself besieged with requests for help in obtaining this wonder drug from all ranks of society. Princess George of Greece sought his advice on whether penicillin could be used for a middle-ear infection.[61] Sir Montagu Norman, Governor of the Bank of England, was another of Fleming's prominent penicillin patients to whom the drug was rushed when he had pneumococcal meningitis, although it was stressed that his case was judged worthy of penicillin on medical grounds and that he was acting as 'a human assay' rather than receiving it through having friends in high places.[62] An appeal from the Swiss Football Association to Stanley Rous, Secretary of the English Football Association, for penicillin to save the life of the Swiss international player Thomas Abegglen was sent to Fleming, who arranged to send supplies of the drug through the Swiss Legation to Zurich.[63] The inevitable reaction to this was the sensationalist newspaper headline 'Germans get penicillin while Britons die. Even soccer players get it. Civilians must have more.'[64] In sending penicillin abroad, Fleming was merely acting in accordance with Foreign Office policy, which was to send penicillin to Allies and neutrals in humanitarian cases or where it was of political advantage, as in the case of Switzerland, which had given assistance to British Prisoners of War.[65] The Foreign Office did, however, turn down a request for penicillin for the baby daughter of the Secretary-General of the Falange Party in Spain, as 'no case of minor political advantage would justify such a reduction of vital stocks of penicillin needed for the war effort'.[66] It actually depended on the individual circumstances of the request as to whether depletion of vital supplies was merited.

Fleming's old friend and former assistant in his work on penicillin, Stuart Craddock, now a general practitioner at Holsworthy in Devon, appealed for penicillin for one of his patients, the Port Reeve. This was one appeal Fleming could not resist. Although he had no right to send it at a time when distribution was on a regional basis, he promised to send penicillin to his old friend on condition it was kept a secret: 'If you could prevent people knowing, and if you are prepared to do the injection, I could let you have some penicillin.'[67] There had been less need for confidentiality earlier when Fleming had used a crude penicillin filtrate, unsuitable for patients, to cure the pet dog of Craddock's small son Iain, during one of his many visits to Holsworthy.[68]

With penicillin in short supply, something of a penicillin mania developed. It was seen as the universal panacea. There was talk of such blessings to come as penicillin toothpaste, signalling an end to dental decay, and penicillin lipstick to be marketed for 'that hygienic kiss'. One newspaper in 1941 described it and other antibiotics as offering 'new hope for wounded soldiers, dark-locks for the grey-haired, hair for the bald, sepsis cured by soil, cheese-mould as a healer, and millions of germs sitting down to dinner which is whisked away as soon as they start'.[69] Such startling claims amused the more knowledgeable. Arthur Mortimer, Deputy Director of Medical Supplies in the Ministry of Supply, had even suggested to Fleming a suitable advertising campaign for the lipstick: 'Kiss whom you like, when you like, how you like and avoid all consequences except matrimony.'[70] When it was later pointed out to Fleming that one of the effects of penicillin was to turn grey hair black, he wryly commented that 'if it does turn grey hair black, you had better take shares in a penicillin company'.[71] Yet one of Fleming's colleagues at St Mary's, the surgeon Arthur Dickson Wright, had such faith in the drug that he could declare that Fleming's discovery 'will have done more people out of a job than any other person at any time' by depriving surgeons, physicians and venereologists of a role.[72]

There was plenty for them to do at St Mary's, where George Bird and Margaret Anderson wards were designated as the penicillin wards to deal with clinical trials under the control of the discoverer of penicillin himself, who had overnight in the eyes of the medical students taken on the aura of the great man.[73] His caution in the proper use of penicillin did not desert him and he insisted that there should be full tests on the susceptibility of an infection to treatment with penicillin before he administered the drug. The results were miraculous to doctors more used to the side effects of the sulphonamides and the lack of any other effective treatments. George Bonney, the house surgeon seconded to work on the penicillin wards, considered the extraordinary cures to be 'magical' with their immediate results, yet observed that Fleming repeatedly warned against inappropriate use of the drug at a time when many doctors hailed it as a once and for all end to infective diseases.[74] Early patients described injections with penicillin as being 'like a rush of hot water'[75] and 'as sharp as a bee sting'.[76] Stan Peart, then a medical student and one of Fleming's early penicillin patients, said 'it looked like mustard and it felt like mustard'.[77] However, this golden miracle was in short supply and could not be wasted if it was likely to prove ineffective. Fleming also knew from his experience with lysozyme and the sulphonamides how adaptable the bacteria could be in developing resistance to their enemies.[78]

It was not only in the clinical testing of penicillin in the wards at St Mary's that Fleming became more and more involved with work on penicillin.[79] Glaxo regularly sent him batches of penicillin for testing to assess their purity, toxicity and likely clinical value. With production methods still so crude, it was no surprise that he found himself rejecting many batches as substandard.[80] He also returned to his old expertise with venereal diseases and studied the effects of penicillin on the sexually transmitted diseases it was proving so effective against in the armed forces.[81]

While Fleming himself continued to work steadily and behind the scenes in his laboratory, the enormous press interest in him had been gaining momentum since the treatment of Harry Lambert in the late summer of 1942. On 27 August 1942, *The Times* published a leading article entitled 'Penicillium', drawing attention to the new drug and its development at Oxford.[82] Almroth Wright, despite his antipathy to chemotherapy, was quick to claim credit for his department and wrote that 'you refrained from putting the laurel wreath for this discovery on anyone's brow . . . on the principle *palmam qui meruit ferat* it should be decreed to Professor Alexander Fleming of this research laboratory. For he is the discoverer of penicillin and was the author also of the original suggestion that this substance might prove to have important applications in medicine.'[83] This bold claim on behalf of the Inoculation Department did not go unchallenged from Oxford, and Robert Robinson countered that 'a laurel wreath, a bouquet at least, and a handsome one should be presented to H.W. Florey'.[84] These were the opening salvos in a war to claim credit for penicillin that was to lead to uneasy relations between St Mary's and Oxford and a breach between Fleming and Florey.

There was immediate press interest in the story. Reporters besieged Fleming at St Mary's and were rewarded with interviews and a story. They went to Oxford and were ignored. Florey, suspicious of all personal publicity, refused to talk to them.[85] In his view, talking to the press was akin to advertising, which was contrary to the ethics of the medical profession, something Almroth Wright had no qualms about. He was also acutely aware that his predecessor as Professor of Pathology at Oxford, Georges Dreyer, had never recovered his reputation after the newspapers had hailed his development of a vaccine against tuberculosis that had later proved ineffective.[86] Piqued at their cold reception at the Sir William Dunn School, the journalists returned to the more welcoming figure of Fleming. With Fleming as the focus of their stories, the tendency was the unfair marginalisation of Florey and his team in coverage of the penicillin story. Imperceptibly, their role was edited out of the story, leaving Fleming as the hero. The *News Chronicle* featured him as their 'Man of the Week'.[87] There was something romantic about the story of a chance discovery that appealed to the public, while Fleming's apparent rags to riches rise from the obscurity of a humble background to his new status as a benefactor to humanity was given full play.[88] Scottish newspapers stressed his Scottish background[89] and the Irish press was able to lay a claim to him through Sareen's background.[90] The BBC even ascribed the first clinical trials to Fleming in a radio broadcast.[91]

Penicillin was good news amidst the gloom of war. It came in a year that had seen the fall of Singapore, Japanese victories throughout South-East Asia, the Red Army in retreat, the sinking of such prestigious battleships as the *Hood*, *Prince of Wales* and the *Repulse*, and the advance of Rommel's forces in North Africa. The Battle of El Alamein in October 1942 may have been the turning point after three years of war, but, as Churchill had said, it was not the beginning of the end but only the end of the beginning. There was more of the hardship of war ahead. Inspiration was sorely needed. Penicillin offered the prospect of life amidst the destruction of war and fitted in with popular interest in postwar reconstruction. The interest in penicillin had its counterpart in the reaction to the publication in December 1942 of the Beveridge Report with its blueprint for a welfare state. Both the Beveridge Report and penicillin offered visions of a better world to come once the war was finally over.

So inspirational was penicillin that it was even given the credit for cures with which it was totally unconnected, especially when it concerned that other focus of wartime mythologizing, Winston Churchill. In December 1943, after attending the Teheran Conference at which Roosevelt, Stalin and Churchill had decided that priority be given to Operation Overlord, the Prime Minister collapsed with pneumonia at Carthage during a brief Tunisian stopover on his way to visit the battlefields of Italy. Lord Moran, Dean of St Mary's Hospital Medical School and, as Charles Wilson, a former fellow student of Fleming's, was in attendance as usual on his most famous and at this time only patient, and he was also able to call in a second opinion from Dr D.E. Bedford. Moran had never used penicillin before and, though it was readily available from Colonel Pulvertaft, the cautious Moran preferred to stick with what he knew rather than risk returning home to a hostile reception if it all went wrong. He did know about the sulphonamides, and it was these that saved Churchill's life, not penicillin. Churchill, as fond of punning as Fleming, said that his life had been saved by M and B, which referred equally to the sulphonamide M and B 693 and to his doctors Moran and Bedford. During his enforced convalescence in Marrakesh he discovered that the sulphonamides were an agreeable accompaniment to the novels of Jane Austen.[92] The newspapers reported Churchill's recovery but claimed that it was thanks to penicillin and to Fleming.[93] The story that Fleming had twice saved the Prime Minister's life grew up, with Fleming or his father having first saved Churchill from drowning as a boy and then later this cure in North Africa. Neither story was true, but put together they made good copy and like many good stories live on as urban myths.[94]

The public wanted to hear about penicillin and it was in the interest of the Ministry of Information to encourage publicity for what was not only a rare good-news story but could also be praised as a matter of national pride as a British achievement. Lord Beaverbrook, the newspaper magnate, friend of Churchill and a former member of the War Cabinet, was a prominent patron of St Mary's Hospital and put his weight behind publicising Fleming's role. As a voluntary hospital dependent upon charitable support, St Mary's needed good publicity in order to survive, and penicillin offered a means of bringing its claims to the generosity of the public before the world. It was a time when high wartime taxation and price rises were having an effect on the income of the traditional supporters of hospitals and other charities. With less money to go around, publicity was even more necessary. Beaverbrook, mindful of his own links with St Mary's, also professed himself to have been anxious that 'justice should be done to this great pioneer', Fleming, and said that 'it seemed to me that this was a duty laid on me as the proprietor of newspapers in Britain, the country which gained a measure of reflected glory on account of Fleming's immense achievement'.[95] Beaverbrook did not think that Britain fully recognised Fleming's achievement, but the full weight of his newspapers, the *Daily Express*, *Sunday Express* and *Evening Standard*, was put behind support for Fleming.

The man at the centre of this media interest was not altogether comfortable with it. As soon as the publicity in *The Times* had appeared in August 1942, Fleming had written to Florey, even before Almroth Wright's letter to the Editor: 'You will have noticed in *The Times* some very undesirable press publicity. I have done my best to stop this sort of thing, but I was not asked about this particular case.'[96] He had also reassured Florey that he had been pleased to see Robinson's letter putting in a claim on Florey's behalf to some of the credit, 'although my work started you off on the penicillin hunt, it was you who have made it a practical proposition, and it is good that you should get the credit. You are lucky in Oxford to be out of range of reporters. They are a persistent lot and I have not been able to dodge them completely.'[97] As the media avalanche continued, he told Florey: 'You can not deplore the personal element that has crept in to penicillin more than I do, and for the moment I am the sufferer . . . I do hope that the people who matter (the others do not count) do not think that we are in opposition. I will certainly do what I can to dispel the idea.'[98]

Despite efforts to censor and even suppress references to penicillin in the newspapers and on the wireless by the General Penicillin Committee, concerned that publicity would only stoke up demands for penicillin that was not yet available,[99] the press frenzy continued unabated throughout 1943 and 1944.[100] The Penicillin Committee finally conceded in 1943 that 'some informed publicity giving value to British work would be timely'.[101] Florey, however, was increasingly resentful of the way in which the undesirable publicity in the press had ignored the efforts of his team and had begun to suspect that Fleming had not been entirely frank in claiming to have tried to discourage the press, just as Florey himself had taken a firm line in refusing to handle media enquiries although his colleague Professor Gardner had seen this as a mistake. In December 1942, he wrote to Sir Henry Dale, President of the Royal Society, to complain that 'I have now quite good evidence from the Director-General of the BBC in fact, and also indirectly from some people at St Mary's, that Fleming is doing his best to see that the whole subject is presented as having been foreseen and worked out by Fleming and that we in this Department just did a few final flourishes'.[102] Dale recommended caution as the whole question of Fleming and publicity was a delicate matter. Fleming was again up for election as a Fellow of the Royal Society, and this time Florey, who had himself been elected a Fellow in 1941, was on the Council; any dispute would reflect badly on the Royal Society.[103]

Fleming was duly elected a Fellow of the Royal Society on 18 March 1943, twenty years after he had first been proposed. His proposers in 1943 included Howard Florey, as well as Almroth Wright and other luminaries of the medical and scientific establishment.[104] His colleagues at St Mary's honoured the distinction by presenting him with an eighteenth-century silver salver. In his speech thanking his friends and colleagues for their gift, Fleming had planned to use a quotation from Burns, 'Would to God the giftie gie us, to see ourselves as others see us', but became flustered and used it out of context, giving the impression that he was actually saying that no one had recognised his talents rather than that he did not see himself as anything out of the ordinary, as he intended.[105] Superficially his relations with Florey remained amicable, and they shared a platform in a discussion on penicillin at the Royal Society of Medicine in November 1943, where 'the two great men of penicillin' both paid tribute to each other's work.[106] They also shared the annual award for 1943 of the American Pharmaceutical Producers' Association. Norman T. Kirk, Surgeon-General of the US Army, broadcast a tribute from Washington to Fleming and Florey, while Fleming replied on behalf of both of them from London.[107] Yet the bulk of the press coverage and acclaim continued to be lionised by Fleming. The newspapers were even interested when he was ill in bed with influenza in December 1943 and a journalist trapped Robert, now a medical student at St Mary's, into saying 'He is mother's despair. It takes her all her time to keep him in bed. The other day, against everybody's advice, he insisted on returning to work. Now he is back in bed again.'[108] He was well enough in January 1944 to be named 'Man of the Year' by *Picture Post*[109] and in May 1944 he was pictured on the front cover of *Time*.[110] As a result of a campaign by *Time*, the sum of $2,720 was raised in contributions from American readers of the magazine and sent to Fleming, who used it for his research, together with a free life subscription to *Time*.[111] Of Florey and his team, there was little mention.

The article in *Time* especially incensed Florey, as it seemed to give excessive praise to Fleming, as did most American newspaper coverage. John Fulton, an old friend of Florey's from their time as fellow Rhodes scholars, took up the cudgels on his behalf and warned Chester Keefer, who was overseeing clinical trials in the United States, that 'he seems utterly infuriated by the recent account of penicillin in *Time* and he hopes that we will exert our best efforts to avoid taking up a collection for the discoverer of penicillin'. Fulton suspected that the Surgeon-General's office might be boosting the claims of Fleming, for whom, 'as you well know, penicillin was merely of technical advantage in the cultivation of soil organisms'.[112] Keefer defended the article in *Time* and recommended that Fulton read Fleming's 1929 paper, which would show that Fleming had actually pointed to therapeutic applications of penicillin while having nothing at all to do with soil organisms. Fulton, however, would not give ground and declared that 'Fleming seemed not to have the imagination to carry out' experiments to demonstrate the clinical usefulness of penicillin that Florey had done.[113]

Florey himself had appealed to the Medical Research Council for help in combating this crescendo of publicity for Fleming. His irritation had turned to annoyance at what he saw as 'the unscrupulousness carried on from within St Mary's calmly to credit Fleming with all the work done here. I have sufficient evidence of one sort or another that this is a deliberate and clever campaign.' Whereas a year earlier in his correspondence with Dale on the subject, he had thought Fleming might be behind it all, he now had a new villain and felt emboldened to write to Mellanby after 'several people – some non-scientists – have asked me if there wasn't something a bit peculiar about the propaganda, and one of them, who is in a good position to know, lays a good deal of it at Lord Moran's door'.[114] The Dean of St Mary's and president of the Royal College of Physicians, nicknamed Corkscrew Charlie for his devious ways, was a more plausible conspirator than Fleming and was not above using his friends in high places, including his patient the

Prime Minister, to further the interests of his beloved hospital and medical school. In a speech to the Royal College of Physicians in March 1944, Churchill had congratulated St Mary's Hospital on its association with penicillin, 'which has broken upon the world just at the moment when human beings are being gashed and torn and poisoned by wounds on the field of war in enormous numbers and when so many other diseases hitherto insoluble cry for treatment'.[115] The words were undoubtedly Churchill's, the inspiration for them Lord Moran's. However, there is a difference between suspicions of dirty dealing from Moran and hard evidence. Mellanby, while accepting Florey's irritation at Fleming's 'unusual attitude' to his public acclaim, declined to become involved and reassured Florey that his work was recognised in the scientific world, where it mattered.[116]

The opportunity for Florey to tell his story to a wider public came when a film was commissioned by ICI to tell the story of penicillin as a great British discovery to counter 'the growing belief abroad (and in this country) that the world would ultimately have to look to the USA for supplies of penicillin'.[117] Florey characteristically wished to downplay the personal element in the film, asking the director Basil Wright to tone down the story of his and Heatley's journey to America[118] and disclaiming any involvement with 'the sort of publicity of the sob stuff character'.[119] Florey also objected to the depiction of Fleming in the film. In one scene, he was shown treating patients in a ward during the flying bomb raids on London, but Florey objected to this on the grounds that it gave the impression that Fleming had pioneered the clinical use of penicillin. When it was pointed out to him that the scene was in its correct chronological place, he reiterated his point that 'all of us here take exception to this, no matter in what place and period of the film'.[120] The shots were removed. Fleming, by contrast, was 'very affable and helpful' during filming and showed none of Florey's paranoia about his depiction in the film.[121]

It was even more galling to Florey when there was a public call for the state to reward Fleming financially for the discovery. The fact that Fleming had not benefited materially from penicillin attracted a lot of press interest with the headline 'New drug earns me nothing, Penicillin Man explains'.[122] After questions were asked in the House of Commons, Clement Attlee, the Deputy Prime Minister, replied that he was aware of the contribution of Fleming and also of the part played by others, but that it was government policy 'to support medical research in progress, and not to offer payments on the basis of results'.[123] A letter in *The Times* gave the response of many people to this statement with a renewed call for a 'sign of the nation's gratitude for a rare and timely service to humanity'.[124] The incident reinforced the public perception of Fleming as a man who had sought and received no reward for his great discovery.

Meanwhile, with the Normandy landings of June 1944, penicillin came into its own on the battlefields for the liberation of Europe. Fleming himself, in a sermon at the Savoy Chapel Royal on the first Sunday after D-Day, said that 'It seems as though Providence has been kind in presenting us with penicillin just at a time when it is most wanted'.[125] Casualties on the invasion beaches of 6 June were injected with immediate doses of penicillin before being 'sent home to live'.[126] It was estimated that it cost £1,000 to treat with penicillin each soldier wounded in combat.[127] Many of the wounded were treated at the base hospital at Basingstoke staffed by St Mary's doctors and nurses. It was a hectic atmosphere with wounded arms sent upstairs and legs downstairs for treatment and little time for sentimentality with so many casualties. On one of the wards, ear, nose and throat patients were moved out so that soldiers with 'blown-up thighs' could be treated with intra-muscular injections of penicillin given by inexperienced physiotherapists. Later, nurses took over the duty of injecting the penicillin, but, often administered in suspension in beeswax and oil and without procaine to ease the pain, these injections at three-hourly intervals were still painful.[128] The sister in charge of that ward remembered that Fleming 'sometimes visited our outpost, always without notice and informally. He was almost always discovered in a quiet corner, sitting on a bed chatting to a patient in a quiet Scottish accent.'[129] Unlike the pomp that accompanied the visits of most of the honorary staff, Fleming simply crept into the ward without a word to the sister.

As the Allied armies made their way across Europe and into Germany, penicillin accompanied them. Although primarily intended to be for the benefit of wounded soldiers, it was sometimes used for the relief of suffering civilians from the liberated countries. John Hofmeyr, a South African student at St Mary's, volunteered to join a civilian relief team to liberated Holland in spring 1945 and found himself in the midst of a typhoid epidemic among the ill-nourished local population. Cornelius, one of the patients in an emergency hospital set up in a one-roomed school, was a hopeless case, suffering not only from typhoid but also from a severe abscess in his leg. Penicillin was begged from the military authorities 50 miles away and kept in a borrowed refrigerator. It was another miracle cure. Soon there were 'M.O.'s from incredible distances coming to beg supplies. Sometimes they brought some pleading relative of a patient dying from meningitis or pneumonia or something.' Hofmeyr, though he was only a junior student, had the 'heartbreaking job' of refusing them and offering the less effective sulphonamides instead. There was not enough penicillin available even for use by the relief team doctors.[130]

Fleming himself was becoming worried that, once it did become more widely available, penicillin might be a threat to the future funding of the Inoculation Department and was canny enough to realise that the penicillin publicity could be used to the advantage of his work rather than for any personal gain. In May 1944, prompted by 'the enthusiastic reception penicillin had found in the whole public press', he suggested that the Inoculation Department and St Mary's Hospital should launch a joint appeal in connection with the forthcoming centenary of the hospital in June 1945. An appeal for the endowment of the Inoculation Department was especially important because, in his opinion, 'it was almost certain that the use of penicillin would supersede that of certain vaccines and the income of the Department would by consequence be adversely affected'.[131] It was agreed that 20 per cent of the income from the centenary appeal should go to the Inoculation Department.[132] The highlight of the centenary was a visit from the Queen, in her role as President of the hospital, to St Mary's on 28 June 1945, when, among many other attractions, she saw an exhibition illustrating the discovery, manufacture and use of penicillin and visited patients in the penicillin wards.[133] As part of the fundraising campaign to rebuild the 'birthplace of penicillin' and endow the Inoculation Department, the Penicillin Train, two railway carriages containing an exhibition on penicillin and the work of St Mary's, toured the rail network of its sponsor the Great Western Railway in southern and western England, attracting great interest wherever it stopped.[134] A massive publicity success, the appeal proved less successful than hoped for by the hospital and raised only £209,370 7s 11d, the victim of postwar impoverishment and uncertainty over the likely fate of endowment funds when the hospitals were nationalised.[135]

Fleming himself missed the centenary celebrations as he was on a triumphant tour of North America in the summer of 1945. However, by the end of the war, the benefits of penicillin were hailed everywhere. He himself was universally acclaimed as the discoverer of the miracle drug, but this publicity had resulted in a breakdown in easy relationships between the man who had first discovered penicillin and the men who brought it into clinical use, although superficially the tension was not so apparent in public. In Britain Fleming was fêted as the discoverer, yet the British enthusiasm was as nothing compared with the reception that awaited him in North America and elsewhere throughout the world in the decade to come.

EIGHT

Challenge for America

The end of the Second World War found Fleming back in the United States from which he had made a mad dash home to London at the outbreak of war six years previously. Then he had been one of a number of delegates at a microbiological congress. Now, his second visit to North America took on more of the character of a triumphal tour, as the modest Scot whose discovery had seemingly vanquished infection was greeted everywhere with all the honour more usually given to a victorious general touring the battlefields on which his reputation had been won. Universally he was greeted as the man who had given the world penicillin, though he had been warned in advance not to expect such treatment: 'I had been told in many quarters it was believed that penicillin originated in America but that I cannot accept, as everywhere in the public press as well as in scientific quarters, I have received my full share of credit for the initiation of the work.'[1] For Fleming it was the opportunity to see for himself the great advances that had been made in North America to enable mass production of penicillin to become a reality.

What struck Fleming most from his triumphant American tour was that 'It is evident that they think more of penicillin in America than in England'.[2] Everywhere he went in the summer of 1945 he was lionised during a series of press conferences, radio interviews and public lectures orchestrated for him by John Cameron, his minder from the British Mission, who confessed that he had fallen 'completely under his spell'.[3] His American tour was a success from the moment he set sail on the *Aquitania* and gave a lecture on the discovery of penicillin to his fellow travellers in mid-voyage. Despite his dislike of such lecturing, he was coming to tailor what he said to his audience, increasingly non-medical. He also joined his shipmates in conversation though was perhaps a better listener than talker.[4]

The tone of the visit was set when he arrived in New York to be greeted by cheering crowds and a police motorcycle escort. The American Association of Penicillin Producers organised a banquet at the Waldorf Hotel in his honour and presented him with a gift of $100,000, which he requested should be given to the Inoculation Department at St Mary's to set up an Alexander Fleming Memorial Fund to encourage

The fledgling bacteriologist Fleming assesses an Opsonic Index, watched over by a photograph of the founder of modern microbiology, Elie Metchnikoff, *c.* 1909. Next to him in the wheelchair is Captain Hayden, incapacitated by polio, whom Fleming had persuaded Wright to employ. *(Alexander Fleming Laboratory Museum, St Mary's NHS Trust)*

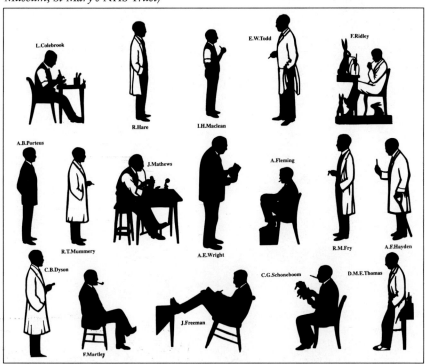

A brotherhood in science, silhouettes of staff of the Inoculation Department in the 1920s. *(Alexander Fleming Laboratory Museum, St Mary's NHS Trust)*

The scene of Fleming's labours: the Clarence Memorial Wing, St Mary's Hospital. *(Alexander Fleming Laboratory Museum, St Mary's NHS Trust)*

'Private 606': sketch by Ronald Gray marking Fleming's success in the London Scottish Regiment and as a 'pox doctor'. *(Alexander Fleming Laboratory Museum, St Mary's NHS Trust)*

A wartime laboratory: Fleming and A.B. Porteous at Wimereux, 1918. *(Alexander Fleming Laboratory Museum, St Mary's NHS Trust)*

'Tear antiseptic': cartoon by J.H. Dowd, suggesting one way of producing lysozyme, 1922. *(Alexander Fleming Laboratory Museum, St Mary's NHS Trust)*

The art of bacteriology: one of Fleming's germ paintings that failed to impress Queen Mary. *(Alexander Fleming Laboratory Museum, St Mary's NHS Trust)*

Family life: Sareen and Robert. *(Alexander Fleming Laboratory Museum, St Mary's NHS Trust)*

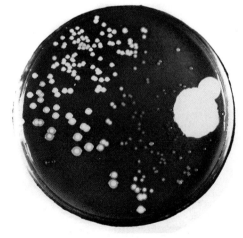

Fleming at the time of the discovery of penicillin. *(Alexander Fleming Laboratory Museum, St Mary's NHS Trust)*

A national treasure: Fleming's 1929 photograph of his petri dish contaminated by a mysterious mould which has inhibited the growth of bacteria. *(Alexander Fleming Laboratory Museum, St Mary's NHS Trust)*

Penicillin in use on the battlefields for the liberation of Europe, Luxembourg, 1944. *(Imperial War Museum, EA52557)*

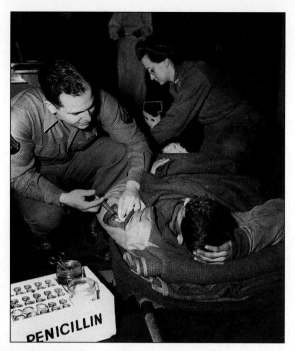

An exhortation to build a penicillin factory to aid the war effort. *(Alexander Fleming Laboratory Museum, St Mary's NHS Trust)*

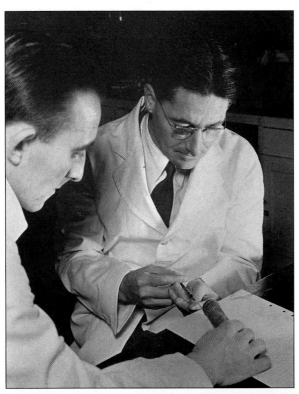

Performing the crucial animal tests: Howard Florey, assisted by Jim Kent, injects a mouse. *(Sir William Dunn School of Pathology, University of Oxford)*

The image of the dedicated scientist: Ernst Chain analysing penicillin, 1944. *(Wolfgang Suschitzky)*

e penicillin girls tending the mould at the Sir William Dunn School of Pathology. *(Sir
lliam Dunn School of Pathology, University of Oxford)

*erican pioneer Andrew Moyer. (United States Department of Agriculture, Agricultural
earch Service, National Center for Agricultural Utilization Research, Peoria, Illinois)

A hero to bullfighters, Barcelona, 1948. *(Alexander Fleming Laboratory Museum, St Mar NHS Trust)*

A 1952 visit to Athens ending with a proposal: Fleming and Amalia at the Acropo *(Alexander Fleming Laboratory Museum, St Mary's NHS Trust)*

future researchers. The fund was to be administered by the University of Pennsylvania, where A.N. Richards, who had done so much to encourage penicillin production in the United States, was Professor of Pharmacology.[5] At Peoria, Illinois, Fleming was a guest of the chief of the fermentation division at the Department of Agriculture Northern Regional Research Laboratory and was able to see for himself the place that over the previous four years had hosted the work necessary for scaling up penicillin production. Over the next few months he also had the opportunity to visit some of the new industrial plants set up for the mass manufacture of penicillin.[6] At Yale he met and was photographed with the first patient to have been treated with penicillin in North America, and by referring to her as 'my patient' caused yet again inadvertent offence to Florey and his team back home in Oxford.[7] In Washington, DC, he was able to see for himself the seat of power where so many high-level policy decisions had been taken. There the Variety Clubs of America presented him with their Humanitarian Award and a cheque for $1,000 at a sumptuous dinner at the Mayfair Hotel attended by the elite of the cabinet, Senate and the international diplomatic corps. However, in many ways the personal high point of his American trip was Commencement Day at Harvard, where not only did he receive an honorary doctorate but he had the opportunity to renew his acquaintance with Roger Lee and the other Harvard men he had first met at Boulogne during the dark days of an earlier war.[8]

Throughout his tour, he was learning how to deal with the press, who were at their most pushy during this trip. John Cameron guided him through the maze of press conferences, public lectures and radio interviews. Fleming was very conscious of the importance of having a mentor such as Cameron in his introduction to the trappings of celebrity and wrote 'without him I should have been rather lost'.[9] Nevertheless, his confidence was built up to such an extent that he could introduce a nationwide broadcast of a dramatised account of his life in which his part was played by matinee idol Ronald Colman. Only once did Cameron see him ruffled by the insistent personal questions hurled at him, such as how he had broken his nose and how his medical studies had been funded. His usual reaction was to retreat into his wonted silences, but at a press conference in Washington he actually told Cameron that he had had enough of it and wanted to go. On another occasion, when pestered by the press as he went down to breakfast at the Biltmore Hotel in New York, he answered their question about what he was thinking with the profound answer that he was indeed thinking of something very important, whether to have one egg or two for his breakfast. His impish sense of humour shone throughout his visit. When asked at a dinner hosted by the American Medical Association in Chicago whether it was true that penicillin could cure a hangover, he replied that 'it isn't that wonderful'.[10] Cameron, who to some extent had tutored and guided him through a gruelling series of media encounters lasting for two months, found that fame did not stop Fleming from being 'one of the most humble men I have ever met; he often used to say "I wonder why it is that they make such a fuss of me"'.[11]

The ceremony and pomp of Fleming's 1945 American tour were in complete contrast to the circumstances in which Howard Florey and his colleague Norman Heatley had brought penicillin to the New World in the summer of 1941. Their mission, on the advice of Sir Edward Mellanby of the Medical Research Council and supported by a travel grant from the Rockefeller Foundation, was to get large-scale production going.[12] Florey's main task was to seek the interest and involvement of companies in the States, as yet still at peace and far removed from the European theatre of war. His personal aim was to obtain North American supplies for his own clinical trials, although this ambition, not surprisingly, was to be frustrated by North American demands for the drug. Travel to the United States in wartime was not easy and far from safe. In April 1941 Heatley and Florey were brought face to face with a reminder of the dangers soon to face them when they went to the cinema to see the Hitchcock thriller *Foreign Correspondent* in which the clipper aeroplane to North America is blown out of the air on the outbreak of the war.[13] Their own dangerous journey was shrouded in secrecy and took three months to organise while all the necessary wartime formalities and permissions were negotiated. Chain was furious when he discovered that this trip had been organised without his knowledge or involvement. Indeed he only learned about it when he saw the packed suitcases in a corner of Florey's office half an hour before Florey and Heatley were due to set off.[14] The quickest way was by air, but there were no direct flights from Britain. Ethel Florey drove her husband and Norman Heatley from Oxford to Whitchurch aerodrome near Bristol, from where they flew to Lisbon on 27 June in a blacked-out aeroplane.[15] There, amidst the bright lights of the capital of neutral Portugal, a haven for spies from both sides, they found themselves stuck for four days before they could get on the next available Clipper flight to New York. Even then the route was far from simple, taking them via the Azores and Bermuda before they finally reached New York on 3 July.

The eve of the Independence Day holiday was not the most propitious time for them to begin their important business, though Florey did manage to make a report to Alan Gregg at the Rockefeller Foundation about the results he had obtained with penicillin so far.[16] Independence Day also gave him the opportunity to visit his children, Paquita and Charles, who had been evacuated to live with his friend John Fulton, a physiologist, at New Haven, Connecticut. It also allowed him to capitalise on a link that gave him access to the help he needed. Fulton, who had been a fellow student of Florey's at Oxford in the 1920s, was an invaluable contact, able to suggest people who might be able to help. The unexpected guests of honour at Lucia Fulton's customary Fourth of July cocktail party, Florey and Heatley were steered towards Ross Harrison, Chairman of the National Research Council and Vice-President of the Board of Scientific Directors of the Rockefeller Institute of Medical Research, with whom they enjoyed fuller discussions the following day.[17] A man with wide contacts in the medical world, Harrison was able to introduce them to Charles Thom, a mycologist at the Bureau of Plant Industry at Beltsville, Maryland, the man who had first correctly identified Fleming's mould as *Penicillium notatum*. Interested by what he heard from Florey and Heatley, Thom took them to Washington on 9 July and introduced them to Percy Wells, acting assistant chief of the Bureau of Agricultural Chemistry and Engineering.[18] Wells immediately thought of the most suitable facilities for continuing their work, ones located in a small town in far-off Illinois.

Up to the time of its involvement in the penicillin project and for many years after, Peoria had been something of a Vaudeville joke, which later caused Fleming to describe it as the 'Wigan of North America'.[19] The proverbial phrase 'Will it play in Peoria?' has come to sum up its role as the epitome of middle America and was to be used by President Harry S. Truman as a benchmark for the acceptability of his policies. Lying on the Illinois river some 150 miles south of Chicago, it was at the heart of the corn belt. Before prohibition, it had been a centre of whisky distilling as well as a market centre for grain and agricultural machinery. Now it was dominated by the newly built Northern Regional Research Laboratory, with its art deco style entrance, referred to locally as the 'Ag Lab'. The Northern Regional Research Laboratory had been established as a New Deal initiative to find alternative uses for agricultural products, chiefly the locally grown corn of the Midwest in this instance. It was one of four regional research laboratories authorised by Congress in 1938 and had opened only towards the end of 1940.[20] It had newly developed fermentation facilities that were essential if the aim of increasing yields was to be successful. A special pilot-type shallow pan aluminium fermenter had been constructed there, which was thought suitable for the penicillin project.[21]

On 9 July, Wells sent a telegram to Orville May, director of the laboratory in Peoria, asking whether it would be possible to use these facilities for the investigation of the production of penicillin from Fleming's mould.[22] The next day a telegram arrived inviting Florey and Heatley to Peoria to discuss the project.[23] While the facilities would be available and the laboratory was happy to cooperate immediately, there still remained a need to discuss the proposed work to make sure that it was an area to which the scientists at Peoria could actually make a contribution. Wells himself had no doubts about this and suggested that they try out a submerged fermentation technique first developed by May in 1935 at Arlington Farms, Virginia, a site later occupied by the Pentagon.[24]

Florey and Heatley arrived at Peoria on 14 July 1941. They held their first meeting with May and his staff immediately on their arrival and then began work the following day. The speed with which it all took place was a reflection of the importance the government of the United States attributed to the work of investigating 'pilot production of bacteriostatic material from Fleming's penicillium in connection with medical defence plans'.[25] While Florey only stayed in Peoria long enough to see that the laboratory was in a position to cooperate fully with this project, Heatley stayed there until the end of November, before going to work for a further six months with the Merck pharmaceutical company at Rahway, New Jersey, where he contributed to the transition of penicillin production from the research laboratory to industrial production.[26] However, the programme to increase penicillin yields that now began under the direction of Robert Coghill, chief of the fermentation division, was to continue for the next four years, work that could truly be described as the basis of all further wartime biological developments of penicillin.

Throughout the journey from Oxford right up until his arrival in Peoria, Heatley had constantly been worried about the condition of the precious freeze-dried samples of penicillin he was carrying. Would the samples stand up to the rigours of the difficult and protracted journey? What effect would the heat of the plane and of first the Portuguese and then the North American summer have on them? His fear was that the high temperatures might have killed the mould.[27] Slowly and painstakingly, the freeze-dried specimens were coaxed into germination at the Ag Lab. Ironically, Heatley's concerns were needless. What he did not know was that spores of Fleming's mould were already in Peoria. The sample sent by Raistrick to Charles Thom for identification in 1934 now formed part of the national mycological collections, which had been transferred to the Northern Regional Research Laboratory in 1940.[28]

Norman Heatley found himself working closely with Andrew Moyer on the difficult task of finding answers to the problem of producing the new drug on an industrial and economical scale.[29] It was not made any easier by a difficult relationship between the two men. Moyer was not the most agreeable of colleagues and has been described by one co-worker as 'a right sonofabitch' to work with.[30] Heatley feared with some justification that Moyer was holding back vital information but believed that he could count on the support of Coghill and his fellow workers at the Ag Lab, all of whom had been friendly and welcoming to the quiet Englishman, if it came to a showdown.[31] The tension was exacerbated by the anti-British and isolationist stance taken by Moyer as war approached, not an uncommon attitude in the American heartlands at that time but one that did not make transatlantic cooperation one whit easier.[32] Heatley even found himself lodging above the headquarters of what he described to Florey as the local Nazi party, but characteristically he accepted the circumstances in which he found himself and settled down to the task before him.[33]

Nevertheless, Moyer, a brilliant chemist, was undoubtedly the right man for the job. In the search for the optimum conditions for the production of penicillin, he soon found that he could increase the yield by substituting lactose for the sucrose used by the Oxford team in their culture medium. He then discovered that by adding corn-steep liquor to the fermentation medium he could increase the yield by ten times. There was nothing remarkable about this decision to use corn-steep liquor, a by-product of the corn wet-milling process. They tried it out in all their fermentation work as a matter of course. Moyer and Coghill had indeed earlier studied the composition of corn-steep liquor and found that it contained phenylacetic acid, which later proved to be useful in stimulating the production of specific forms of penicillin.[34] Later still, as a result of these studies it was found that the addition of penicillin precursors, such as phenylacetic acid, to the fermentation medium, pioneered at Peoria, further increased the yield of the antibiotic. This form of penicillin, which was later to be shown to have a benzyl side chain, was christened Penicillin G and for many years was the most widely preferred type of penicillin in clinical use.[35]

By the time Heatley left Peoria at the end of November 1941 after training the staff there in his methods of penicillin assay, he and Moyer were able to report to Coghill that 'the study has resulted in a greatly improved method for penicillin production whereby yields are increased twelve-fold over those previously reported; the essential features of the new method are the additions of corn steeping liquor and of neutralizing agents to the medium'.[36] These yields had followed on from five days' incubation of the mould by growing it on the surface of the growth medium. They had tested variations in the make-up of the nutrient media, temperature and other environmental conditions. They had also experimented with growing the organism in rotary drums and vats.[37]

The surface culture method of growing the mould used at Oxford was inefficient and uneconomical compared to growth in submerged culture. When grown on the surface of a culture medium, the penicillium mould could penetrate no more than one or two millimetres below the surface, so that a large surface area was required to grow any significant quantity of penicillin. This in turn required an enormous number of culture flasks, either closed bottles or open trays. Unless the penicillin could be grown in submerged tanks or vats, it seemed that it would be well-nigh impossible to produce it in sufficient quantities for widespread clinical use. The next step, having found a growth medium that greatly increased yields of penicillin, was to experiment with growing the mould in deep tanks below the surface of the culture medium, but it was here that the team at Peoria found a new difficulty. The problem was that the strain of *Penicillium notatum* brought to Peoria from Oxford produced traces of penicillin only when grown in submerged culture in a constantly aerated and agitated mixture in deep tanks.[38] The search was on for a faster-growing strain of penicillium.

At first it had been thought that only the Fleming strain of *Penicillium notatum* actually produced penicillin, but then the researchers observed that most strains of the chrysogenum–notatum group of penicillia moulds produced it in greater or lesser quantities. Another strain of the fungus, originally sent from Biourge's laboratory in Belgium, was found in the culture collections of the laboratory at Peoria, which produced a more stable form of penicillin but with lower yields.[39] Under the direction of Kenneth B. Raper, staff at the Northern Regional Research Laboratory screened strains of the mould sought from around the world with the help of the Army Transport Command until they found one capable of producing sufficient penicillin in submerged culture. Raper believed that there might be an organism in soil that could produce larger quantities of penicillin. As a result, samples of soil were delivered daily to Peoria from all parts of the world in bottles, paper bags and paper cartons. Good penicillin-producing strains of the mould were found as far away as Cape Town, Chungkin and Bombay, but ironically the best of all was actually found in Peoria itself.[40]

In virtually all the accounts of the discovery of this faster-growing strain of penicillin, credit for finding it is given to Mary Hunt, a researcher at the Northern Regional Research Laboratory who earned herself the nickname 'Mouldy Mary' on account of her assiduous search for moulds in local markets, bakeries and cheese stores.[41] Fleming was fond of telling her story.[42] The legend goes that, having been employed to search for moulds, she found the most productive strain, *Penicillium chrysogenum*, on a mouldy cantaloupe melon in a Peoria market. Or did she? As so often in the story of penicillin, the truth is slightly different from the legend. An unnamed Peoria housewife actually brought in a mouldy melon. 'Mouldy Mary', despite her nickname and her unusual quest, was not responsible for what was an important find.[43] The new mould produced much higher yields of penicillin when cultivated in submerged conditions. The productivity of this mould was further increased after exposure to X-rays at the Carnegie Institute and ultraviolet radiation at the University of Wisconsin.[44]

While Heatley had made appreciable advances with his scientific work on penicillin in collaboration with North American colleagues at Peoria, described by one journalist as a 'microbe zoo',[45] Florey had more mixed fortunes in his attempts to win over the American chemical industry. On leaving Peoria, he began what he described as a 'carpet bagging' tour of the North American chemical industry, accompanied for most of the time by Norman Heatley, visiting Philadelphia, Toronto and the mid-Atlantic States. In some places there was encouragement but as yet no offers of practical help. In others the reception was much more discouraging. Merck had been conducting research at Rahway, New Jersey, since 1940 as part of a much wider study of antibacterial substances instigated by Selman Waksman of Rutgers University in 1939. E.R. Squibb of New Brunswick had considered the possibility of penicillin work in 1937 but had been deterred by an unfavourable internal report on the prospects of such work. Lederle had been interested in penicillin for over a year but was uncommunicative so as to protect its commercial interests. Pfizer too was interested and considering some work on penicillin.[46] Although many of these companies had already started some research into penicillin before the arrival of Florey, there were understandable fears about embarking on an expensive project with a drug that at that stage had only been used on staphylococcal infections in limited clinical trials. What also held them back was the fear that, if the chemists could find some means of synthesising penicillin, any investment in production from the mould might be rendered worthless overnight. The rival firms were also suspicious of each other. The interest was there but something extra was needed to get the project off the ground.

However, Florey did enjoy the confidence of Alfred Newton Richards, Chairman of the Committee on Medical Research of the Office of Scientific Research and Development, set up to coordinate scientific research with the needs of national defence with an eye to the by now imminent war. This new body was also to have responsibility for the Manhattan Project, which led to the development of the atom bomb.[47] Florey had briefly worked in Richards's laboratory at the University of Pennsylvania in 1925. Richards indeed was well placed to facilitate cooperation between government, the universities and big business, as he was a consultant to Merck as well as Vice-President for Medical Affairs at the University of Pennsylvania. Meanwhile Vannevar Bush, Director of the Office of Scientific Research and Development, wielded great influence with the White House and was able to push the case for prioritising penicillin as high as President Roosevelt.[48] Florey visited him on 7 August 1941 and received assurances that he would give every possible support to the production of penicillin.[49]

Richards wasted little time in mobilising those sections of American industry in a position to push forward penicillin production. At a meeting of the Committee on Medical Research held on 2 October he was authorised to 'suggest to interested persons the desirability of a concerted programme of research on penicillin involving the pooling of information and results'.[50] He consequently convened a meeting of government officials and representatives of the chemical industry in Washington, DC, on 8 October 1941. It was important enough for Vannevar Bush himself to be present. Charles Thom represented the Department of Agriculture, while industry was involved through high-level representatives of Squibb, Merck, Pfizer and Lederle, four of the major pharmaceutical companies that had already shown an interest. Priority was given to the production of penicillin, and plans were discussed for a collaborative programme, both between companies and with universities.[51] There was much talk but little progress, and a second conference held in mid-November was no more productive.[52]

Everything had changed by the time of the third meeting held at the University Club in New York on 17 December 1941, and there was now no holding back by anyone. Ten days after the shock attack on Pearl Harbor and America's entry into the war, penicillin production was more than ever a priority.[53] The changed climate was also fostered by favourable reports from Coghill on the successful use of corn-steep liquor at Peoria.[54] In particular, George Merck, President of Merck, was now more than ever convinced that mass production of penicillin might just possibly be feasible, although he had been openly sceptical right up until he heard Coghill's report and had actually declared that even with the best facilities available to his company it was not humanly possible to produce even the kilo of penicillin that Florey had requested for his clinical trials. Now George Merck was confident enough to commit $781,000 to the project and promise the Office for Scientific Research and Development a bottle of synthetic penicillin by New Year's Day 1943.[55] His confidence was misplaced, but, with his belief that 'success depends upon people', he threw his weight behind production from the mould.[56]

However, the outbreak of war was to have mixed results for penicillin production. While the antibiotic was obviously of great value to the war effort, other things, as in wartime Britain, were considered of greater importance. The War Production Board gave priority to rubber, essential for so many things from tyres to boots, now that the Japanese had severed imports from the Far East. To aid the quest for alternatives, the United States Department of Justice allowed chemical, rubber and petroleum companies freely to pool and exchange commercial information. This move, which was so at odds with normal competitive instincts in business and also against the spirit of anti-trust legislation with its fear of cartels and monopolies, set a precedent for the exchange of information between competing industrial firms, which was to encourage cooperation in developing penicillin commercially. Nevertheless, it was not until 7 December 1943 that the Attorney General exempted penicillin from the operation of the anti-trust laws, an exemption given to no other drug.[57] Until this time, pharmaceutical firms had pooled information but only by violating the legislation with official connivance.[58] Moreover, the War Production Board was able to allocate some building materials, raw materials and manpower for penicillin production, and encouraged cooperation.[59] Tax relief was given to firms to offset the risk of plant being made obsolete by the advent of synthetic penicillin. An 85 per cent tax on excess profits also encouraged investment in research and development. However patriotic these hard-headed industrialists might have been, there was still a point at which it was better to retain as much profit as possible with the so-called 15 cent dollar rather than lose it to government coffers even if it was to support the war effort.[60] Yet the profits from penicillin, considerable as they may have been later, were an unknown quantity when the pharmaceutical and chemical industrialists committed themselves to the considerable financial risks of penicillin production.[61]

Undoubtedly the pharmaceutical and chemical industries rose magnificently to the challenge of scaling up production to a manufacturing scale. Collaboration and the sharing of expertise between companies through the mediation of the Committee on Medical Research enabled the transition to mass manufacturing to progress more rapidly and smoothly than would have been possible in peacetime, when the usual commercial rivalries would have operated.

Each company played its part, according to its own brand of expertise or previous production experience. Merck and Squibb, for example, joined in a collaborative programme in February 1942 and agreed to make their data available to other companies and to hand over all the penicillin they produced for distribution for clinical trials through the Committee on Medical Research.[62] Patriotism and government direction did not entirely overcome normal commercial considerations and the pooling of information between rival firms was not always as effective as it might have been, as Albert Elder, coordinator of the Penicillin Program from 1943, acknowledged when he wrote that 'progress could have been much more rapid with a free interchange of material. One industry man said that as he saw my job, I was to go from one plant to another collecting honey, but I was not to distribute pollen along the way.'[63] Individual firms were very much aware of their own postwar interests, when it would be an advantage to be ahead of the game in meeting mass demand for penicillin.[64]

The big players initially were Merck, Squibb, Pfizer, Abbot and Winthrop, all of whom gambled large sums of money on bringing penicillin into clinical use. It was risky to invest so heavily in this new relatively untried drug, but it was a risk that was to pay handsome dividends for all of them in the future. John Smith of Pfizer described the penicillium mould as being 'as temperamental as an opera singer'.[65] It was largely for this reason that, while the work of the Northern Regional Research Laboratory had conclusively shown that the future for large-scale production lay in the use of deep-tank fermentation, most of the penicillin being produced in the United States actually continued to be produced in shallow layers in flasks, bottles and pans. Merck and Squibb indeed concentrated on the enlargement of their pilot plants, working from the assumption that the drug would soon be synthesised and fermentation plants would prove to be unnecessary.[66] The Chester County Mushroom Laboratories in West Chester, Pennsylvania, became a collaborator in the penicillin project to produce penicillin by surface culture only after its technical director, G. Raymond Rettew, convinced Richards and Coghill that the similarities between the growth of mushrooms and penicillium mould were enough to give his company a strong advantage in the drive to production.[67] It was left to a new player in the drugs industry to take the necessary steps towards establishing a commercial-scale fermentation plant.

It was involvement in the race for penicillin that had indeed brought one of the major players in the modern multinational pharmaceutical industry into the pharmaceutical field in the first place. Pfizer was in origin a pioneer of deep-vat fermentation techniques for the production of citric acid for the food and drink industry. Such techniques were vital for the successful scaling-up of penicillin production and Pfizer was able to adapt these processes for the production of penicillin. Work on penicillin began in the summer of 1941 and by October supplies were being made available for testing at the University of Columbia.[68] This involvement was driven by John L. Smith, the pugnacious and somewhat unorthodox Vice-President of Pfizer, backed by the chief chemical engineer John E. McKeen, who was quick to follow up the scientific work at Peoria into submerged culture.[69] Unlike some of the more traditional pharmaceutical companies, there was more of an entrepreneurial spirit at Pfizer under Smith, who was not afraid of trying out the new and untested, especially since his firm was a newcomer to the drugs industry anyway. He was, nonetheless, concerned about the possibility of contamination of the firm's other more obviously profitable biological processes by penicillin and other micro-organisms and moved much more slowly from commercial considerations than he might otherwise have done.[70] By 1943 Pfizer was producing penicillin in 50-gallon tanks in a pilot plant, and then at Brooklyn opened the first plant to produce penicillin in 7,000-gallon tanks on a mass scale by submerged culture.[71] A disused ice plant a few blocks away from the Pfizer works in Brooklyn was bought and fitted with stainless steel fermenters. With materials in short supply, equipment, including a second-hand elevator brought over from Long Island and a redundant steam boiler from Indiana, was as ever scrounged and improvised.[72] As an incentive to greater efforts in construction, posters on the walls urged the men to work harder to complete the factory to help win the war and a note in their pay packets reminded them that 'on this job you are creating a plant that will mean life and death to many men in the armed forces . . . the quicker our work is done, the quicker penicillin will be saving our fighting men'.[73] By the end of the war, the Brooklyn plant was producing more than half the total world production of penicillin.[74] Major-General George Lull, Deputy Surgeon-General of the War Department, congratulated the firm on 'the service rendered by the world's largest producer of penicillin'.[75] Not to be outdone, Merck and Commercial Solvents were soon following hard on their heels with the introduction of deep-fermentation techniques.[76]

Both the management of Pfizer and visitors noticed the 'co-operation, friendship and esprit de corps of all workers on the project' at Pfizer.[77] The hourly workers were very well treated and on their days off were given tickets to watch the Brooklyn Dodgers, the local baseball team owned by their boss, but there were signs of dissatisfaction among the professional staff, who dreaded the frequent visits from McKeen, 'an aggressive in your face type' all too ready to grill research staff on what progress they had made with their work at a time when 'it was all improvisation'.[78] Total dedication was expected and some workers might find themselves working sixteen hours in one day, with double shifts and even triple shifts not unknown.[79] Such commitment was also expected and found at other plants, such as Merck in New Jersey, where over a period of six months workers stayed day and night on occasion to get a successful production run.[80] There was a sense that such all-out effort would help to win the war, and many of the scientists, managers and production workers were young men with the determination and stamina to make the penicillin project a success.

Not all production, which since July 1943 had been under the supervision of the War Production Board, was on such an industrial scale as that at Pfizer. Surface culture continued and was officially encouraged because at first there was no certainty that submerged culture would succeed. Indeed throughout the war, the official attitude was that synthesis was always just round that elusive corner.[81] There seemed little point in investing money in expensive methods of production if they were soon to be superseded and if there were cheaper if less efficient methods available. Ronald Hare, in charge of penicillin production at the Connaught Laboratories in Toronto and a former colleague of Fleming, was scathing about some smaller North American factories 'started by amateurs who seemed to be doing it as much for fun as from patriotic or pecuniary motives'. One of these was a firetrap in a basement full of flammable liquids presided over by a gum-chewing chemist, while another businessman was reusing old whisky bottles in a derelict Brooklyn factory.[82]

Nevertheless the future lay with submerged culture. Britain began to consider the postwar penicillin needs of the civil population in 1944 when the whole question of postwar reconstruction was in the air generally. Plans were put in place for the building of two large modern plants at Speke, near Liverpool, by Distillers and at Barnard Castle, County Durham, by Glaxo, which were intended to have the capacity to meet British peacetime demands. The original intention was that both factories should use the shallow-tray method, of production.[83] Then the Ministry of Supply sent Harry Jephcott of Glaxo and William Boon of ICI to inspect deep-fermentation plants in the United States. They were immediately won over to the superior method, and, on their return to Britain, the plans for the two new plants were changed. Work had already begun on construction of the Barnard Castle site, but the Speke factory could now be designed for submerged-culture production from the start. Glaxo signed agreements with Merck and Squibb for the purchase of the new technology and Distillers came to a similar arrangement with Commercial Solvents.[84]

As in Britain, military pressure encouraged American penicillin production. For a long time, the American military authorities had been aware of the shortcomings of sulphonamides with their debilitating side effects such as mental confusion, vomiting or nausea. Military doctors now welcomed the opportunity to try out penicillin. The armed forces offered a source of human guinea pigs for trials of the new drug. Trials involving wounded soldiers at a pilot penicillin unit at Bushnell Hospital, Brigham, Utah, began on 1 April 1943 at a time when enough penicillin was already being produced to consider its possible widescale use in the treatment of wounded soldiers.[85] A special ward was set up for penicillin therapy, and each patient was given a separate room in an attempt to avoid cross-infection as far as possible. Major Champ Lyons, a pre-war surgeon at Massachusetts General Hospital, Boston, and 'quite an inspiration' to his new military colleagues,[86] who in turn were 'alert and anxious to co-operate with us' in 'an extraordinary opportunity' that could 'shorten the period of convalescence by years and . . . return men to active service',[87] was placed in charge of the unit. Here he collaborated with Major Frank B. Queen, chief of laboratory services at Bushnell in what were effectively the first large-scale clinical trials of the new drug.[88] On 3 June 1943 a second clinical unit was established at Halloran General Hospital, Staten Island, New York.[89] These two units became penicillin therapy schools for medical officers from other military hospitals, who attended for one-month training periods and participated in the clinical testing programme, which was in turn extended to nine other military hospitals. Trainees were given the opportunity to determine the cases to be treated and the details and procedures in their treatment. They then forwarded the case notes to the Army Surgical Consultants Division, which used them to devise clinical protocols for front-line doctors.[90] These trials at Bushnell and Halloran convinced the army of the importance of penicillin to the war effort and intensified demands for the prioritisation of its production. The Surgeon-General, Norman T. Kirk, himself wrote to Richards for information on the status of penicillin production in June 1943 and was reassured that industrial expansion plans were on course.[91] This pressure intensified as demands for use on the battlefields grew and penicillin proved itself in the theatre of war as much as in the operating theatre.[92]

Even with all the will to succeed on the part of the pharmaceutical industry, it was impossible to produce penicillin quickly enough for the armed forces, which became increasingly impatient of the War

Production Board's inability to meet production targets. At a meeting in June 1943, hosted by the National Academy of Sciences, the War Production Board had promised 200 billion units of penicillin a month,[93] but this had proved over-ambitious, and the mere 400 million units actually produced in the first five months of the production process proved frustrating to military doctors, who had expected much more. Their complaints led directly to the appointment of a 'penicillin czar', a trouble-shooter charged with coordinating production.[94] Albert Elder, a chemist, was appointed as programme coordinator in 1943 and was able to bring some order to the chaos of supplying industry with the needful resources to scale up production.[95] The task of ensuring that there were enough motors, filters, centrifuges, sterilisers, vacuum pumps, heat exchangers, drying ovens and other necessities available for when the manufacturers required them was perhaps the easy part of his job at this time of shortage. Much more difficult was dealing with the widespread official attitude that the way forward lay with the synthesis of penicillin. He was even 'ridiculed by some of my close scientific friends for allowing myself to be associated with what obviously was to be a flop', and it was only because the army took the attitude that 'a bird in the hand was worth two in the bush' that fermentation production was scaled up to meet the demand rather than wait for synthesis before making the investment in plant.[96]

Wartime security considerations also restricted access to all aspects of penicillin production in the United States from March 1942 and only a limited amount of information was passed over to England, where the Committee on Medical Research set up an office in the US Embassy in London to coordinate American and British research and production. Florey complained that he had made available all the information on his work to American producers, but he was finding it well-nigh impossible to receive any information from them.[97] It was a refrain constantly picked up by British firms and the British government throughout the war.[98] By contrast there was a much more relaxed attitude among the usually more uptight British and there was no similar restriction on the publication of clinical data in the United Kingdom, though from 1942 publication of chemical information relating to production methods was banned in case it was of value to the enemy.[99] There was much discussion in Britain in 1944 of putting penicillin on the secret list as a 'munition of war', but it had already been so well publicised as to which firms were producing it and where that such action would have been redundant.[100] The British Penicillin Synthesis Committee was much readier to publish research data than the Office of Scientific Research and Development and there were disagreements over what should be considered secret or not in the race to synthesise penicillin, although generally the informal agreements to pool information worked well.[101] Among the British scientists there were some who would have preferred more secrecy. In November 1944, one member of the Penicillin Synthesis Committee, Professor Heilbron, 'wondered whether we were not making a free gift to our enemies of vital information'. Sir Robert Robinson, chairing the meeting, pointed out 'that there was undoubtedly leakage of information which would in any case reach Germany and delay in publication was, therefore, likely to be disadvantageous to British and American workers'.[102] Behind the needs of researchers for good data was the pressure for penicillin to treat sick people.

Demand was enormous, especially following the publicity surrounding the treatment in March 1942 of the first patient, Mrs Anne Sheafe Miller of New Haven, Connecticut, the 33-year-old wife of Ogden Miller, the athletics director at Yale. Anne Miller was dying from streptococcal septicaemia following a miscarriage. For four weeks her temperature had been above 106°F and her chart 'looked like a geological elevation of the high sierras'.[103] Not even sulpha drugs could bring down the fever. Luckily her physician, John Bumstead, was also treating John Fulton at that time and he was able to persuade Fulton to bring influence to bear to obtain a sample of penicillin. It took three days for 5.5 grams of this scarce drug produced by Merck in New Jersey to be flown to New Haven from Washington and delivered to the hospital by a state trooper. Penicillin was given by intravenous drip, and overnight Mrs Miller's temperature fell and her appetite returned.[104] Miracle cure though it may have been, it was not actually the first time a patient had been treated with penicillin by injection in the United States. Dr M.H. Dawson of Columbia University and the Presbyterian Hospital, New York, had been inspired by the 1940 *Lancet* paper on penicillin to inject it into three patients on 15 October 1940, before Florey used it systemically on Albert Alexander, but the dosage had been far too small to induce any improvement in the patients.[105]

Greater publicity came with the release of penicillin for the treatment of staphylococcal infections in the respiratory tracts of victims of the Cocoanut Grove nightclub fire in Boston on the evening of Saturday November 1942. The Cocoanut Grove was a fashionable, if slightly disreputable, nightspot, in the midtown theatre district of Boston, which was particularly crowded on the night of the fire with junior officers on weekend leave from their units, a wedding party, football supporters who had spent their afternoon at a game between Holy Cross and Boston College and fans of the cowboy film star Buck Jones, who was making a guest appearance at the nightclub. The fire had started when an artificial palm tree decorating the club caught light and flames spread through the bars. Fire exits were locked and panic ensued. That night 484 of the club's patrons, including the bridegroom celebrating his wedding, the film star Buck Jones, and many soldiers and sailors died of burns or suffocation. Hospitals in Boston were overwhelmed with the casualties and the dying were laid out in rows in hospital corridors. Many of the victims were so badly burned that they could be identified only by their effects, but in other cases where the casualty had suffocated there were no marks on the bodies and it was noticed that even the fuzz on the men's neckties remained unaffected.[106] Respiratory infections were a major problem for many of the survivors regardless of whether or not they were badly burned. Already the value of penicillin in treating burns victims had been shown by Flight-Lieutenant D.C. Bodenham working with the RAF from June 1942.[107] Now the Cocoanut Grove fire offered American doctors the opportunity to test the effects of penicillin on staphylococcal infection in the respiratory tracts of burns victims, and penicillin was released at once with some urgency to Champ Lyons, surgeon at Massachusetts General Hospital. Supplies of the drug were low, and chemists at Merck worked round the clock in order to supply 32 litres of penicillin by the morning of 2 December 1942. As a result of the low doses of penicillin available for administration to these cases, it was impossible for Lyons and his colleagues fully to appraise the efficacy of penicillin therapy, although it was observed that the effect of penicillin on deep burns was to keep the wound clear of the expected active or invasive infection.[108]

The case of infant Patricia Malone, suffering from septicaemia, further tugged a nation's heart strings in the summer of 1943. It all began with a call to the city desk of the Randolph Hearst-owned *New York Journal-American* late in the afternoon of 12 August 1943 from the girl's father asking for help, as doctors at the Lutheran Hospital, New York City, had told him that the only hope of saving his daughter's life was the new wonder drug penicillin. The newspaper responded to the appeal by contacting all the drug companies in New York, to no avail. Within ten minutes of the call from Lawrence Malone, the newspaper had contacted both A.N. Richards and Chester Keefer for the release of a stock of penicillin to save the life of this little girl. Both of them contacted Dr Collitti, her physician at the Lutheran Hospital, and arrangements were made for the Squibb Laboratories at New Brunswick to release a supply. Reporters from the newspaper then picked up Dr Collitti in a car and with a police escort rushed him to the Squibb Laboratories and back to the Lutheran Hospital. Even with an escort and no obstacles in their path, the journey still took two hours, while Patricia's condition continued to deteriorate. Within five and a half hours of her father's desperate appeal for help, she was at last given penicillin by continuous intravenous drip. She rapidly improved and six weeks later was able to return home fully restored to health.[109]

While these civilian cases may have captured the headlines, penicillin remained available largely only for military use, and the patriotic press was ever ready to stress the contribution the drug was making towards winning the war, while simultaneously reminding their civilian readers that soon it would be available for them too. The New York based *Liberty, the Magazine of a Free People* in July 1944 told the story of one anonymous case of a soldier whose life had been saved by penicillin at an army camp somewhere in New England in November 1943. This 33-year-old soldier was slowly and surely dying of a streptococcal infection that had destroyed his blood cells and riddled his body with abscesses. As in so many other reported cases, an appeal went out for the penicillin that was his only hope of life. Then followed a frantic ambulance dash to take the dying soldier from his own army camp to the nearest source of penicillin at Lovell General Hospital, Fort Devens, Massachusetts. On his arrival, the doctors at Lovell General considered that it was too late even for penicillin to do any good, but they connected him to a continuous intravenous drip all the same. Expecting an autopsy report, the pathologist at the hospital back at his own base was surprised to be informed 'Patient is recovering'. Once again, penicillin had saved a life.[110]

Such reports only stoked up the demand for release of penicillin. Dr Chester Keefer of Boston, Chairman of the National Research Council Committee on Chemotherapy, charged with the rationing of penicillin supplies for civilian use, was inundated with heart-rending requests for this life-saving substance, all as cogent as in the cases of Anne Miller and Patricia Malone. Appeals were made to Eleanor Roosevelt to intervene to obtain penicillin for the dying sweetheart of a serving soldier.[111] With 85 per cent of penicillin production going to meet military demands throughout the war, there was very little available for civilian use, and a strong case had to be made for every application. On the one hand were the very strong personal factors relating to individual patients whose lives could be saved if they could only be given the drug. Against these individual needs was the demand for scientific data to assess the clinical effectiveness of penicillin and its use in non-life-threatening situations. If penicillin was to be understood and used effectively, it was essential to collect data on its dosage, methods of administration, length of treatment and any adverse reactions. Somehow Keefer had to reconcile these competing interests and keep everyone happy.[112] Amazingly, he actually managed to do so until April 1944, when there was so much penicillin being produced that it was beyond the capacity of one man to manage its equitable distribution. Now the Penicillin Producers' Industry Advisory Committee took on the responsibility of devising a plan for its distribution through nominated hospitals. At first there were only 1,000 hospitals in the United States on this list, with the Chicago-based Civilian Penicillin Distribution Unit acting as a clearing house for orders for the drug.[113] By 1945 the number of depot hospitals holding supplies of penicillin had increased to 2,700, and they in turn supplied a further 5,000 hospitals.[114]

Nevertheless, despite all attempts to control the distribution of penicillin officially, there were mavericks prepared to buck the system if they thought they knew of a worthy case. John L. Smith, the small, stiff and entrepreneurial vice-president of Pfizer and part-owner of the Brooklyn Dodgers, was approached in June 1943 by Leo Loewe, a physician at the Jewish Hospital in Brooklyn, for some penicillin to treat Laurette DesRosier, a young girl dying of the heart condition endocarditis.[115] At that stage it was considered an unsuitable disease for treatment with penicillin because of the high quantities of the drug required and the length of time it would have to be administered to do any good. Smith explained that he could not personally release any penicillin, as it was all allocated through official channels. Nevertheless, he was persuaded to visit the girl in hospital. He was so moved by what he saw that he agreed to break all the regulations and release the drug. So interested was he in the progress of the case that he visited the hospital daily during the girl's treatment and saw for himself the amazing results of penicillin. Noted more for his interest in baseball than in penicillin, an interest that was to provide an instant bond between himself and Fleming when they met, Smith now became a convert to the miracle of penicillin. Not only did he lead Pfizer into developing a deep-fermentation plant, but he also continued to break the guidelines laid down by Chester Keefer forbidding the use of the drug in cases of acute endocarditis and continued to supply Loewe and his colleagues with penicillin for use in further trials involving such cases. Technically, they were breaking the law, but these trials were successful and eventually Keefer himself was forced to admit that penicillin was of value in the treatment of endocarditis and that it was good that some patients suffering from this disease had been given the opportunity to live. John Smith himself, having cheerfully broken all the rules to supply the penicillin used in their treatment, was so interested in these patients that he gave up many of his weekends to visit them, just as he had been so keen to see every stage of Laurette's recovery.[116]

Fortunately, production increased from 21 billion Oxford units in 1943 to 6.8 trillion units in 1945, while prices fell from $200 per million units in 1943 to $6 per million units in 1945. In the summer of 1945 monthly production figures for penicillin briefly fell as a result of a shortage of corn-steep liquor, but that was only a temporary blip. The speed at which production increased was astounding, and as mass production rose the unit costs of producing it fell to affordable levels.[117] By March 1945, restrictions on the civilian supply of penicillin could be lifted.[118] The dream of penicillin being available for all was at last realised, even before war had given way to peacetime. John Sheehan has written that 'only the Manhattan Project leading to the development of the atomic bomb is equalled by the efforts of the Office of Scientific Research and Development during World War II to produce a synthetic penicillin',[119] but in its scale of effort and its success the production of penicillin by fermentation methods is also comparable to the Manhattan Project. The antibiotic and atomic ages both came into being at the same time. The effect of the Second World War had been to override commercial rivalries and allow for the transmission of information between two Allied nations, between government bodies and commercial companies and between competing firms. This was not always smooth nor as effective as it might have been in an ideal world, but it did take place. War is destructive and the priority given to the sinews of war may have been an impediment to more peaceable development, but it did give a greater sense of urgency and an impetus to cooperation without which the history of penicillin would have been very different. Coghill spoke truly when he stated that 'Penicillin is a more or less direct . . . by-product of the war. It has probably saved more lives and eased much more suffering than the whole war has cost us.'[120]

Not only had penicillin become possible thanks to wartime conditions, but it had been developed against the unfolding drama of a world at war. It had itself played a part in the winning of that war by helping to heal the war-wounded. That and its role in that other ever-present war against infection had been dramatised in the pages of the popular press. It was little wonder that its discoverer should be hailed so triumphantly on his North American tour of 1945, even though for him his visit was a personal opportunity to see the advances made on the other side of the Atlantic. The adulation he received then launched him onto a new phase of his life and a new character as a world figure, an unexpected role but one for which he was eminently suited, as his reception in the United States had shown very clearly.

NINE

World Ambassador

Fleming's North American tour of 1945 marked the beginning of a new phase of his life as he entered on a public career for which nothing in his character or previous experience had prepared him. As worldwide acclaim and honours were showered on this laconic, shy, unassuming man approaching retirement, he was expected to take his place as a public figure who in a very important sense belonged to the world. Surprisingly, he was a great success in his new role and seemed to have been cut out for it from the start. Everyone wanted to know him and the public liked what it saw of the great man, who at first seemed surprised by all the attention and then grew accustomed to it but never lost the natural modesty and pawky, impish sense of humour that were his trademark. Indeed, to an age that had seen enough of larger-than-life figures such as Hitler, Stalin and Mussolini, it was that lack of pretension that perhaps made him all the more popular.

The honours began to flood in even as penicillin came into more widespread use during the war. In May 1944, Fleming was elected a Fellow of the Royal College of Physicians and in the July Honours List it was announced that he and Florey were both to be knighted. Inevitably, the press made more of Fleming's knighthood than Florey's, which struck a sour note at Oxford. Fleming himself was delighted, but was a little disappointed to find that the actual ceremony was conducted in the basement of Buckingham Palace rather than in the grander surroundings customary in peacetime, but no chances were being taken at the time of the V-bomb attacks on London. After the investiture, he returned to St Mary's to find one of the Inoculation Department tea parties in progress presided over by Wright on one of his by now infrequent visits there. No one said anything to their newly knighted colleague and Wright continued with his monologue on the virtues of vaccine therapy and the faults of chemotherapy. Then Craxton, the department secretary, entered with some papers for Wright to sign. Dismissively yet pointedly, he told Craxton not to bother him with 'such trivial things. *Doctor* Fleming will deal with them.' Sir Alexander meekly left the room to attend to them. As soon as Wright had gone home, everyone crowded around Fleming and a party was held to celebrate his new honourable status. Fleming gave Clayden money to buy beer and everyone from the tea lady up enjoyed the party, with the notable exception of the absent Director of the Inoculation Department.[1] Fleming insisted on personally waiting on the secretaries, laboratory assistants and domestics at this party in his honour, all of whom felt immensely honoured that Sir Alexander had actually poured their drinks for them.[2]

Other honours followed with the award of the John Scott Medal and Prize of the City Guild of Philadelphia, the Charles Mickle Fellowship of the University of Toronto and the Robert Campbell Medal of the Ulster Medical Society. Wartime restrictions on travel meant that the only trip Fleming could make to collect his award in person was to Belfast. After delivering the Campbell Oration, he was driven to the station to catch the boat train to Larne, only to find that he had left his lantern slides at the University of Belfast. While the driver returned to retrieve them, the stationmaster held the train back, and the complaints of the other passengers subsided when they discovered who had caused the delay. Meanwhile, Fleming sat in his carriage reading and displaying a total lack of concern.[3] Already his reputation was such that there was nothing people would not do for him as a thank-you for the benefits his discovery of penicillin had seemingly brought. Early in 1945, he was elected President of the newly founded Society of General Microbiology. In his inaugural address, he confessed that 'Other and more distinguished members were asked to assume the presidency, but they were sufficiently strong-minded to refuse it. But, true to Scottish tradition never to refuse anything, when it came to my turn I accepted.'[4] This was not entirely true, for, while Fleming did accept most of the honours that came his way, he did turn down those offers that might in some way compromise his principles. On a postwar visit to Italy, he was offered an editorial role with a new journal of pharmacy; the duties would be negligible and it promised to be a reputable and impressive publication, but he refused 'as things might go in I disapproved of'.[5]

His true public life can be said to have begun with the end of the war and the resumption of the opportunity to travel, albeit with restrictions. May 1945 was a busy time for him amidst the national celebrations of victory in Europe. On 2 May he was made an Honorary Freeman and Liveryman of the Dyers' Company, one of the major livery companies of the City of London. At the ceremony he recalled his time as a junior clerk running errands between his own company and other firms. Then on 17 May, he was made an Honorary Freeman of the Borough of Paddington, in which he had studied and worked for approaching half a

century. He was subsequently to receive in October 1946 the Freedom
of Darvel, in which he had been born, and in March 1949 of the
Borough of Chelsea, in which he lived, completing the hat-trick of being
an honorary Freeman of the three places that had been such an
important part of his life.[6] Such honours took him back to his own past,
but it was the triumphs of the present day that were henceforward to be
to the fore. A few days after the Paddington ceremony, he was due to set
out for a tour of North America organised by the British Council. It was
a high-profile visit, and, before setting off, he was interviewed for the
BBC by Bebe Daniels, the Hollywood actress who had made a second
career for herself on British radio with her husband Ben Lyons as stars
of the popular wartime radio programme *Hi Gang*. She arrived at
St Mary's for her appointment and was surprised to find that there was
no entourage of secretaries and aides protecting Fleming from visitors.
Instead a lone technician directed her to his room. She found him bent
intently over a bunsen burner, obviously engaged in important work. He
looked up and asked her if she would like some tea; he had been boiling
water. Such unexpected informality won her over immediately, as it was
to entrance many who came into contact with the great man, who
proved far less intimidating in person than they had expected before
they met him.[7]

He was lionised during his North American tour and the fuss
continued when he returned to London at the end of August. After only a
short time at home, he was off on his travels again, this time a shorter
journey to Paris as the guest of the French government. Once again on his
arrival at Le Bourget he was able to play the game of fooling the
assembled reporters when they mistook one of his fellow passengers for
Fleming. This man was tall, dark, bearded and impressive in manner and
looked much more like everyone's image of a great scientist than Fleming
himself did. One of the reporters asked Fleming whether this man was
indeed the discoverer of penicillin, to which Fleming nodded, either
because his grasp of French was imperfect or as a private joke. Only
when Fleming was greeted by a reception party that included Louis
Pasteur's grandson Professor Pasteur Vallery-Radot and the Director of
the Pasteur Institute, Jacques Tréfouël, was the guest of honour correctly
identified by the French press.[8] For Fleming there was then the ordeal of
an official reception and a broadcast before he could be taken to Paris,
where even his eminence did not permit him to be given rationed butter
with his breakfast when he lacked the necessary coupons. The following
day a visit to the Gobelins tapestry factory, where he was presented with
a small piece of tapestry, was followed by a reception at the Académie de
Médecine, of which he was made an honorary member. The third day of

his visit was equally packed with official functions. He had been scheduled to meet General de Gaulle in the morning, but this meeting was postponed until the afternoon. Instead the Director of the Louvre gave him a personal tour of the collections, before it was time for lunch at the French Foreign Office. After a lengthy lunch and even longer speeches, he finally met de Gaulle, who 'presented me with Commander of the L[egion] of H[onour]. (Hung around neck and kissed both cheeks.)' There was almost no time to pause before an official dinner presided over by the doctor and author Georges Duhamel and attended by doctors, politicians, trade unionists, writers and artists such as Paul Eluard and Le Corbusier. The fourth day of his visit centred on the Pasteur Institute with a tour, reception and lunch at which he was presented with the Pasteur Medal, as well as the opportunity to see the treatment of a carbuncle with penicillin. On his last full day, there was a visit to the Hospital for Sick Children and more cases being treated with penicillin. It ended with a reception at the Hôtel de Ville at which the President of the French Academy announced that he was to be granted honorary membership. Everywhere he went he was greeted by cheering crowds.[9] It was a tough schedule and one that was to be repeated many times all over the world. Nevertheless, he was still mindful of the role he had played in North America as a representative of his country's interests. He observed the situation regarding penicillin production in France and noted in his diary, 'in France only 10,000 Roux bottles a day making penicillin. Great chance for England to organise at small cost a larger bottle plant or to help with advice. Send Raistrick and someone from Boots, Glaxo (who can talk French and who is quite familiar with actual bottle production).They seem to want practical help.'[10] This brief note was followed up in his report to the Ministry of Supply on his French trip:

> I gather that penicillin was used as a means of furthering friendly relations through entertaining and honouring me as a British representative. It is clear that they are badly in need of penicillin. In the long run they will un-doubtedly make their own supply but in the meantime they will have to get it from us or from America, and I suggest that without much trouble or cost certain British propaganda could be made.[11]

Arriving home from France on 8 September after a delay at the aerodrome, Fleming was again off on his travels on 14 September 1945 for a nine-day trip to Italy, where he was greeted by representatives of state, church and medicine, but was overawed by none of them.[12] He was also given a papal audience, where, despite his Presbyterian upbringing, he bowed and kissed the papal ring. He found the Pope 'very cordial' and knowledgeable about penicillin.[13] Fleming was presented with a papal medal. His response was to put his hand into his pocket and pull out a mounted specimen of the penicillin culture, which he handed to Pius XII with minimal ceremony. This culture was a 'rather home-grown specimen', which he had made up at short notice and sealed with elastoplast.[14] As soon as he returned home he sent a replacement for it to the Vatican.[15] Perhaps even more important to his country than this diplomatic round were the visits he paid to British military hospitals in Italy, where he took a 'roguish pleasure in the thought of the brass having to wait' while he talked to humbler bacteriologists, doctors and patients.[16]

On 28 September, he was off to Copenhagen and would have accepted an ad hoc invitation to fly to Oslo to lecture had it been possible for his hosts to arrange transport at such short notice.[17] His travels then tailed off until the end of November, when he was invited to Belgium. As ever, he was given lavish hospitality, but it was the more ordinary details and cases in which his penicillin had been efficacious that caught his attention. He was received by the Prince Regent at the Royal Palace in Brussels and noted that he suffered from boils and that he was a 'simple, homely young man. Perfect English. Mixes his own cocktails.'[18] Fleming's response was to send a small supply of one of the staphylococcal toxoid vaccines produced by the Inoculation Department to the Prince Regent's physician for the treatment of the troublesome boils.[19] The Belgium trip, however, was really notable for the fact that Fleming was the recipient of three honorary degrees in two days from the Universities of Brussels, Louvain and Liège. The University of Louvain had conferred honorary degrees on certain British subjects after the Liberation: Churchill, Montgomery and Fleming. In his acceptance speech, Fleming regretted that they could not have all been presented together, as the presence of two war leaders and orators would have taken the spotlight off him and 'you would have expected little of me, a simple laboratory worker who sits at a bench playing with test tubes and microbes'.[20]

However, despite such engaging displays of self-deprecation, 1945 was to end with perhaps the greatest accolade of all, the Nobel Prize for Medicine.[21] On 25 October a telegram had arrived announcing that he was to share it with Florey and Chain. It was not the first time that Fleming's name had been coupled with that of this high honour. He had been hotly tipped as the recipient of the 1944 award, and many newspapers had indeed announced him as the winner on the authority of reports of a news broadcast from Switzerland naming him as the laureate for that year. The *Daily Mail* also reported that it was likely that some of the Nobel funds would be used to reward his 'close collaborator' Howard Florey.[22] The false reports emanating from Berne embarrassed Fleming when he received congratulations on his success and had to admit that, despite newspaper reports, the Nobel Prize had gone elsewhere: 'It is very nice to get your congratulations about the Nobel Prize, but it would have been better if I had got the Prize.'[23]

The Nobel Prize had not been awarded since 1939 and it would have been very surprising had Fleming not been nominated in 1944, such was the sensational impact of penicillin on medicine. Indeed, Fleming and Florey jointly had first been nominated in 1943, but at that stage the full potential of penicillin was only to be guessed at, and it was not considered worthwhile to undertake a full examination until there was enough evidence from clinical trials to assess its value.[24] They were again both nominated in 1944, with Chain's name also added to the nomination, and this time their claims to be awarded the Prize were submitted to detailed scrutiny.[25] However, nomination and election were very different, and the Karolinska Institute in Stockholm, charged under the terms of Alfred Nobel's will with deciding on the laureates for the Prize for Medicine or Physiology, had other candidates to consider. The 1944 Nobel Prize was awarded to Joseph Erlanger and Herbert Spencer Gasser for their work on the structure of nerve fibres.

Fleming, Florey and Chain were again nominated in 1945, the majority of nominations once more being for Fleming.[26] Wartime postal disruptions in continental Europe meant that not all the nominations were received in time to be counted for consideration when making the award. Although invitations to nominate had been sent out in September 1944, many of them had been received only at the end of April 1945, with the result that many of the nominations had arrived too late for them to count, although they had been looked at.[27] The general response from previous laureates and those asked to nominate for the 1945 prize in North America, Britain and continental Europe was that the discovery of penicillin merited the award of a Nobel Prize and that Fleming undoubtedly deserved the accolade together with Florey. Behind the scenes in letters and telegrams to the Swedish legation in New York and to Liljestrand in Stockholm, Florey's friend John Fulton pressed strongly for the award to be given to Florey alone, claiming that this was not only his own opinion but also that of a large group of doctors and scientists in the United States.[28] The large number of nominations received from the United States for Fleming and his reception in North America make Fulton's claim to be representative suspect, given his strongly partisan stance and animosity towards Fleming on Florey's behalf from the very beginning of the press attention on Fleming. The reports commissioned by the Nobel Committee from Professors Liljestrand, Kristenson and Hellerström were remarkably unanimous in concluding that Fleming deserved half the Prize, as he had made the primary discovery from which all else had flowed, while the remainder of the award should be shared between Florey and Chain, whose work had made the therapeutic use of penicillin a real possibility.[29] This time there was no doubt at all as to who deserved the 1945 Nobel Prize for Medicine, and it was an award in tune with both informed scientific opinion and popular sentiment. Cecil Weir of the Ministry of Supply wrote that 'it is very good for British science that this British discovery is being accorded such a well deserved award, that your marvellous work is receiving such unstinted honour'.[30]

On 6 December, Fleming flew to Stockholm, where, amidst the official round, he was able to enjoy the gaiety, bright lights and well-stocked shops of a country that had escaped the ravages of war. In particular, he noted how all the shops were decorated for Christmas.[31] This was at a time when his own country was preparing for its first peacetime Christmas in six years, but where austerity still ruled. On all his overseas trips in the immediate postwar period, Fleming relished the opportunity to go shopping and buy goods that were unobtainable or rationed at home. Similarly, the diaries of his travels are full of lists of the food he ate, an understandable reaction to the privations of rationing at home, which was perhaps becoming even more stringent in peacetime than during the war.

The Nobel Prize ceremony on 10 December, the first to be held since the outbreak of war, was a glittering occasion, with full evening dress and decorations being worn. Fleming had difficulty tying the Légion d'Honneur around his neck, but was pleased when he managed, as he was the only holder of that particular award at the ceremony. He was impressed by the fanfare of trumpets as the winners were ushered onto the platform of the Koncerthus, decorated with the bust of Alfred Nobel and bedecked with flowers. As well as the 1945 laureates, there were present some of the award winners from previous years, including Corneille Heymans, who had won in 1939 and was to become a great friend of Fleming's, and Herbert Spencer Gasser, who had stolen the honours in 1944 when the world expected Fleming to win. Afterwards he sat next to the Crown Princess of Sweden at the banquet held in the Blue Hall of the Stockholm Stadtshuset, which despite its name was actually walled with red brick in an attempt to recreate the feel of an Italian Renaissance palazzo. Then everyone adjourned to a students' singsong and dance in the opulent surroundings of the Golden Hall with its Byzantine-style gilded decorations. He did not return to his hotel until three o'clock in the morning, despite having to deliver his official Nobel lecture that day. After the lecture, he had dinner with the King. It was an exhausting schedule, after which 'early to bed it should have been, but when we got back to our hotel we adjourned to the bar and drank Swedish beer for a long time. Among us there was an Argentine woman poet who got a Nobel Prize but couldn't stand up to the drink.'[32] Fleming could stand up to the alcohol easily, but he failed to identify the correct nationality of Chilean poetess Gabrielle Mistral.

It had certainly been an exciting year for Fleming, who hitherto had not been a great traveller. It was only the start, however, of a globe-trotting career that was to take him all over the world. Now the pattern had been set for the rest of his life. The itinerary of overseas trips undertaken in subsequent years takes on a certain regularity and sense of routine. In 1946, he visited Italy, France for the Pasteur celebrations and Brazil for the Inter-American Medical Congress. In 1947, he was in Vienna and in 1948 Spain. He was back in Italy and the United States in 1949. In 1950, his schedule was punitive, with trips to the United States, Eire, Brazil, Italy, Belgium and Sweden. In 1951, he slowed down with just one foreign trip on a World Health Organisation visit to Pakistan, which was arduous enough in itself. In 1952, he went to Belgium, Switzerland and Greece, with visits to India, the United States, Italy and Greece and to Cuba the following year. The New World was again his destination in 1954 with tours of the United States, Canada, Mexico and Brazil. Everywhere he went, there was the same round of speeches, dinners, formal receptions, meetings with dignitaries and honours and awards. The novelty soon wore off and it all became somewhat repetitious, yet Fleming continued to undertake his official duties as assiduously as George VI or Elizabeth II carried out their state duties, regardless of personal inclination and a retiring personality.

The international nature of the honours heaped upon Fleming was not without its problems at a time of political tension. There was no obstacle to accepting awards from countries closely tied to Britain or in which there was official interest in extending British influence, but as the Iron Curtain descended, there were difficulties with countries within the Soviet bloc. Effectively a barrier had been erected that prevented the honouring of foreign scientists in an atmosphere of suspicion that made it unwise to be too friendly towards international figures from the other ideological camp, even if their work did transcend national boundaries and was of supranational significance. Very few honours came Fleming's way from Eastern Europe, and one that did he was unable to accept. In 1948, Charles University in Prague celebrated its 600th anniversary by awarding honorary degrees to distinguished figures in the arts and sciences. Invitations to accept the award were sent out in February 1948 to attend a ceremony on 8 April.[33] Fleming was unable to attend the ceremony in person, but assured the Czechoslovak ambassador that he would ask the British ambassador in Prague to collect the honorary doctorate on his behalf.[34] He also wrote to Ernest Bevin, the Foreign Secretary, about the degree and was informed by the Foreign Office that the British ambassador to Czechoslovakia was not only unwilling to represent him at the degree ceremony but that indeed 'I expect that you like the others will by now have decided to decline the Charles' University's offer'.[35] In the short time since the offer had been made, the Communist hold on Czechoslovakia had been tightened, non-Communist ministers had tendered their resignations, the Foreign Minister, Jan Masaryk, had fallen to his death in mysterious circumstances and the Rector and senior officials of Charles University had been replaced by men sympathetic to the new regime. The Foreign Office could not tell Fleming what to do, but he was himself well aware of the delicate political situation and had no desire to bolster a regime of which he disapproved. After considering the matter, he decided to decline the honorary degree: 'as I know so little about the new constitution of the University, I think it would be better if the matter were left over until affairs in the University have settled down again.'[36] It was to be a long time before the situation had normalised enough for the doctorate to be awarded and by then Fleming had long been dead. In 1993, with the return of democracy following the Velvet Revolution of 1989, the authorities of Charles University decided to confer the unawarded degrees of 1948 with the certificates bearing the original award date of 8 April 1948 but with an accompanying certificate explaining the reason for the delay.[37] Originally declined for political reasons, the honour still had ideological overtones when finally awarded forty-five years later marking the restoration of freedom and democracy.[38]

Fleming's attitude to all this attention was mixed. Stuart Craddock believed that 'he thoroughly enjoyed it all, but it was quite obvious that although he liked the friendly atmosphere of these welcomes, he enjoyed the whole affair because it was interesting and something new'.[39] Bill Frankland, who came into daily contact with him in Almroth Wright ward at St Mary's as registrar, found a certain weariness in his chief whenever a new invitation came in, though he would eventually accept them and do what was asked.[40] The requests might be to accept an honour, give a lecture or even to be a judge at a sheepdog trial.[41] Even when he was in the midst of the novelty of a situation he enjoyed, he could find it a bit much and wish he were home, as he confessed in a rare personal comment in his diary of his 1946 Italian trip: 'If I stayed here another week I should be very lonely in a place like this. There seem to be all sorts but mainly business.'[42] His unassuming personal manner was best suited to informal gatherings, yet he accepted that he must attend formal events. After receiving the Gold Medal of the Royal College of Surgeons on 14 November 1946, he suggested to his friend Dr G.E. Breen that they should escape to the Chelsea Arts Club for a game of snooker, and surprised his fellow members by bursting in on them in full evening dress and dripping with medals. It had not occurred to him to change before going into his bohemian retreat. Breen commented that he was 'at his best at informal gatherings. Formality and protocol made him uneasy.'[43]

Fleming developed his own strategy to cope with all the formality and protocol. On meeting him after his return from an overseas trip to receive yet another honour, Breen asked him what he found to say on all these occasions. Fleming's answer was easy: 'I always tell them that they are a fine lot of chaps. That's enough.'[44] Nevertheless, he still found it worth commenting when a dinner held in his honour at the Palazzo Torino in Turin proved informal by English standards with everyone in lounge suits and 'no saying what good boys are we'.[45] Whatever the occasion, however informal it might be, he still suffered nerves before it, though appearing outwardly calm enough. He told Roger Lee, 'I am sorry that I can't get used to all this fuss, but I suppose I have to put up with it. It is very nice to look back on when it is all finished, but at the time I can not get rid of the scared rabbit feeling.'[46]

Why then did he put up with it all? Perhaps it was partly because he did actually enjoy the travel and the events once he had played his part. There was also a sense of duty, since this public role seemed to be expected of the discoverer of penicillin. He realised that he was representing his country's interests. The British Council considered him to have been their most successful and popular lecturer in Vienna following his visit there in April 1947 and that his week in Austria had been of more value than the three lecturers sent the previous year put together.[47] Hugh Clegg, editor of the *British Medical Journal*, summed it up to Fleming's biographer André Maurois:

I have the impression that few people realise what a magnificent ambassador for Britain Fleming was when he went abroad. Modest to the point of shyness, by no means an orator on public occasions, he impressed those he met with his simplicity and essential humility. With it all was a naive schoolboy delight in simple pleasures.[48]

Certainly John Cameron agreed with this assessment of the man he had seen charm America in the summer of 1945.[49] Fleming himself was well aware of his importance as an envoy for his country, whether he wanted to be or not. His motive for visiting North America in 1945 had been professional and concerned with seeing for himself how penicillin had been developed there, but 'when I arrived in America, I found that our representatives, both in the supply and information services, thought that the most important aspect of my visit would be in respect of international amity and that it was very important that I should not discourage publicity'. As a result, 'in many cases, against my personal wish', he had given talks, broadcasts, interviews and press conferences.[50] He found it embarrassing to be treated as a celebrity and frustrating that his fame outshone his professional standing. During his first visit to Spain in 1948, he noted that the British consul in Barcelona was 'greatly pleased that I had come to Spain as that more than anything would do a great deal to further good relations between Spain and our country', but complained that 'It seems to me that as an ambassador I am of more importance than as a medical figure'.[51]

Fleming's triumphal tour of Spain in 1948, described by André Maurois as having taken on 'the appearance of an apotheosis', was perhaps the high point of Fleming's travels and the most rapturous of his receptions anywhere.[52] The first part of the tour, arranged by Professor Lluis Trias de Bes, a cardiologist at the Hospital Municipal de Infecciososos de Nuestra Sénora del Mar in Barcelona, was as usual arduous, with the customary deluge of honours, decorations and receptions. What marked it out from other trips was the scale of the popular enthusiasm and the gratitude shown from people whose lives had been saved by penicillin and who now knelt before him to kiss his hands. Nurses at the Hospital de Nuestra Sénora del Mar queued up for his autograph and when out of devilment he substituted 'Bright eyes' for the name of one nurse he considered pretty, he was convinced that she felt she had scored over her fellow nurses.[54] His lectures to the Royal Academy of Medicine of Barcelona were rapturously received, and before his final lecture a choir of students sang a hymn of praise in Latin verses composed in his honour.[55] The prior and monks of the monastery at Montserrat were pleased by remarks that Fleming considered commonplace and placed a sample of penicillin that he presented to them among the holy treasures of the sanctuary.[56] A balcony appearance at the town hall of Barcelona was greeted with cheers and applause. Walking through los Ramblas, he was recognised by everyone and showered with gifts of carnations.[57] At a bullfight, he received an ovation from the crowds, while the toreadors insisted on being photographed with him. At half-time during a football match between Ireland and Spain, he was given a microphone to make an extempore broadcast of his thoughts on the game. Dining at a small restaurant in Barcelona, an unplanned visit so as to avoid meeting a prominent Fascist who was dining at Fleming's hotel, he was embarrassed to find that the proprietor refused to accept any payment. Elsewhere he was showered with so many presents that it was necessary to buy an extra suitcase to pack them in. An optician who had been cured with penicillin offered him a pair of gold spectacles, so Fleming chose a pair identical to his own. He felt that 'everywhere I have been, I have found everyone most demonstrative, a little too much for my own comfort'.[58] He had the 'impression that I was Winston or Princess Elizabeth',[59] and even had he been visiting royalty he could not have been more widely acclaimed. At a cabaret he was introduced to the exiled Queen of Italy during a song dedicated to him by the singer Josephine Baker and had to acknowledge another ovation while talking to the Queen, prompting him to wonder what she thought of it all.[60] At an alfresco lunch with a Barcelona businessman, Fleming was disconcerted to find his host had concealed a microphone in an overhanging bush to record the conversation.[61]

Seville attempted to outdo the hospitality of Barcelona,[62] and Madrid outshone them both. Fleming's schedule in Madrid, organised by his great admirer Florencio Bustinza Lachiondo, was more punishing than ever, but he made no complaint about it, to Bustinza's great relief. Bustinza, a Liverpool-born, Madrid-based physiologist, was one of his most ardent and eloquent admirers.[63] He had first become interested in penicillin during the war after hearing Spanish broadcasts on the subject by Dr E. Martinez Alonso, translated from scripts prepared by Fleming.[64] This inspired him to study all the available literature, obtain a specimen of the penicillin mould and make his own bacteriological observations. His book *De Pasteur à Fleming* on the history of antibacterial agents followed and was dedicated to Fleming.[65] This enabled him to make personal contact with his hero, who thanked him for having sent a copy. Fleming's handwriting alone was to impress Bustinza, who could detect in it his 'spiritual nobility'. This inflamed him with an even greater desire to meet for himself the great man whom he 'admired for his genius'.[66] His dream came true in the autumn of 1945 when he visited Fleming in his laboratory and was impressed with the cordiality of his welcome and Fleming's 'air of distinction, sweetness, generosity and sincerity, which, with his entrancing modesty and simplicity, captivated me at once'.[67] It was nothing less than pure hero worship from a medical researcher who was by no means undistinguished himself but saw in Fleming the shades of Pasteur, Koch, Behring and Metchnikoff, the pioneers of bacteriology. His role in organising Fleming's visit to Madrid proved to be Bustinza's own moment of glory and sealed his friendship with Fleming. Until his own death in 1982, Bustinza was to continue to promote Fleming's reputation in Spain and to prize their friendship as one of the most important in his own life beyond his own family circle.

Nothing was spared by Bustinza to make Fleming's stay in Madrid a success. A visit to his own laboratory and the Anglo-American Hospital was followed by a lecture on success at the British Institute. A reception after the speech was followed by a banquet hosted by the Duke of Alba and a grand ball. The highlight of the visit was a ceremony at the University of Madrid, where the Rector conferred on him an honorary doctorate and the Minister of Education, not to be outdone, invested him with the sash and Grand Cross of the Order of Alphonso X, amidst wild applause. Bustinza read out the citation, emphasising the patience, perseverance, self-sacrifice and altruism of Fleming's career. He also had the honour of translating Fleming's speech into Spanish for the benefit of the audience. Throughout the visit to Madrid, he was constantly at Fleming's side, interpreting for him, helping him to acknowledge the well-wishes and gifts from admirers, arranging care for Sareen Fleming, who had been taken ill, and even entertaining Fleming by joining in with his games to while away times when they had to wait for a reception.[68]

Fleming felt uncomfortable at being showered with gifts if he could not give anything in return and soon found that the most appreciated gift was likely to be the most symbolic, a specimen of the penicillium mould. Using his usual ingenuity and imaginative approach to laboratory techniques, he invented a method of growing the penicillium on discs of blotting paper, which he then fixed with formalin and mounted between sheets of spectacle glass enclosed by tortoiseshell or gold rims.[69] These he gave as gifts. At the height of the V-bomb raids in the summer of 1944, the Queen paid an unannounced visit to the hospital and was presented with one of Fleming's mould medallions, which apparently prompted a humorous remark from the King on her return from the visit that they already had enough mould on the walls of Windsor without being given more.[70] Other grateful recipients included Churchill and Roosevelt, friends, colleagues and many of the people he met on his numerous travels. These insignificant-looking artefacts soon took on the status of holy relics, and indeed one of them, given by Fleming to Edgar Lawley, Vice-Chairman of the St Mary's Board of Governors and a Trustee of the

Wright Fleming Institute, in 1952, was actually mounted in a gold desk stand reminiscent of the medieval reliquaries used to house saints' body parts or fragments of the true cross.[71]

Back at home Fleming had had to adjust, like everyone else, to the return to peace that had made his travels possible. The house in Danvers Street had been repaired, and he returned to live there with Sareen and Robert. Sareen's sister Elizabeth returned to her upstairs flat. They took possession of The Dhoon again, which had been requisitioned by the Royal Air Force as billets for officers during the war. At both houses, there was a backlog of maintenance and cleaning to be faced by Sareen. Nor was it easy to travel from one to the other in those days of petrol rationing. Fleming had bought a large shed from the Pegrams, a former artists' studio, to set up in the garden at The Dhoon, which he now equipped as a private laboratory so that he could take work home with him and spend longer periods at The Dhoon away from St Mary's. The 'Little Lab', decorated with prints of British birds, became a favourite retreat for him. Restoring his garden to its former condition also preoccupied him. His gardening pursuits led him to play a trick on his sister-in-law Ida, who had a highly prized rockery in her garden at Radlett. Fleming offered her some unusual seedlings, which he assured her would be a worthy addition to her alpines. They turned out to be cabbages. Ida, though, was used to her brother-in-law's tricks and, according to her husband, 'pretended to be very cross but as a matter of fact she had smelt a rat from the beginning owing to Alec's excessive anxiety for their welfare'.[72]

On 24 June 1946 Almroth Wright, approaching the age of 85, at last retired, his departure from office eased by a lump sum of £5,000 and an annual pension the exact equivalent of his salary of £2,500 a year. It was a generous retirement package, perhaps reflecting the eagerness of the house committee of the Inoculation Department chaired by Sir Andrew Duncan to encourage the Old Man to give up the reins. By this time, the old rivalry for the succession to Wright was no longer an issue. Freeman was 69 and beyond the usual retirement age, though age did not stop him from continuing to work in the Allergy Clinic for many more years to come. Fleming himself, at 65, was two years off the University of London retirement age for his Chair in Bacteriology. However, there was no doubt that someone as distinguished as the discoverer of penicillin should be appointed as the new Director of the Inoculation Department and Principal of the Institute of Therapeutic Research at an annual salary of £3,000.[73] He had effectively run the department since 1939, but now finally had the real authority to do things, or would have done had Almroth Wright not attempted to outflank him.

During one of Fleming's frequent absences abroad, Wright had ensured that the older members of the Inoculation Department should have tenure. This left him with a lot of dead wood in what had become something of a geriatric institution during Wright's later years and with no room for manœuvre had he wished to introduce change. As a result, Fleming had to devote time to issues arising from the situation and staff bequeathed to him by Wright. There were dissatisfaction and conflict, which he was called upon to resolve, and he had to try to find a way of smoothing over personality clashes within the laboratory. One member of staff, Mummery, had not published any papers for many years, and Fleming had to speak to him about this lack of activity, since 'if we all did that the lab reputation must go down'.[74] What he could not do was use the sanction of dismissal, thanks to Wright. He also had to show sensitivity towards staff disappointed at lack of recognition or promotion. Himmelweit had been unhappy at not being made assistant director. Fleming realised that, despite Himmelweit's complaints about not receiving a better salary, 'money [is] not the important thing but status'.[75] For younger members of staff, salary could be important. In one case, John Freeman recommended a pay rise to a registrar in the Allergy Clinic on the grounds that he was an ex-prisoner of war in the Far East with a wife and children to support. Fleming was not impressed by such appeals to personal circumstances but asked the more cogent question as to the quality of the man's work before agreeing to the requested salary increase.[76]

He was deluged with requests from young researchers all over the world wishing to work with him.[77] There were very few established posts available, but it was possible to fit in a few researchers who were willing to take junior positions or had the means to support themselves. Even if he was unable to offer them a post, he was always ready to offer advice to anyone who sought it, however humble. An impoverished young Italian approached him for a job to enable him to study and become a scientist, and, although Fleming could not give him the job he sought, he did tell him how to gain a qualification and encouraged him in his aim of becoming a chemist.[78] However, researchers hoping to be led down exciting new lines of research by Fleming were disappointed. In his sixties and with massive demands on his time as Principal of the Wright Fleming Institute and as a lecturer, Fleming could not be expected to undertake major new research projects and was content to let his department continue along the lines established by Wright.

Fleming was an efficient and competent but uninspired administrator, since it was not within the management sphere that his interests lay. In many ways his rule as principal was 'as autocratic as Wright's'.[79] He hated to be too personally involved in the affairs of his staff and was quite isolated as the man at the top. C.B. Dyson doubted that 'he had a *real* friend in the Lab, though he was looked up to and admired'.[80] It was perhaps inevitable that Fleming's position should now appear so aloof. Always reserved and even shadowy in character, he was marked out from his contemporaries and younger colleagues as the great man whose discovery had changed medicine and he now bore the overall burden of responsibility for the fortunes of the Wright Fleming Institute. At times this could take on the appearance of a parsimony that seemed to confirm the Scottish stereotype of meanness, though perhaps it was as much the product of the economical ethos of the voluntary hospital system. On one occasion, when the expenditure of the Wright Fleming Institute had exceeded its income by some £3,000, Fleming reacted by reducing an order for three tubes of a particular chemical, costing 1s 6d each, to one tube and suggested that the staff could make up the chemical themselves if they really needed it, even though to have done so would have represented over £40 in labour costs.[81] While such self-reliant improvisation would have been appropriate in Fleming's youth, when the only way of obtaining many items of equipment or laboratory supplies was to make them oneself, it was no longer necessary nor economical in the postwar period.

Many of the staff felt a lack of firm leadership from a principal who was often absent on public engagements and lecture tours. His usual method of dealing with personnel issues was to comment, 'Why are some people so difficult? We will discuss the matter again tomorrow.' As a result of this procrastination and only too well aware of his employer's detestation of routine administration, Victor Craxton, the secretary of the institute, troubled him as little as possible.[82] The technician Clayden, who had been part of the Inoculation Department since the heady days before the First World War, even went so far as to consider that 'in my humble opinion, he should have left the administration to another and devoted himself to his scientific research'.[83]

Despite the many demands on him, Fleming did continue to carry out research as a bacteriologist, though inevitably this postwar scientific work had to take a back seat to his public role and was not of the same significance as his earlier studies. He continued to investigate the effects of penicillin.[84] However, in the treatment of many of his patients he continued to rely upon the use of vaccines.[85] With his Greek colleague Amalia Voureka, he began a study of the bacillus *Proteus vulgaris*, notable for its use of long flagellae to propel itself. Dr Voureka's observation that its movement was stimulated by light especially delighted him and stirred him to devise demonstrations of this.[86] Dr A. Pijper of the Instituut vir Patologie of Pretoria corresponded with Fleming for over a year on the subject of flagella and the motility of bacteria, considering him an expert on the subject, until Fleming finally admitted that 'I had never been especially interested in flagella except that I had to teach bacteriology and I had spent some time in trying to find a good way of demonstrating them to students'.[87]

There was also the problem for the new principal of the position that the Inoculation Department would enjoy when the new National Health Service came into force in July 1948. The National Health Service Act of 1946 had effectively nationalised the voluntary hospitals. Teaching hospitals were allowed to retain some autonomy with their own Boards of Governors, henceforth to be appointed by the Minister of Health, and were able to maintain control over their endowment funds. However, the London hospital-based medical schools were now to become independent institutions within the University of London, separate from their parent hospitals though continuing to be closely linked. The dilemma for Fleming was to determine the best place for the Inoculation Department within the new scheme, or even whether or not it should seek independence. Colonel Parkes, House Governor of St Mary's, advised him that they would be 'much safer under the umbrella of the hospital or school', but warned him that there was a danger that the hospital might be linked with a regional laboratory for its pathology rather than with the Inoculation Department.[88] While Huggett, Professor of Physiology, assured him that the medical school would go a long way to accommodate the interests of Fleming's department, others were concerned that the Inoculation Department would gain nothing from such an association and the school would gain everything. Anyway, any advantages might only be short term as 'the Schools [are] going to be taken over by the Government in a few years and if we joined the School we would have no more security than if we stayed out'.[89] It was a difficult position for Fleming, but his ability to control his feelings and weigh up the options stood him in good stead while navigating his way through the quagmire of negotiations. Merlin Pryce indeed believed that 'the keynote of his success as a negotiator was his conciliatory nature lacking in pugnaciousness but nevertheless firm'.[90] Tact and concision made him a doughty opponent in committees and at meetings. After weighing up all the options, Fleming and the Chairman of the house committee Andrew Duncan were in agreement that the best collaboration would be with St Mary's Hospital Medical School, if the independence of the Inoculation Department could be guaranteed.[91] This was the solution adopted, though it proved difficult to wed the commercial aspects of

Almroth Wright's policy for the Inoculation Department with the academic demands of an institution allied to a university.[92]

Fleming, in so many ways a Conservative by instinct, was opposed to the new National Health Service, which came into force on 5 July 1948. In this he was little different from the majority of the medical establishment, who feared the loss of status nationalisation of health services could bring. It was an embarrassment to him when on holiday in Scotland in August 1947 he was accosted by the Minister of Health, despite his hopes that Aneurin Bevan, whom he had immediately recognised, had not seen him.[93] He was to encounter Bevan again in 1953 during a visit to India, when, as a member of the World Health Organisation delegation studying Indian medical services, he found himself listening to a speech by Bevan on social medicine. The audience recognised Fleming and called on him to speak. Hostile as he was to state intervention in medicine, he began his usual account of the discovery of penicillin and the true ends of research by stating that he lacked the previous speaker's oratorical skills, but 'when I speak, I give you the facts; Bevan has to draw upon his imagination'.[94]

Nevertheless, whatever his attitude may have been to a National Health Service, Fleming had no choice but to accept it. He continued to have responsibility for patients in Almroth Wright ward and his name was above each patient's bed, but most of the routine work was left to his juniors. Patients were referred to him as the discoverer of penicillin from across the country and from abroad. While his visits to the patients on the ward were rare, he did insist on receiving reports on them from his registrar at ten o'clock every morning. Bill Frankland, whose task this was, 'learnt within one week that he really wasn't interested in what was happening to the patients', but was quite happy to talk about other things that he was doing.[95] Yet, despite his reluctance to see them in the ward, Fleming was prepared to take great pains to ensure that his patients received the best treatment possible, taking considerable time to prepare a vaccine for one man suffering from multiple boils though he never actually saw the patient. Similarly, although his visits to the ward were rare, he was still keen to keep his finger on the pulse of what was going on and was able to make shrewd judgements on the medical and nursing staff. The ward sister on Almroth Wright ward from 1947 to 1955 was engaged to be married. Bill Frankland, who was friendly with the sister concerned, asked Fleming whether it would be possible to hold the wedding reception in the library of the Wright Fleming Institute. Reluctantly, Fleming agreed on condition that it would be a one-off use of the library and then commented, 'What a pity she is getting married. We will now lose her.' Frankland hastened to reassure him that Sister

Almroth Wright[96] would not be leaving on her marriage and Fleming replied, 'Now I do not mind that she is getting married.' What had struck Frankland was that Fleming was able to sum up the character and capabilities of a nurse he hardly ever saw and regret that she might be leaving the job she filled so competently.[97]

He had to retire as Professor of Bacteriology in 1948 at the statutory age of 67, but was allowed to continue as principal of the Wright Fleming Institute. There was a precedent for this with the long tenure of Almroth Wright, but above all it was the eminence of Fleming himself that ensured him lifelong tenure if he desired it.

Pleasure in his success was soured for him by impending personal sorrow. Sareen Fleming's health had begun to fail soon after the end of the war, but after she had taken ill at the very peak of her husband's success during their visit to Spain in 1948, the decline was rapid. At first she had enjoyed the success and acclaim showered on her husband, but as she became more unwell the public occasions became more of a burden to her and there was even criticism of her as seeming to be awkward and ill at ease at such events. Eventually as Parkinson's disease got its grip on her, she was unable to attend them, and her husband was left to face them alone. When she became unwell in Madrid in 1948, Fleming had been concerned but not unduly alarmed, putting it down to a gastrointestinal upset.[98] If only it had been something so easily treatable, he would not have so soon lost the mainstay of his personal life. Their son Robert later suspected that she was also suffering from an undiagnosed brain tumour as well as Parkinson's disease and noted that she was in great pain towards the end.[99] Sareen came under the care of Fleming's old friend G.W.B. James, who had been appointed as psychiatrist to St Mary's Hospital in 1927. She was first admitted to the Lindo Wing, the private wing of St Mary's, before being treated for a time in a private nursing home run by James. Fleming's own views on mental and neurological diseases were very much linked to his concerns as a bacteriologist and, according to James, he 'never appreciated the conception of the unconscious mental processes'. On the contrary, he believed that 'infection was probably the principal cause of major and minor disturbances of the mind'.[100]

Despite the worsening of Sareen's condition, Fleming kept up the round of public appearances with a visit to Rome to attend a meeting of the Pontifical Academy of Sciences and a long-planned visit to the United States in June 1949 to inaugurate the Oklahoma Foundation for Medical Research. In his speech there, he stressed the importance of the role of the individual worker who, as in the cases of Pasteur, Wright and Fleming himself, often carried out his best research without lavish equipment and in the humblest of surroundings compared to the palatial marble halls of the foundation he was opening: 'if the worker wins, the palace becomes an ordinary laboratory; if the palace wins he is lost.'[101] During his trip, he was received at the White House by President Truman and, complete with resplendent headdress, installed as an Honorary Chief Doy-Gei-Taun ('Great Maker of Medicine') of the Kiowa tribe of native Americans.[102] Straight from his transatlantic voyage, he went to Verona to attend the International Congress of Medicine and receive the Freedom of Verona.[103] It was all a distraction from Sareen's distressing illness, which remained his chief concern. The official opening of the Leo pharmaceutical factory in Italy was postponed until Lady Fleming was well enough to travel to Rome with her husband for the ceremony.[104]

The end came soon enough and Sareen Fleming died on 8 October 1949.[105] Never one to share his feelings, Fleming seemed to retreat into himself even more than ever. His colleagues remarked on his drawn and haggard appearance. A neighbour Peggy McMillan had been distressed shortly before his wife's death when she saw signs that he was upset when he replied to her enquiry about Sareen with the comment that 'My discovery cannot help her. It couldn't save John.'[106] Now a grieving widower, he returned to his laboratory and perhaps for the first time ever kept the door closed. At home he was lonely, despite the company of his son Robert and nephew Harold Montgomery, both students at St Mary's.[107] Silent, somewhat gloomy, mealtimes were often shared with his widowed sister-in-law Elizabeth, still suffering from depression since the loss of her husband John and now mourning the loss of her more gregarious twin sister.[108] There were fewer visits to The Dhoon and Fleming spent more time at Radlett with his brother Robert, even more so after his son Robert qualified and began his National Service.[109] That first Christmas without Sareen, 'the empty chair was very obvious'.[110]

One way of coping with this was to continue with his round of official visits, though the pleasure they gave him had begun to pall and the invitations were perhaps less frequent than they had been in the first flush of the penicillin celebrity. Less attention was paid to smoothing his path on his visits and in Rome for the Congress of Chest Medicine in September 1950 he found to his surprise that for the first time in many years he was not met at the aerodrome on arrival.[111] Nevertheless, his travels continued and in January 1950 he was off to Dublin to collect another honorary degree and the following month to Leeds to receive the Addingham Medal, before in March taking himself off on a month-long lecture tour of the United States, where he considered there was 'too much homage'.[112] While the centre of reverent attention at the Roanoke Country Club, Virginia, he amused himself by watching 'the women's hats and the men's ties. The men beat them for gaudiness.'[113] In June he lectured in Milan on antibiotics, but did not really enjoy his visit and confessed that he had 'just had enough of trying to understand bad English and I shall be very glad to get home'.[114] However, in August his pleasure in travel revived when he was again the centre of attention at the Fifth International Congress of Microbiology in Rio de Janeiro, despite some initial reservations about accepting a free round trip to the congress when 'there were so many younger and more energetic microbiologists who may have made more important contributions to the work of the Congress'.[115] The dilemma was solved when, in addition to the places reserved for a British delegation, a personal invitation was issued to him to attend. Everywhere he went he was recognised from his photographs, and the shopping trips he so enjoyed became an embarrassment for him as shopkeepers tried to force gifts on him of anything he fancied. He considered it to have been the most successful congress he had ever attended, with more opportunities than usual for people to mingle and exchange opinions, but he did find it trying: 'for some reason I appeared to be the most notorious person at the Congress but this had its disadvantages as I was followed by photographers and could never relax and do some of the things I would have liked to have done.'[116] He was the star turn at the congress, and his example of when to stand or sit during an elaborate ritual that was part of a special service in the cathedral at Petropolis was followed by all the congress delegates, since they assumed that he knew all about the ceremony. He later admitted that, being short, he had stood up when there was something he particularly wished to see.[117]

While Fleming was fêted more abroad than in his own country, there was one honour from Britain that especially pleased him, nomination as Rector of the University of Edinburgh in 1951. This was a three-year honorary position with little real power but the holder was actually elected by the students themselves. The current Rector was the comedy actor Alastair Sim, while Fleming's most serious opponent was the fabulously wealthy playboy the Aga Khan. Passions ran high among the students during the election campaign and there was even a possibility that the messenger bearing Fleming's acceptance might be kidnapped by the rival camp.[118] Such fears of dirty tricks proved unfounded: Fleming won by a landslide and, following his inauguration as Rector on 19 February 1952, was carried in his rectoral robes on the shoulders of the students through the streets of Edinburgh. Letters of congratulation poured in, many of them assuming that the post was more than an honorary one. Denis Dooley, a former research assistant, joked that 'there appears little else that you can become except Pope'.[119]

By now Fleming's eminence was such that he was in great demand on the world stage of microbiology and was considered an ideal figure to encourage the development of microbiology and medicine in the Third World. In April 1951 he was invited to attend the All Pakistan Medical Conference and was faced with another gruelling programme. However, it was not all work and he had time to sightsee between the lectures, speeches and lunches in his honour, at one of which he was amused to find himself in the position of loaning a grey suit to a Glaxo production manager from Bombay who had arrived unaware of the dress code for the occasion.[120] However, his greatest pleasure came from meeting with old comrades from his London Scottish Regiment days and being escorted to the airport by the Pipes and Drums of the Pakistan Army Medical Corps band.[121] The congress in Pakistan had been held under the aegis of the United Nations Educational, Scientific and Cultural Organisation, which appointed him to its Commission of International Scientific Conferences. He rarely spoke at these CISC meetings in Paris, only too conscious that 'they pay too much attention to what I say [and] I must be careful', though he was a shrewd observer of his colleagues and made perceptive notes on their characters in the privacy of his diary.[122]

The World Health Organisation also called on his services for a delegation to India in January 1953 to study Indian medical services. Inevitably Fleming was deluged with the expected signs of adoration and invitations to speak, but since he was in India as part of a team carrying out a very specific programme with Indian medical schools he was not free to accept such invitations.[123] However, there was time to experience all that the Indian subcontinent could offer and to do some shopping. He asked his fellow Nobel laureate and delegate Corneille Heymans of Ghent for advice on choosing a wedding ring and went shopping for scarves, blouses and a sari, as well as ordering a diamond engagement ring made to his own specifications.[124] Although few people knew it yet, Fleming was preparing for remarriage.

Fleming was not cut out for widowhood or the single life. His domestic life had always been made comfortable for him, first by his mother and sister and then by Sareen, and he enjoyed feminine company. In his early days he had given the impression of not being interested in girls, though this was far from the case, and later comments on his shyness with the opposite sex surprised those who had known him as a young man.[125] In his diaries, he invariably noted any particularly attractive women who came his way.[126] The actress Marlene Dietrich had a crush on him, invited him to dinner and cast his horoscope, in return for which he put his hand into his pocket and

presented her with one of his mould medallions.[127] Sareen Fleming
had told one of her friends that Alec would remarry after her death
but that the lucky woman would have to do the asking herself.[128]
Certainly he did not need to do the chasing. He was attractive to
women despite being in his late sixties when he was widowed and
there were several women seriously interested in him.[129] However, the
victor was to be one of his colleagues, Dr Amalia Voureka, who had
slowly but surely made herself indispensable to him in the years since
she had joined the Inoculation Department in October 1946 with a
British Council bursary.

The very appointment by the new principal of a female research
worker in the formerly all-male Inoculation Department had been a
revolutionary step in itself. Wright himself barely tolerated her
presence during his rare visits to his old department, while she
considered him a dinosaur and resented not at first being allowed to
take her meals with the other staff through his continuing influence.
Fleming, however, was impressed by his recruit and, after first
suggesting that she do work in the field of allergy, which did not appeal
to her, invited her to work with him. The daughter of a Greek doctor,
Amalia Coutsouris was born in Constantinople in 1912. Her family
had fled from the Ottoman Empire to Athens, leaving everything
behind them, on Greece's entry into the First World War. Amalia had
trained as a doctor and married a young architect, Manoli Voureka,
before the Second World War had brought more disruption into her
life. The young couple had both become actively involved in the Greek
resistance movement, first by helping escaping Greek and British
soldiers, Jews and resistance workers and then by carrying radio
transmitters around, hidden in supposed sacks of potatoes. They were
both arrested by the German occupation forces in November 1941.
After six months in Averof Prison, Amalia was released, only to return
to her resistance activities. By the end of the war her home and
Manoli's architect's studio were in ruins and her marriage to her crop-
headed architect was over. Eager to make a new life for herself, she had
applied for a British Council scholarship to study in London, topping
the list of forty-five applicants.[130] When her scholarship ended, Fleming
first obtained an extension of six months on it and then appointed her
as the first holder of a research scholarship endowed by Ben May, who
also donated a phase-contrast microscope. From the start, Amalia
became devoted to her mentor, whose 'extraordinary ideas seemed to
radiate vitality, intelligence and humanity'.[131]

A fluent linguist, Amalia Voureka soon became invaluable in acting
as an interpreter for overseas visitors to the institute and in translating

Fleming's speeches into other languages for publication. He himself spoke only English, but in November 1950 he delivered a speech in French for the first time in Brussels at a meeting in honour of the 80th birthday of the bacteriologist Jules Bordet. Amalia had translated the speech into French for him and then recorded it for him at slow and normal speeds on a tape recorder so that he could practise the pronunciation. His efforts were well received, though he himself considered it to be 'very bad' and noted that he was asked to repeat part of his speech in English, not French, for broadcast to the Belgian Congo.[132] Amalia was also increasingly acting as his escort at social receptions. However, while he was in Stockholm in December 1950 to attend the Nobel Prize Jubilee celebrations,[133] Amalia went on holiday to Athens, where she was offered and accepted a job as head of bacteriology at the Evangelismos Hospital. She did not take up the post for another year and in that time she grew closer to Fleming, spending a great deal of time in his company. In June 1951, he took her for the weekend to The Dhoon for the first time and they spent part of the summer there with Amalia working in his little laboratory in the garden. She left for Athens in December 1951 and found awaiting her there a portrait of Fleming by John Wheatley that she had admired at the Royal Academy, which Fleming had secretly bought for her.

It seemed as if the romance was over almost before it had begun in earnest. However, they continued to correspond and in the summer of 1952, while attending a meeting of the World Health Organisation in Switzerland, Fleming volunteered to represent UNESCO at a meeting to be held in Athens. Amalia met him at the airport on 7 October and was his constant companion for the next month, ostensibly as his guide and interpreter. It was a triumphal visit almost on the same scale as his Spanish apotheosis. His first lecture at the University of Athens was attended by the Prime Minister, Archbishop and a host of other dignitaries, with crowds outside waiting for a glimpse of their hero.

At the ceremony also at the University of Athens conferring an honorary MD on Fleming, Professor George Joakimoglou declared that the discovery of penicillin had 'also caused much distress, and I thought you should be told. In our country many doctors used to specialise in V.D. This brought to them much wealth and a luxurious life. After the advent of penicillin the whole branch is practically demolished and its previously successful practitioners have to turn to another specialty.'[134] This may not have been popular with a section of the medical profession in Greece, but it added to Fleming's immense popularity there. Joakimoglou's views were later refuted by the Spanish physician

Dr Martinez Alonso, who believed that the demand for penicillin could actually increase the work of the VD specialist and remarked that 'The wages of sin are now negligible. A few shots of penicillin put you on your feet in no time (or in whatever position you may want) and you can start all over again. If the road back from sin is paved with nothing more lethal or painful than a few million units of Sir Alexander's discovery, why not indulge?'[135] Despite the constant theme of venereal disease running through Fleming's career, the image of him as a harbinger of the permissive society is an unfamiliar one but one that would probably have amused him.

There was much else to entertain him in Greece. Everywhere he went, he was overwhelmed by the kindliness he received from the highest, including the Duke of Edinburgh's sister, with whom he shared the role of guest of honour at a dinner, to the lowest, the peasants who knelt before him and kissed his hand. His travels around Greece in an official car were accompanied by a police motorcycle escort, even when nothing more than tourist visits to Corinth, Epidaurus, Mycenae, Olympia and Delphi.[136] He received the freedom of Athens, Salonika and Kastoria and had a private luncheon with King Paul and Queen Frederika, at which the Queen was delighted to be presented with a penicillin button.[137] He also met Amalia's friends and won their approval. On his last day, 9 November, Amalia cooked dinner for him in her flat. As he was leaving, he muttered something and Amalia had to ask him to repeat it. It was a proposal. In his diary for that day, a few unimportant notes are followed by a space and then a single word: 'Yes!'[138]

Fleming might have been overjoyed to be accepted, but the engagement was kept secret. Bill Frankland, his registrar, had been invited to give a paper in Paris and told his chief that he would be late in giving his usual daily report on patients in Almroth Wright ward. He was surprised when Fleming uncharacteristically questioned him about the time of the flight. He was delayed on his return and found himself face to face with an abashed Fleming at the airport. Later he realised that Fleming must have been returning to London from a weekend in Paris with Amalia.[139] Bustinza was one of the few people to find out about the wedding when he wrote asking for Amalia's address and was told that it would soon be Fleming's own in Chelsea.[140] Amalia returned to London on 3 April 1953 and was disconcerted at being greeted by the doubly grim-visaged Alexander and Elizabeth Fleming. He had invited his sister-in-law to meet his new wife to reassure her that nothing would change in their relationship, but it was not the welcome Amalia had expected. For once secrecy paid off and they were married at Chelsea Registry Office, followed by a service of blessing at the Greek Orthodox cathedral in

Moscow Road, Bayswater, on 9 April 1953 in the presence of close friends and family, without press attention.[141]

After a reception and week's stay at Claridge's Hotel, the newly married couple set off on a successful lecture tour of Cuba, where Fleming was made an honorary member of eight learned societies and academies, an honorary professor of the University of Havana, Grand Commander of the Order of Carlos Findlay and holder of the Grand Cross of Honour and Merit. When the heat at the Country Club that had been booked by the British Embassy became too much for Amalia, their official guide Dr Margarita Tamargo arranged for them to transfer to a seaside hotel. Cuba was followed by another exhausting lecture tour of the United States, where even during a three-day fishing trip Fleming took time off to lecture and visit local hospitals. Returning home, they began their married life, whose routine was very similar to the one Fleming had shared with Sareen, though as a concession to his new wife he returned home from the Chelsea Arts Club half an hour earlier than was his wont.

The marriage was not popular with his colleagues at St Mary's, where Amalia was not greatly liked. The age difference of thirty-one years scandalised many people and Amalia was perceived to be arrogant. Men and women often reacted to her differently, men finding something glamorous in her very foreignness while many of her women critics considered her dowdy. However, even Amalia's staunchest critics conceded that Fleming seemed to be much happier and more at ease and that a light seemed to have returned to his eyes since his marriage.[142] She was very protective of him and encouraged him to stop smoking after he had a bout of pneumonia in October 1953. Shortly before his death, he was visited by Alec Zaiger in his laboratory and both men were smoking. Fleming had just finished his cigarette when Amalia came in and Fleming was quick to tell her that it was Mr Zaiger who was smoking not him.[143] It was customary each Christmas for Fleming to be offered a drink in the sister's sitting room after cutting the turkey for the patients, wearing a chef's hat one of them had made for him.[144] One Christmas after his marriage, he was offered the usual glass of whisky by the sister; Amalia's face was thunderous with disapproval but he calmly enjoyed his whisky anyway.[145]

Amalia relished the opportunity to travel with her husband, who was happy to take on yet more lecture tours to satisfy her desire to see the world. Attendance at the Sixth International Congress of Microbiology in Rome in September 1953 gave the Flemings the opportunity to get to know better Ernst Chain, now working at the Istituto Superiore di Sanità, a relationship eased by the instant rapport between Amalia and

Chain.[146] After a brief visit to Athens, they returned home to prepare for a trip to Nice, where Fleming was due to speak at the opening of 'Les Journées Médicales' on 28 October 1953. Two days before the conference, he went down with pneumonia, and Amalia travelled to Nice instead to deliver the speech on his behalf.[147] He was given penicillin for the very first time and commented that 'I should not be here now if it had not been for penicillin'.[148] Before he was fully recovered, he went to Edinburgh University to install the Duke of Edinburgh as Chancellor in mid-November. The following February saw an extended tour of the United States, Canada, Mexico and Brazil. Amalia had particularly wished to visit South America and jumped at an invitation for her husband to open a penicillin plant for Wyeth in Mexico. However, the tour, at the invitation of the American Academy of General Practice, was partly funded, without any public fuss, by Pfizer, and Fleming, eager to indulge his young wife, found himself in the embarrassing position of asking Pfizer if the firm had any objections to the publicity a trip partly funded by them would give to one of their rivals.[149] Amalia enjoyed her time in Latin America, but it proved to be the last major overseas tour undertaken by her husband. Indeed there was to be only one more trip abroad for him, a short visit to Bordeaux in November 1954, marked by the award of an honorary degree, freedom of the city, an official banquet and a tour of the vineyards. In retrospect it took on the glow of a pleasant farewell to his role in representing his country abroad.

It was now twenty-five years since the publication of the first paper on penicillin on 10 May 1929. On 29 May 1954, his colleagues at St Mary's presented Fleming with two Georgian silver soup tureens to mark the silver jubilee of this event. The Duke of Edinburgh, who made the presentation in the library of the medical school, remarked that soup tureens were a suitable present to commemorate experiments that had begun with a meat broth. Fleming, wearing cufflinks hurriedly bought at Woolworth's by Amalia since her husband had forgotten to put his own links into his shirt cuffs, in turn presented Prince Philip with another of his mould medallions, the second one he had given him within six months.[150] Handing it to his equerry, Prince Philip was heard to remark that 'every time I meet this chap Fleming, he gives me one of these bloody things'.[151] Another mould medallion was produced later in the year when Queen Elizabeth the Queen Mother laid the foundation stone of the Centenary Wing of the Medical School. The culture was placed in a time capsule alongside a copy of Sir Zachary Cope's newly published *History of St Mary's Hospital Medical School* and a stopwatch marking the exact time at which medical student Roger Bannister had recently run the 4-minute mile.[152]

Fleming was now beginning to look forward to retirement and announced his resignation as director of the Wright Fleming Institute from January 1955.[153] He did arrange to keep on his personal laboratory at the institute and at a valedictory dinner given by his colleagues announced that he intended to be around St Mary's for many years to come.[154] He fell ill with influenza in February and never really recovered his vitality after that. A weekend at The Dhoon was disturbed on 5 March by the news that the Chelsea flat had been broken into and some of Amalia's jewellery and a camera stolen, though the thieves had abandoned in the street the safe containing his medals. Outwardly he remained unperturbed and occupied himself over the next week with playing with a stereo-realist projector he had recently received as a gift from America.[155] He was also preparing for a British Council sponsored lecture tour to Istanbul, Ankara, Beirut and Greece, due to start on 17 March, which Amalia thought would do him good.[156]

On the morning of Thursday 10 March, he was given an anti-typhoid inoculation and commented that he had a sore arm after it. He spent the evening with his son Robert and Robert's fiancée Kathleen, showing off his latest toy, and awoke the next morning in good spirits. Ahead of him was a luncheon party at the Savoy and dinner with Eleanor Roosevelt and Douglas Fairbanks Junior. Then he felt sick, experienced a pain in the chest and vomited. At first he would not let Amalia disturb his doctor and when she called Dr Hunt told him that there was no urgency and that he should see his other patients first. He told Amalia that he didn't think it was his heart only minutes before he died of a massive coronary thrombosis. His general practitioner Dr Hunt later said that Fleming had always been remarkably healthy considering the long hours he kept, the hard work he undertook, his chain-smoking and his capacity to absorb alcohol without ill effects.[157]

News of his death was greeted with shock. Messages of condolence poured in from all over the world.[158] A day of national mourning was declared in the Dominican Republic.[159] In the Greek village of Arachova and all over Greece, the flags were at half mast.[160] A death mask was made of his face at the request of a Californian sculptor, and Bustinza, in London for the funeral at Golders Green crematorium, obtained a copy of it. In Barcelona flowers were laid in tribute to him, reminiscent of the flowers heaped upon him during his 1948 visit, and Don Gregorio Maranon expressed his belief that Fleming would now be sitting at God's right hand.[161] In death as in the last decade of his life, he remained the property of the world.

TEN

Miracle Cure

If the discovery and development of penicillin could be said to have had any lasting legacy, it would surely be the launch of the antibiotic age in medicine. Fleming, together with Florey and his colleagues, had made a gift of penicillin to the world that was to lead to the development of other antibiotics, yet they were to be castigated for not taking out patents that would have protected their discoveries and methods. Certainly they did not amass great personal riches from it, nor would they have wanted to do so.[1] Similarly, Fleming has been criticised for failing to establish a school of thought around him. Colonel Walter Parkes, former House Governor of St Mary's, wrote that 'unhappily he never built up a group of young men who would continue what he had begun'.[2] The question is why anyone might have expected it of him. It was not in the nature of the man to build up a research institute as Wright had done and he was not a team builder in the way that Florey had been. In many ways he was the last of the nineteenth-century lone researchers. He was also, for all the youthfulness of his spirit and the spring in his step, very much the old man of penicillin. Florey was in his early forties at the time of the development of penicillin and his associates much younger, while in North America the sense of a young dynamic country was reflected in the youthful enthusiasm of the scientists working on the problem of mass production, synthesis and clinical testing. All of them had long and fruitful careers ahead, whereas Fleming's scientific achievements were in his own salad days. He had nothing to prove and no need to thrust himself forward for a future career. He was also remarkably loyal to Almroth Wright and content to follow the lines laid down by the man who had been the greatest influence on him.

The drive to remake the Wright Fleming Institute in his own image was not there and neither was the money. Selman Waksman had used the financial rewards from streptomycin, the second of the great antibiotics to be discovered, to build 'a temple dedicated to the study of the smallest things, the microbes' in the Waksman Institute of Microbiology at Rutgers University, but, after all, he had patented his discovery.[3] During one of his lectures to students in July 1949, Waksman had commented on the stupidity of Fleming in not patenting penicillin. The following week he introduced his graduate students to his great friend Fleming, for whom he expressed the utmost respect.[4] Waksman was not alone in seeing Fleming as commercially naive. One of the questions most frequently asked about Fleming is why he did not make any money from penicillin. Fleming's own explanation was that it had never occurred to him. The common assumption is that he altruistically gave penicillin freely to the world, which indeed he did.[5] However, patenting it would not have been an option. Under the patent law at the time he could not have patented a substance occurring in nature.

Florey and his team at Oxford, in contrast to Fleming, could have patented any new processes they developed to purify penicillin, but failed to do so. Chain, coming from a family background in industrial chemistry, was alive to the importance of taking out patents, but Florey subscribed to the contemporary medical ethics that equated patenting and commercial practices with the despised purveyors of patent medicines. There were passionate arguments between the two men on the subject, but Florey could call on the support of Sir Edward Mellanby and Sir Henry Dale, doyens of the scientific establishment, in his contention that patenting would be unethical. They overruled Chain's arguments that patenting could bring in much-needed royalties to support the work of the Sir William Dunn School, and that if they did not take patents someone else might and they would then have to pay out royalties to use the methods and equipment they had devised.[6]

Chain's fears were not realised but only because the development of deep-fermentation methods of production in the United States, using a different strain of mould and a different culture medium, superseded the methods developed in Oxford. These were patented and caused bad feeling on both sides of the Atlantic. Postwar British politicians took up the myth of lost opportunities as this became the archetypal example of British entrepreneurship: developing an idea only for it to be exploited by another country. It was a myth closely bound up with British national identity and the need to come to terms with a new postwar role following the loss of Empire. In January 1945 Andrew Moyer took out British patents on the processes he and Heatley had developed in Peoria. As a Federal employee, he had to assign his United States rights to the Department of Agriculture[7] but was free to take out patents overseas. Having no compunction about asserting what he saw as his own rights, he applied for the patents without the knowledge of Norman Heatley, who might have had a claim to a share in them.[8] Merck too asserted claims for royalties for deep fermentation, to the resentment of British firms.[9] Against the background of new Anglo-American military cooperation in 1952, Vannevar Bush, former head of the Office of

Scientific Research and Development, asked the lawyer John T. Connor to investigate and refute claims that 'America stole penicillin' from the British.[10] Connor argued successfully that when new British deep-fermentation plants were built they licensed the procedures from American firms such as Merck, Squibb and Commercial Solvents with the requisite expertise developed in the States. However, one solid outcome of the controversy was the establishment of the National Research Development Corporation in 1948 to assist the development of new British inventions through providing finance and advice on such matters as patenting to avoid any further such perceived losses to the nation as that of penicillin.[11]

Concern was not only about the loss of economic rewards, but also of the missed diplomatic and status benefits arising from antibiotics. Cooperation and collaboration between the wartime Allies had given way to national rivalries in penicillin as in many other areas with the end of the war. With the liberation of Europe came questions as to what penicillin supplies and what information on production could be released to both Allies and neutral countries. In 1946 the British Foreign Office was so concerned that the United States was benefiting diplomatically from the supply of penicillin to Bulgaria 'not only to enhance their prestige vis-à-vis the Russians, who have no penicillin at all, but to consolidate their own situation as a humanitarian and altruistic people' that it became a matter of national urgency for the British Embassy to supply British penicillin as a reminder that the drug was one of the most important achievements of a British scientist.[12] Britain was also opposed to American plans to develop penicillin production in postwar Germany. One official even commented that 'the Germans have existed for many centuries now without penicillin and I am not sure that they need it now'.[13] In the unforgiving mood of the postwar occupation of Germany, the only justification for even giving penicillin to the former enemy was to safeguard troops stationed there from gonorrhoea and prevent the spread of ultra-virulent strains of streptococcus back to Britain that could have caused an epidemic among an austerity-weary people.[14] If there was opposition to the defeated and disarmed enemy being given access to penicillin technology, there was even more to its export to a former ally once the Cold War had begun in earnest. It was feared that fermentation equipment might be of benefit to the Russians in developing biological weapons.[15]

The Americans did not have it all their own way, and Selman Waksman was to find that he had not always been any smarter than Fleming when it came to exploiting his own rights. He had been careful to take out patents for streptomycin and confided to his diary in 1945 that the British were 'caustic that we are asking for a royalty for streptomycin, apparently not so much in a spirit of scientific research as in a spirit of jealousy that they were not able to do likewise for penicillin'.[16] Unfortunately, a careless slip meant that his British rights were not as secure as he believed. Samples of *Streptomyces griseus* had been sent to the Lister Institute, the depository for the British National Type Culture collections, during the war when transatlantic communications were difficult and, by an oversight, had been distributed on request to British pharmaceutical companies without informing them of the rights of Rutgers University over streptomycin. By 1947, Glaxo, Distillers and Boots were planning to manufacture streptomycin and were prepared to contest any claims for the payment of royalties. Waksman's lawyers warned him that litigation might not go his way and he himself was concerned that he would be the target of bad publicity in view of the widespread feeling in Britain that, since penicillin had been freely given to the world without hope of any financial reward for St Mary's or Oxford University, the Americans should reciprocate with streptomycin. Sir Harry Jephcott, Chairman of Glaxo, had suggested a way out whereby the British manufacturers of streptomycin might be persuaded to establish a fund for Waksman similar to the one provided by the American producers of penicillin for Fleming. Waksman, making the best of the situation, could then announce to the world that 'in view of the fact that penicillin was given by the British scientists to the rest of the world for the alleviation of human ailments . . . the American scientific group concerned with the discovery and development of streptomycin are only too happy to reciprocate in giving the benefit of these discoveries to the British people'.[17]

Yet penicillin, whether protected by patents or not, was important in providing the impetus to the discovery and development of other antibiotics. There was at last the possibility of a cure for such once life-threatening diseases as the heart condition bacterial endocarditis, meningococcal meningitis and septic wound infections. Death in childbirth no longer haunted expectant mothers. The misery of chronic infections of the bones and joints or of the ear and sinuses was eased. Despite fears that the role of the doctor and surgeon might be minimised with a means of controlling infection, antibiotics actually opened up new possibilities. By offering protection against hospital-acquired infection, more complex procedures were possible in such areas as organ transplantation where the immune systems of the patients had been compromised. The pre-antibiotic age now seemed like the dark ages of modern medicine compared to the golden sun of the antibiotic age.

Yet the seeds of future problems were there from the beginning, as Fleming, with his experience of the ways in which bacteria could acquire resistance, was only too well aware. At a time when penicillin was often seen as the universal panacea by the public at large and by many doctors, he urged caution. In his Nobel Lecture in 1945, he ended with a warning:

> The time may come when penicillin can easily be bought by anyone in the shops. Then there is the danger that the ignorant man may easily underdose himself and by exposing his microbes to non-lethal quantities of the drug make them resistant . . . Mr X. has a sore throat. He buys penicillin and gives himself not enough to kill the streptococci but enough to educate them to resist penicillin. He then infects his wife. Mrs X. gets pneumonia and is treated with penicillin. As the streptococci are now resistant to penicillin the treatment fails. Mrs X. dies. Who is primarily responsible for Mrs X.'s death? Why Mr X., whose negligent use of penicillin changed the nature of the microbe. Moral: if you use penicillin, use enough.[18]

Within a few years, this prediction had become a reality, as more and more bacteria became resistant to penicillin.[19] This they did by producing an enzyme, penicillinase, which destroyed it. The genetic information that controlled this process could in turn be transferred to sensitive bacteria, making them resistant too.[20] Fleming was aware of these dangers and warned of them in many lectures. However, he was not infallible on all aspects of his discovery. He never accepted that penicillin could cause allergic reactions, believing these to be caused not by penicillin but by the impurities in the preparations then available. In 1950, he asked his registrar, the up-and-coming allergist Bill Frankland, to contribute a chapter on allergy to the second edition of his book on penicillin. Frankland concluded that, 'with increasing use of penicillin, allergic reactions would become more common'.[21] Fleming insisted that he change this to 'the more recent penicillin preparations rarely cause local or general reactions'.[22] Frankland has been proved right, but fortunately penicillin had given the impetus to the search for other antibiotics that could be given to those people allergic to penicillin.

It was Florey and others, not Fleming at the tail end of his career, who would continue the antibiotic revolution. Florey had indeed laid out the principles for the development of new antibiotics in his own Nobel Lecture. First there was the screening of microbes to identify those that produced an antibiotic substance, followed by the extraction of that substance.[23] It would then be tested on animals to see if it were poisonous before human trials could take place. These principles became the basis of work on all new antibiotics. Streptomycin, the second of the major antibiotics to be discovered, was isolated by Selman Waksman and his colleagues Albert Schatz and Elizabeth Bugie at the New Jersey Agricultural Experimentation Station at Rutgers University in 1944 by adopting a scattergun approach, blasting off enough pellets until one finally scored a hit. He and his colleagues screened thousands of soil microbes before finding any with antibiotic properties. Even then some of the antimicrobial substances were toxic to man. One of his students, Hubert Lechavalier, screened just 172 cultures of the bacteria actinomycetes and scored two hits with neomycin and candicicin. However, it was the isolation of streptomycin from the gullet of a chicken that really hit the jackpot. This was active against the scourge of tuberculosis, against which penicillin was ineffective.[24] Fleming took an interest in its British trials under his successor as Professor of Bacteriology, Robert Cruickshank, in the Almroth Wright ward at St Mary's.[25]

The other more focused approach to the development of new antibiotics depended much more upon reasoning than it did on comprehensive searching. Sometimes it too was the result of chance observation, just as it had been with Fleming's penicillin. The cephalosporin group of antibiotics was discovered when Giuseppe Brotzu, Professor of Bacteriology at Cagliari University, reasoned that sewage, a source of typhus, might contain organisms that were antagonistic to pathogenic bacteria. In 1945 he isolated *Cephalosporium acremonium* from the sewage off the coast of Sardinia. In crude broth, the culture was not poisonous and proved effective in treating boils and other local infections. However, Brotzu was unable to interest the local pharmaceutical industry. Nor could he find a journal ready to publish his findings. He sought the advice of Florey and sent a copy of a reprint of a paper on the subject in an issue of the journal *Lavori dell'Istituto d'Igiene di Cagliari*. It was a journal that did not exist. He had invented it himself solely to add weight to what he was sending Florey, who happily took up further work on this new antibiotic.[26]

The early screening efforts produced a steady stream of new antibiotics throughout the 1940s and 1950s.[27] Most of them were developed in partnerships between academics and industrialists. Just as the role of the lone researcher in a private laboratory had given way to research institutes and university laboratories in the early twentieth century, there was now a move towards larger-scale effort and cooperation between universities and commerce. Fleming, although a member of a research institute linked to both a hospital and a medical school, essentially worked on his own. For his discovery to be developed, teamwork had been essential, but this had been carried out in a university laboratory that was still in many ways isolated from the partnership with industry so necessary to get mass production under way. Now it was recognised that one institution could not go it alone. Waksman, recognising this, had teamed up with Merck in 1938, although when streptomycin proved so profitable he had found a way out of the agreement to share royalties with that company.[28] The partnerships later forged in the development of penicillin in wartime conditions pointed to the future. Pharmaceutical companies began to set up their own research laboratories to run in-house screening programmes, but they also funded basic research in the universities. The potential profits from antibiotics were so vast that the pharmaceutical firms were driven to invest heavily, even though there was no guarantee of any return on the investment, as it was impossible to predict just where the next discovery might come from. Yet the risks were worth taking for those who dared to venture their capital.

One partnership forged in the 1950s, at a time when bacterial resistance was becoming a major problem, was between Ernst Chain and the patent medicine manufacturers Beecham, keen to move into the field of antibiotics. The parting of the ways between Chain and Florey had become inevitable soon after the end of the war, when Florey had let it be known that Chain did not have 'any future here such as you would like'.[29] In 1948 Chain moved to Rome as scientific director of the International Research Centre at the Istituto Superiore di Sanità. In 1955 he accepted the offer of a consultancy to advise Beecham on citric and tartaric acid production. Before long, Chain and Beecham had entered into an agreement for research into the development of new penicillins by the chemical modification of the penicillin molecule. Beecham's desire to be involved in antibiotic production coincided with Chain's belief in the need for 'a research unit in chemical industrial microbiology which would be *al pari* with the American corresponding organisations'.[30]

The old dream of being able to synthesise penicillin, which had buoyed up hope of an easy and quick means of manufacturing it, had been burst already with an understanding of the structure of the substance. During the war, no less than 130 British scientists in 11 different research groups and 299 Americans in 21 groups had worked on the structure of penicillin, and synthesis always seemed to be just around the corner.[31] It was just as well that production from the mould had begun instead of waiting for the development of ways of making it artificially, or it might not have come into use until after the war. By 1943 the components of the penicillin molecule were known, but what proved elusive was an understanding of how this combination of sulphur, carbon, hydrogen, oxygen and nitrogen fitted together. Edward Abraham, Ernst Chain, Wilson Baker and Robert Robinson at Oxford established that it consisted of a nucleus and side chain, its nucleus being 'a thiazolidine ring fused to a beta-lactam ring'.[32] Only in 1945 was the precise molecular configuration of the molecule confirmed by Dorothy Hodgkin, using techniques of X-ray crystallography. She had become involved in the synthesis project after meeting Chain on a walk in the University Parks and later went on to receive the 1964 Nobel Prize for Chemistry for her contribution to X-ray crystallography, including the work on the structure of penicillin.[33] It was now realised that penicillin would be too difficult and too expensive to synthesise industrially and it was not until 1957 that it was actually synthesised in a laboratory by John Sheehan of Massachusetts Institute of Technology.[34] However, the fact that there were at least four different types of penicillin active against different bacteria depending on the nature of the side chain raised the possibility of being able to modify the structure of the molecule to produce new antibiotics.

Chain insisted that, if the project had any chance of success, key staff from Beecham should be seconded to work with him in Rome to be indoctrinated in his methods and ideas. A pilot fermenter similar to Chain's own in Rome was constructed at the Beecham Research Laboratories at Brockham Park, which had been opened by Fleming in 1947. Here a youthful research team, including George Rolinson, Ralph Batchelor, Peter Doyle and John Nayler, achieved a breakthrough with the isolation from penicillin fermentation solutions of the molecular core or nucleus of penicillin, 6-amino penicillanic acid, usually referred to as 6-APA. Having removed the original side chain from the natural nucleus, they next found a means of adding different chemical side chains. Brockham Park had a total fermentation capacity of only 90 gallons, which was too small to allow the production of more than an ounce of pure 6-APA in any one batch. Nevertheless by June 1958 the team was able to create twelve new penicillins a month. This success and the potential to create an almost limitless number of these semi-synthetic penicillins encouraged Beecham to construct a new pharmaceutical plant at Worthing with giant fermenters capable of meeting the production needs of the new antibiotics.[35]

The first of the new generation of semi-synthetic penicillins became available in 1959 and was followed by many other new weapons in the fight against penicillinase-producing bacteria.[36] Yet the respite was only temporary in the continuous battle between man and microbes. More and more bacteria began to produce an enzyme called beta-lactamase, which was capable of inactivating many penicillins and related antibiotics, leaving the bacteria free to flourish and grow. In the 1980s, clavulanate, which incorporates its own defence against beta-lactamase, was developed as a fix for this problem. When bacteria that produce beta-lactamase enzymes are exposed to a penicillin combined with clavulanate, the bacteria swell up and burst as the penicillin destroys their cell walls. The modern generation of penicillin therapies using clavulanate offered a new lease of life for penicillin.[37]

All this development work was expensive for the pharmaceutical companies. Development costs were increased as the drugs industry became more regulated. In Britain, initial toxicity testing in animals became mandatory, followed by several stages of clinical testing in humans before approval could be given for a new drug to be released to the general public. The whole process of innovation became more complicated and expensive. New products were protected by patent laws for up to twenty years from their initial discovery, but by the time a new drug had gone through the hoops of testing and been approved there might be no more than eight or ten years at the most for a pharmaceutical company to recoup its costs. By 1978 the development time for a new drug was ten years and average development costs had risen from £5,000,000 in the 1960s to £150,000,000 by the 1990s. As regulation rose, innovation declined and fewer new drugs were developed.[38] At the same time, governments throughout the world were acting to contain the escalating costs of healthcare, threatening the high profit margins the pharmaceutical companies had come to expect and that were considered fundamental to their ability to continue their lavish funding of research and development. The response of many of the companies was to seek a greater share of global markets through more aggressive marketing of products. It was also to consolidate and redefine corporate functions. ICI responded with a policy of floating off its pharmaceutical and biosciences businesses to form a new company, Zeneca, which would focus on a core business of pharmaceuticals.[39] Other companies merged to give themselves higher international profiles, including Beecham, which merged with Smith Kline Beckman to form SmithKline Beecham, and Glaxo, which merged with Burroughs Wellcome; only a few years later a further merger saw the emergence of GlaxoSmithKline from SmithKline Beecham and Glaxo Wellcome. Increasingly a greater scale was necessary for efficient research and development and marketing, whether or not the company concentrated on its core pharmaceuticals or moved into an integrated healthcare business.[40] Yet, for all the money poured into the research programmes, there are fewer new antibiotics in development than in the past.

Today, after more than sixty years of antibiotics, there are fears that the antibiotic age may be coming to an end with the rise of superbugs resistant to most antibiotics, especially the much publicised methicillin-resistant *Staphylococcus aureus* (MRSA) first observed in 1960.[41] Methicillin-resistant strains soon spread throughout Britain and then vanished in the late 1960s, only to re-emerge as a problem in the 1980s. Only one antibiotic, vancomycin, remains as the last line of defence against MRSA. Even it was being breached in the early twenty-first century. The press periodically stokes up fears of a return to the dark pre-antibiotic age. In reaction to earlier over-prescribing and inappropriate use of antibiotics, doctors are now more cautious in their prescription.[42] The widespread use of antibiotics in animal foodstuffs to fatten up animals is also blamed for resistance, although penicillin has also had its benefits in veterinary medicine.[43] The doomsday scenario is that we will soon return to the situation before Fleming's discovery, as if it had never been made. The hope is that alternative approaches to the fight against infection, such as the development of vaccines and gene therapy, will prove fruitful. How it will all end remains unknowable, just as in 1928 few could have dreamt of the effects antibiotics would have on the lives of everyone.

ELEVEN

Living Legend

Death was not the end of the cult of celebrity for Fleming. The interment of his ashes in the crypt of St Paul's Cathedral as part of the pantheon of such national heroes as Christopher Wren, Lord Nelson and the Duke of Wellington marked his apotheosis as a British icon. The ceremony on 18 March 1955 took on the trappings of an unofficial state funeral, with police clearing the route to the cathedral taken by the cortège. Crowds gathered outside, while inside St Paul's the congregation was made up of representatives of the academic and medical establishment, pharmaceutical companies, embassies and the many hundreds of people who saw him as their friend. The turn-out from St Mary's Hospital was impressive and would probably have pleased him more than the official contingents.[1] An alabaster casket containing his ashes was interred in the crypt beneath a simple stone inscribed with his initials. A year later, Amalia unveiled a commemorative plaque of pentelic marble quarried from the same stone used to build the Parthenon in Athens. It was designed by his old friend Dyson-Smith and bore the thistle of Scotland and the fleur-de-lis of St Mary's.

After Fleming's death, Amalia very much took on the role of the professional widow, devoting herself to the perpetuation of his memory and achievements. Deeply suicidal after her husband's death,[2] she told Chain that her husband had been 'my God and my world, and I have nothing left now'.[3] Her scientific work took a back seat while she devoted all her time to collecting materials for the Maurois biography, sorting out her husband's papers and arranging displays of his honours in the Wright Fleming Institute. Her desire to perpetuate her husband in some way was so intense that she voted for the first time in her life in the May 1955 general election but cast her vote not according to her own preference for the Labour Party but as she knew her late husband would have voted, since 'it made me think I was bringing him back to life for a few seconds when I gave his vote to the Conservatives'.[4]

Nothing could bring him back to Amalia, but already his reputation had taken on a life of its own. The Fleming mythology indeed had begun during his lifetime. Fleming himself kept a scrapbook that he labelled the 'Fleming myth', in which he collected the many inaccurate stories told about himself and his discovery. It was the responsibility of Howard Hughes, the reader in bacteriology, and Fleming's secretary Pauline Hunter to keep the file up to date.[5] In many ways Fleming was a blank canvas upon whom people could hang their own image. Quiet and very much inclined to keep his thoughts and emotions to himself, he, by his very silence, allowed people to imagine him as being anything they wanted, whether as a young man rising from rags to riches or as the tool of a divinity marking him out as fit to be the one to transmit a blessing to mankind. With his self-effacing, modest demeanour, he humanised medicine and science at a time when, with such new developments as the atom bomb, science could be frightening.

His taciturnity, which made the inner man somewhat unfathomable, had some advantages in his dealings with the press as he was not tempted to make sweeping statements or indiscreet comments that could have hit the headlines. After a gruelling interview with a Spanish reporter questioning him, through an interpreter, on his thoughts about the imminence of another world war and why Spanish science was so backward, subjects that could have had diplomatic repercussions, Fleming reflected, 'the thought occurred to me that if I had been born with a talkative nature I would soon have found myself in trouble'.[6] The resultant newspaper article reported that he had given the reply 'no' to the many long and involved questions.[7] While his political views may not have been quoted out of context to embarrass him, he could find himself inadvertently being interpreted and fêted from a political stance that was not his own. During a visit to Turin in 1946, he was greeted by the Communist mayor as a 'representative of the working man', to which he replied that he was a 'good workman and that was the only way to success'.[8] However, that was not the end of the matter, for on his return from a dinner in his honour the following day, he received a phone call from a journalist about a 'Communist demonstration tomorrow in Milan in my honour. That's a new one.'[9] Despite his amusement at being depicted as a working-class hero, he did or said nothing to destroy such an illusion, but left people to see him as they wished.

Fleming came to be seen as an authority on penicillin in all its applications and received requests for information about it from all over the world. In inviting him to write a preface to an issue devoted to antibiotics of a magazine for American physicians, the editor wrote that, 'We feel there could be no more authoritative, no more inspiring a manner to introduce the subject to the pages of M.D. for the young men of medicine who are its readers than by prefacing it with your words'.[10] A Hungarian doctor actually forwarded him a paper on the arcane subject of the secretion of penicillin in the urogenital organs and addressed him as 'the greatest living authority on this question', something Fleming would never himself have claimed.[11] When attending the 1946 Inter-American Medical Congress in Rio de Janeiro in 1946, he was importuned by a doctor who had tried unsuccessfully to use penicillin three times but each attempt had resulted in a violent rash; he wrote that 'to me personally your presence here is providential for there is something in connection with the use I have made of penicillin that I believe only yourself could elucidate'.[12] It was a subject on which Fleming could not really help, but he was always ready to do his best to assist, while never pretending to know any more than he did. When a Madrid orthodontist appealed for advice on the use of penicillin in a difficult case of an abscess that nothing could clear up, Fleming replied that he had nothing more to suggest than a larger dose of penicillin and tests on the bacteria causing the infection to see how sensitive they were to penicillin.[13] Equally penicillin and its discoverer were an inspiration for younger researchers to study the subject. These young men were eager to send details of the slight advances they had made in the subject to the master for his comments or sometimes merely his approval, such as an article on penicillin and tropical medicine sent by Maurizio Mariotti of Ancona.[14] Mariotti described himself as a young doctor who had enthusiastically followed the story of the discovery of penicillin and the subsequent work on it and as a result had made a study of the application of penicillin in the field of tropical medicine as part of a course he was studying at the University of Rome.[15]

Fleming himself was well aware that he had a part to play as a source of inspiration for younger doctors around the world. In 1951, he was invited to attend the All Pakistan Medical Conference, but declined after confusion over the dates and an attempt by the organisers of the conference to shift responsibility for bearing his expenses onto an outside body. In turning down the invitation he wrote that 'I had hoped that I might have been of some use in stimulating medical research in Pakistan, and the stimulation of medical research is something close to my heart'.[16] He had only a few months earlier contributed an exhibit on penicillin to the Museum of the New Central Drug Research Unit newly established by the Indian government.[17] Pakistan could not be outdone by India in deriving inspiration for its young doctors from the discoverer of penicillin and a fresh invitation was extended by the Pakistan Medical Association for a visit that would actively promote medical research in Pakistan. Fleming was happy to accept a programme with this aim centred upon him, though he requested that the organisers 'do not work me too hard'.[18] His gruelling schedule of lectures in Karachi over three days included lectures on modern trends in antibiotics and 'How Pakistani Children can Grow to be the Research Workers of Tomorrow', a talk to students at the Dow Medical College, and chairing a symposium on the 'Problem of Medical Research in Pakistan'.[19] Following independence and the partition of the Indian subcontinent, Fleming, both on this occasion and in his inclusion in a World Health Organisation visiting team to India in 1953,[20] was playing a small but important part in maintaining British influence in the former Indian Empire.

Penicillin indeed had an important role in promoting Britain abroad. Fleming himself had 'come to personify and embody the spirit and achievements of British research in the subjects allied to chemistry'.[21] In 1947, the organisers of a public exhibition at the Science Museum in conjunction with an International Congress of Pure and Applied Chemistry invited Fleming to loan some exhibits for a showcase on penicillin and urged on him the importance of putting on a good display: 'With so many overseas visitors, it is surely in the common British interest to make the penicillin showcase as lively and comprehensive as possible. I do not think anyone will mind small samples omitted for lack of space, but we should be ashamed to see the case sparsely filled for lack of enthusiasm on the part of the original workers.'[22] Penicillin was a matter of national pride and as such it was prominently featured during the Festival of Britain as one of the modern scientific accomplishments of which the country could be proud.[23] As an achievement it was very much bound up with the postwar re-examination of national identity, although it had come to be seen, however inaccurately, as a paradigm of the failure of national entrepreneurship, with the perceived failure to capitalise on a British discovery only to see it exploited abroad.[24]

Inevitably, the Fleming name was to acquire such a cachet that there were many people who would have liked to use it commercially for their own gain. Product endorsement went alongside celebrity. Fleming was aware of this, though he personally never capitalised on it for personal benefit. He asked that any fees for lecturing, broadcasting or articles be paid to the Inoculation Department or other charitable funds connected with St Mary's.[25] Others were less scrupulous and Fleming knew full well that some of the many requests for him to pose for photographs had commercial motives. While visiting a Spanish pharmaceutical company in 1948, he posed for a large number of photographs 'which I suspect will be used purely for advertisement'.[26] He may have accepted reluctantly such uses of his image, but when there were direct attempts to exploit his name he stood up to them. Two young Uruguayan entrepreneurs named their firm in Montevideo

Laboratorio Fleming, ostensibly in homage to a great scientist but actually to capitalise on the name to prop up a flagging business. Fleming objected to this and refused consent for such a use of his name, which would appear to endorse a firm of which he knew nothing and with which he had no connection: 'While I am alive, I cannot agree to my name being used in such a way.'[27] At the same time he was quite happy for his name to be used as the title of one of the sections of the Red Cross Society Cadet Unit at Urmstone[28] and as the name of a nursing home in Johannesburg, South Africa.[29]

Such was the recognition factor of the Fleming name and interest in him that it is surprising that it was not until 1953 that a biography was published. There had been books and articles on the penicillin story, with which he had cooperated, but he had always set his face against a biography during his lifetime.[30] In 1951, Mary Milne, who as a highly respected matron of St Mary's had come to personify the hospital during the war, approached him on behalf of the writer L.J. Ludovici with a request that he allow him to write a biography. His initial response was that 'a biography does not appeal to me',[31] but, swayed by his regard for Miss Milne and the promises of Ludovici that he would be able to censor whatever appeared in print, he agreed to 'give you what assistance I can in your studies and I am very glad to have your assurance that nothing will be published without my consent'.[32] He asked his friends to cooperate with Ludovici and warned them, 'don't tell them anything too bad about me'.[33] The laudatory biography appeared in 1952 while Fleming and Amalia were in Greece, although Fleming had believed that his consent to the book was conditional on it not appearing during his lifetime. His brother Robert tried in vain to take out an injunction against publication, but there was little that could be done as the book was not defamatory.[34] What perhaps made it somewhat embarrassing was its depiction of Fleming as an inconsolable widower at a time that he was contemplating happiness in a new marriage. In time he became reconciled to its flattering portrait and even autographed copies for colleagues.

Amalia Fleming had no such reservations about the need for an authorised biography of her late husband. Her choice fell on André Maurois, whose biography of Shelley, *Ariel*, had been a literary and critical success. Maurois had first come across Fleming and Almroth Wright as a military liaison officer during the First World War, experiences he was to use to good effect as inspiration for his novel *The Strange Silences of Colonel Bramble*. This novel told the story of a taciturn Scot characterised by quiet humour, reserve, intelligence and independence. Despite appearances, Fleming was not the inspiration for this character, although Dr G.W.B. James, then a battalion medical officer and former fellow student of Fleming's at St Mary's, inspired the paradoxical character of Dr O'Grady in the novel.[35] Nevertheless, when he came to write his *Life of Sir Alexander Fleming*, Maurois was unable to resist entitling one of his chapters 'The Silences of Professor Fleming'. Moreover, he found a certain satisfaction in the reflection that he had begun his literary career with a novel about a taciturn Scot and now in old age was writing the biography of another who also displayed that mixture of quiet humour, loyalty, independence and reserve that Maurois himself found so attractive. At first he was hesitant to take on a medical and scientific biography, but Amalia was determined to have her choice of author.[36] The resultant book is perhaps as much Amalia's in interpretation as it was Maurois's in style. The romance of the discovery is stressed in the first half of the book, while the second half reads very much as a love story. She was said to have rejected the first draft on the grounds that Sir Almroth Wright stole the page just as in his lifetime he had stolen the limelight from Fleming.[37]

The inevitable reaction to the adulation given to Fleming resulted in attempts to topple him from his pedestal and redress the balance in favour of the work of the Oxford team,[38] yet books written for children continued to toe the hero-worshipping line of the exemplar of the modest man who could achieve much despite humble origins.[39]

What is surprising considering the romanticised accounts of Fleming's life and of the discovery of penicillin, whether for children or for adults, was that it never received the Hollywood treatment. Myron Selznick made approaches to Fleming and Florey in 1944, but the response was unenthusiastic.[40] There was a rumour in 1945 that a film version was to be made of a recently published pulp-magazine-style book, *Yellow Magic*, by the popular writer J.D. Ratcliffe.[41] It was reported that Fleming had actually given his permission to be played by a top Hollywood actor, unlikely as that actually was.[42] The reported casting of Barry Fitzgerald, a scene-stealer normally playing whimsical Irishman roles, as Fleming was not perhaps the most appropriate choice and nothing came of the venture.[43] Fleming's response to a subsequent approach from Boris Sokoloff to make a film in 1948 concentrating on his 'memorable fight for recognition'[44] met with the response that 'it might be alright if I were dead and could look down from heaven and see it. It is different when you are still trying to do a job of work.'[45] The time for such a biographical film had passed and, apart from a BBC television play in 1970 by Ian Curteis,[46] the story of Fleming has not yet received a further twist or distortion through the eyes of the film-maker, though penicillin was to play a crucial part in the 1949 film, Orson

Welles's *The Third Man*, written by Graham Greene about a penicillin racket selling diluted penicillin on the black market to Viennese hospitals filled with dying children.[47]

He was also memorialised in more conventional ways. One of the windows of St James's Church, Paddington, had been blown out during the Blitz. Its replacement, designed by Arthur Buss and installed in 1952, depicted scenes and personalities from the history of Paddington, including Brunel and the Great Western Railway, Lord Baden-Powell, the Blitz and the discovery of penicillin.[48] A plaque was also placed outside the room in which penicillin had been discovered 'to the glory of God and immeasurable benefit to mankind'. Further memorials were erected after his death, including a bust in Chelsea Town Hall, a memorial garden at Darvel, a memorial stone at Lochfield Farm and blue plaques at St Mary's Hospital, 20 Danvers Street and The Dhoon.[49] The Department of Health and Social Security was for many years housed in Alexander Fleming House at Elephant and Castle, London. Yet all these public monuments in Britain were subdued compared with the fuss made in some other countries.

Fleming's reputation in Mediterranean countries was phenomenal. In Spain his fame was further fanned through the efforts of Florencio Bustinza, who had championed his visit to Madrid in 1948. It was partly through Bustinza's efforts that a large and imposing memorial was created in Gijón. A sum of 500,000 pesetas had been raised by public subscription for a monument to Fleming consisting of a bust on a 15-foot-high plinth set up in a monumental garden with a pool.[50] Bustinza obtained Fleming's approval for this, suitable photographs for the use of the sculptor and a promise to be present at the unveiling. Sadly for Bustinza and the citizens of Gijón, the monument was not completed until after Fleming's death, when it was unveiled by his widow.[51] Elsewhere in Spain are other monuments to Fleming. In Barcelona, the Plaça Doctor Fleming contains a bust of Fleming and two plaques, one erected by the firemen of Barcelona and the other by the city's abattoir workers. Both groups had been the recipients of the benefits of penicillin and were keen to show their gratitude. For many years, the Pharmaceutical College of Barcelona paid annual homage to Fleming by laying flowers in front of his bust.[52] The tributes are repeated throughout Spain in plaques, statues and the names of streets and squares.

The pattern is repeated in Italy. In Milan and its surrounding area alone there are three streets and two clinics named after Fleming .[53] In Brescia there is a school named after him and at Mazzano a bronze statue by the sculptor Angelo Aimé was unveiled in 1975.[54] Despite Fleming's unhappiness at any commercial use of his name, he was prescient enough to know that he could not prevent it after his death, as indeed happened. The name of Alexander Fleming continued to have such a cachet in Italy in the mid-1970s that it was adopted for what became one of the leading private clinical pathology laboratory services there, the Fleming Labs, providing a diagnostic referral service for over 700 private and public laboratories.[55]

In Greece, Fleming was equally revered and his reputation there is tied in with the troubled postwar history of that fragile cradle of democracy. Unlike Spain, where penicillin came too late for use in the Spanish Civil War, Greece was to see the benefits of antibiotics during its civil war, which broke out with the liberation of the country in 1944 and then was reignited in 1947. The importance of penicillin in the treatment of military casualties and civilian victims of civil war was honoured by the conferring on both Fleming and his Greek wife of the title of Honorary Chairman of the Medical Committee for Orphans in Greece in recognition of the humanitarian benefits of penicillin, which helped the Orphans in Greece Foundation with the rehabilitation of war-injured children.[56]

His fame in Greece was further enhanced through his second wife, who became something of a national heroine for her resistance to the junta of the Colonels in 1967.[57] Once her work had been completed in arranging Fleming's papers and without her husband to bind her to her adopted country, she began to consider the possibility of a return to her native Greece. The Wright Fleming Institute was breaking free of its origins under Wright and seeking to build a scientific profile that did not merely rest on Fleming's reputation. It was an atmosphere in which Lady Fleming no longer felt as comfortable as she had done in her husband's time and in her early widowhood.[58] In 1965, she deposited some of the Fleming papers with the British Library and began to make her own arrangements to return to Athens.

Her return home in March 1967 was not the best timing for as outspoken a lady as Amalia Fleming. Five weeks later a coup d'état took place installing the right-wing junta of the Colonels. Amalia was no stranger to resistance to dictatorships. She had been imprisoned for resistance activities against the German occupying forces during the Second World War, but it was her opposition to the junta on humanitarian grounds that was to seal her reputation in her homeland. After attempting in 1971 to help the escape from prison of a young poet, Alexandros Panagoulis, condemned to death for an attempt on the life of the Prime Minister, George Papadopoulis, she was arrested. As the widow of Sir Alexander Fleming, she had some protection from the treatment usually meted out by the Greek military police to most opponents of the regime. Such considerations did not stop her from being deprived of sleep and water, threatened with torture and, more bizarrely, even being offered a ministerial position if she would support the junta. Sentenced by a military court to sixteen months' imprisonment, she refused to consider the possibility of deportation to England and learned new skills from her fellow prisoners, such as how to pick locks. An appeal was made in a letter to *The Times* from prominent British scientists appealing for clemency 'because of her very special position as the widow of Sir Alexander Fleming' and her diabetic condition. She was soon released on medical grounds but stripped of her Greek citizenship and unwillingly deported to Britain.[59] After the fall of the junta in 1974, she returned to Greece a national heroine and later served as a Greek delegate to the Council of Europe.

Amalia's ambition on returning home had been to set up a research institute devoted to molecular biology and medical research in her husband's memory. The Hellenic Foundation for Basic Medical Research Alexander Fleming was established in 1965, funded entirely by the Greek government apart from £600 that Amalia as founder had donated.[60] Despite funding from the royal government, there was to be no state interference in the running of Amalia's institute, which Ernst Chain thought would give her 'a very great deal of personal satisfaction and give your life a new meaning'.[61] In 1969 land was donated at Vari in Attika for the building of a research institute, but Amalia's political activities brought progress to a halt. On her return from exile, she had to begin again. After her death in 1986, the grandly named foundation had little to its name but the land it owned and was kept alive by her friends.[62] For a time there were problems with drug dealers occupying the site, but a new state-sponsored initiative offered hopes of realising Amalia's dream in 1995 when the Biomedical Sciences Research Centre Alexander Fleming was set up and given the buildings at Vari. The aim of the centre, which began operation in 1997, was to develop modern cutting-edge research in the biomedical sciences in Greece.[63]

Amalia Fleming's effort to get a research institute established in Greece in her husband's memory was paralleled by the fate of a Fleming Memorial Fund launched in Britain. At the time of Fleming's death, he had been a keen and active supporter of the Centenary Appeal for St Mary's Hospital Medical School. At once the question had arisen of launching a nationwide appeal in his memory and the medical school had decided to sideline its own fundraising venture, with the full support of its Patron, Queen Elizabeth the Queen Mother.[64] The Duke of Edinburgh, who in the early 1950s was forging a role for himself as a patron of British science in the way the Prince Consort had done a century earlier,[65] was recruited to head the fund and presided over a meeting held at Buckingham Palace attended by representatives of universities, learned societies and professional bodies.[66] The medical and scientific establishment gave approval to the fund, but it was opposed by Florey and his colleagues, who might have supported a 'Penicillin Memorial Research Fund' but would not even hear of an appeal bearing Fleming's name let alone the erection of a statue to him.[67] It was a debacle and Prince Philip wisely withdrew before he could be drawn into the embarrassing dispute.[68] It was not until over two years later in 1958 that Florey finally agreed to support a Fleming Memorial Fund, realising to his chagrin that the brand name of Fleming was too valuable not to use.[69] The initial idea that the beneficiaries of the appeal should be the Wright Fleming Institute and William Dunn School was unacceptable to Chain[70] and when it was eventually launched in March 1961 it took the form of an international appeal to support medical research in general with grants to existing institutions for specific purposes.[71] The moment for the appeal had passed and the results were not as lucrative as had been anticipated by the time it was wound up in 1963.[72] Marotta, president of the Italian branch of the appeal, considered that penicillin 'had lost the glamour it had fifteen years ago as the revolutionary medical discovery of our times, but is now considered a common and everyday drug'.[73]

The Wright Fleming Institute was also changing at this time and Fleming's name was no longer so honoured at the scene of his labours. There was a conscious reaction against the old Inoculation Department ethos and the Fleming connections were downplayed as the institute repositioned itself as a modern forward-looking research centre.[74] Moreover, vaccine production, the main prop of the institute in Fleming's day, was no longer viable on such a small scale, and in 1967 it had no choice for survival but to merge with St Mary's Hospital Medical School.[75] With increased academic vigour in the 1960s, the past no longer seemed to matter and indeed was seen as a block to modernity. It was to be another twenty years before interest in Fleming at St Mary's slowly reawakened with exhibitions and associated conferences to mark the fiftieth anniversary of the discovery of penicillin in 1978 and the centenary of Fleming's birth in 1981. Nevertheless, it was not until a time of uncertainty in the 1990s that interest in Fleming really took off again at the institution with which his name was so closely associated. There was a need to find security in a sense of identity rooted in the past as the hospital went through the trauma of National Health Service reorganisation and St Mary's Hospital Medical School faced oblivion following its incorporation into Imperial College Faculty of Medicine. The Fleming legend was re-embraced as a symbol of community pride. A museum was opened in 1993 featuring Fleming's laboratory as a permanent memorial and that same year a bas-relief was commissioned for the exterior of the Medical School buildings bearing the defiant assertion 'Fleming discovered penicillin'.[76]

It was not as if the general public needed to be reminded. People had never forgotten Fleming's name in the wider world. When the approach of a new millennium concentrated minds on the achievements of the old, it was inevitable that the discovery of penicillin should be seen as one of the defining moments of the twentieth century. Although he was not the only person to play an important part in engineering the great antibiotic revolution in medicine, it was Fleming who was remembered as the 'Penicillin Man'. Readers of the *Scotsman* voted for Fleming as Scot of the century.[77] The Alexander Fleming Laboratory Museum was declared an International Historic Chemical Landmark in November 1999 by the American Chemical Society.[78] Readers of *The Times* voted for penicillin as a national millennium treasure in 2000.[79] This fame continues on a roll and shows no sign of abating in the twenty-first century.

Some fifty years after his death, Fleming's name remains a universal household word.[80] His discovery is the best known of medicines, its name used as synonymous with antibiotics by the general public for whom there is little distinction between one antibiotic and another. Even in an age when fears that the antibiotic age in medicine may be no more than an interlude in the savage, ever-present war between man and microbes, the blessings of penicillin and the other antibiotics are still appreciated. Penicillin has made a real difference to the lives of all of us. No longer are the joys of the birth of a baby in the developed world overlain by common fears that the mother may die of puerperal sepsis. No one can expect to die as the result of an infected scratch from a rosebush or a simple cut. As the discoverer of this miracle drug, Fleming is still seen as the benefactor of humanity even in these more cynical times when science can be seen as frightening rather than a blessing and doctors are no longer seen as lofty Olympians whose judgement is not to be challenged. Representing the kindly and humane face of medical advance, Fleming remains on his pedestal as a hero of medicine. Yet it was all down to a simple chance observation, as he himself freely admitted. This good luck had made him perhaps the best-known and most revered doctor in the world.

Honours Awarded to Sir Alexander Fleming

The worldwide impact of the discovery of penicillin was phenomenal and reflected in the numerous honours Fleming received as the discoverer of penicillin beginning in 1943 and continuing right up to his death and in one case beyond. Fleming himself was characteristically just as proud of his 1903 medal from the London Scottish Regiment Swimming Club, his 1908 *Daily Telegraph* Rifle Club Medal, his 1909 Territorial Force Efficiency Medal and even the West Middlesex Golf Club monthly medal he won in 1914. These minor honours, along with his academic achievements including the University of London Gold Medal and the St Mary's Hospital Medical School Cheadle Gold Medal in Clinical Medicine, both of which he won in 1908, pale in significance alongside the awards that came as the result of penicillin, yet to Fleming they were just as valued as the honours listed below. The honours may have been showered upon him, but he resisted inflating his own importance to himself.

Fellow, Royal Society, 11 March 1943

Award of Distinction, American Pharmaceutical Manufacturers Association, 13 December 1943

Foreign Associate, Royal Physiographic Society of Lund, Sweden, 8 March 1944

Honorary Fellow, Royal College of Physicians of England, 21 May 1944

Knight Batchelor, 4 July 1944

John Scott Medal and Prize, City Guild of Philadelphia, 21 July 1944

Charles Mickle Fellowship, University of Toronto for year 1944, 10 December 1944

First Lister Memorial Lecturer, Society of Chemical Industry for 1944

Robert Campbell Orator, Ulster Medical Society, 1944

Honorary Freeman and Liveryman, Dyers' Company of the City of London, 2 May 1945

Freedom of Borough of Paddington, 17 May 1945

Honorary D. Sc., University of Princeton, 13 June 1945

Honorary D. Sc., University of Pennsylvania, 18 June 1945

Honorary S. Sc., Harvard University, 28 June 1945

Honorary Fellow, Medical Chirurgical Society, Montreal, 9 July 1945

Cameron Prize in Practical Therapeutics, University of Edinburgh, 11 July 1945

Humanitarian Award of Variety Clubs of America, 25 July 1945

Medal of Honour, Military Medicine Service, France, 31 August 1945

Commander of the Order of Public Health, France, 5 September 1945

Commander of Legion d'Honneur, France, 18 September 1945

Honorary MD, University of Rome, 18 September 1945

Honorary MD, University of Brussels, 6 October 1945

Honorary Member, Philadelphia College of Pharmacy and Science, 5 November 1945

Honorary Member, Jutland Medical Society, 18 November 1945

Honorary MD, University of Louvain, 30 November 1945

Nobel Laureate in Physiology or Medicine, 10 December 1945 (jointly with Sir Howard Florey and Dr Ernst Chain)

Honorary MD, University of Paris, 15 December 1945

Medal of Honour of Canadian Pharmaceutical Manufacturers, 1945

President, Society of General Microbiology, 1945

Honorary D.Sc., University of Durham, 1945

Honorary Member, Royal Society of New Zealand, 1945

Honorary MD, University of Liège, 1945

Medal of City of Liège, 1945

Moxon Medal, Royal College of Physicians of England, 1945

Corresponding Member, National Society of Natural Sciences and Mathematics, Cherbourg, 1945

Honorary Member, Royal Medical Society of Edinburgh, 1945

Honorary Fellow, Jutland Medical Society, 1945

Cutter Lecturer, Harvard University, 1945

Foreign Associate, Academy of Medicine, Paris, 1945

Honorary MD, University of Vienna, 1945

Honorary Member, Society of American Bacteriologists, 1945

Honorary Award of Schroeder Foundation, 1945

Corresponding Member, Academy of Sciences, Institute of France, 11 February 1946

Member, Pontifical Academy of Sciences, 12 March 1946

Honorary Professor, University of Brazil, 10 April 1946

Fellow, Royal Danish Academy of Sciences and Letters, 12 April 1946

Honorary Member, Academy of Medicine, Buenos Aires, 6 June 1946

Honorary Member, Pathological Section, Royal Society of Medicine, 2 July 1946

Honorary D.Sc., University of Dublin, 3 July 1946

Honorary MD, University of Athens, 6 July 1946

Honorary D.Sc., Queen's University, Belfast, 10 July 1946

Honorary Member, College of Surgeons of Brazil, 5 September 1946

Honorary Member, Academy of Medicine, Turin, 4 October 1946

Freedom of Burgh of Darvel, 26 October 1946

Gold Medal, Royal College of Surgeons of England, 14 November 1946

Honorary Fellow, Institute of Medical Laboratory Technology, 1946

Harben Gold Medal, Royal Institute of Public Health and Hygiene, 1946

Knight of Mark Twain, USA, 1946

Honorary Member, Philadelphia College of Pharmacy and Science, 1946

Honorary Fellow, Royal College of Physicians of Edinburgh, 1946

Medal in Therapeutics, Worshipful Society of Apothecaries, London, 1946

Albert Gold Medal, Royal Society of Arts, 1946

Foreign Honorary Member, Royal Academy of Medicine, Brussels, 1946

Honorary President, Centre of Information and Study of Antibiotics, Milan, 1946

Honorary Member, Academy of Medicine, Brazil, 1946

Honorary Member, Medical Society of Lombardy, 1946

Honorary Member, Shut-Ins Association of America, 1946

Citation of Order of the Purple Heart, USA, 11 May 1947 (collected on Fleming's behalf by his friend the actress and broadcaster Bebe Daniels)

Honorary Fellow, Greek Surgical Society, 26 May 1947

Gold Medal, Royal Society of Medicine, 17 June 1947

Honorary LLD, St Andrew's University, 4 September 1947

Member, Lynceorum Academy, Rome, 5 October 1947

Medal for Merit, USA, 13 October 1947

Corresponding Member, Société Philomatique, Paris 1946

Honorary Member, Society of Arts, Vienna, 1947

Honorary Member, Royal Society of Edinburgh, 1947

Fellow of Academie Septentrionale, France 1947

Member of Athenaeum, London, 19 January 1948

Honorary MD, Charles University, Prague, awarded 8 April 1948 but

actually conferred posthumously on 7 April 1993

Honorary MD, University of Graz, 3 May 1948

Honorary D.Sc., University of London, 26 May 1948

Honorary Member, Royal Academy of Medicine, Barcelona, 3 June 1948

Honorary President, Medical Society of Hospitals of Barcelona, 5 June 1948

Honorary Member, Spanish Society of Hygiene, 8 June 1948

Honorary Member, Royal Academy of Medicine, Seville, 8 June 1948

Gold Medal, Royal Academy of Medicine, Seville, 8 June 1948

Honorary Member, Ateneo, Seville, 8 June 1948

Grand Cross of Alphonso X el Sabio, Spain, 11 June 1948

Honorary D.Sc., University of Madrid, 12 June 1948

Honorary Member, Royal Academy of Medicine, Madrid, 13 June 1948

Emeritus Professor of Bacteriology, University of London, 1 October 1948

Addingham Medal, University of Leeds, 1948

Freedom of Borough of Chelsea, 16 March 1949

Honorary Member, Institute of the History of Medicine, Brazil, 17 May 1949

Actonian Prize, July 1949

Freedom of City of Verona, 12 July 1949

Grand Cross of the Order of Phoenix, Greece, 16 September 1949

Honorary D.Sc., University of Bristol, 19 October 1949

Honorary Life Member, 4-H Clubs, USA, 1949

Chief Doy-Gei-Taun ('Maker of Great Medicine'), Kiowa Tribe, USA, 1949

Grand Cross of Order of Chypre, 1949

Past Grand Warden, United Grand Lodge of England, 1949

Permanent Honorary Member, Caledonian Club, 1949

Honorary Member, Savage Club, 1949

Honorary Member, Society for the Study of Infectious Diseases and Parasitology, Italy, 1949

Honorary D.Sc., National University of Ireland, 3 July 1950

Honorary Member, National Society for the Prevention of Blindness, 21 July 1950

Gold Medal, American College of Chest Physicians, 1950

Member, Royal International Academy of Parnassus, 16 February 1951

Honorary Member, Pakistan Medical Association, 8 April 1951

Honorary Member, National Institute of Sciences of India, 1951

Sir Devaprasad Sarvadhikary Gold Medal, University of Calcutta, 1951

Lord Rector, University of Edinburgh, installed 19 February 1952

Cross of Officer of Merito Insigni, Belgian National Foundation of Charity, 12 May 1952

Honorary MD, University of Salonika, 8 October 1952

Honorary Member, Greek Society of Paediatricians, 10 October 1952

Honorary Citizen of Salonika, 16 October 1952

Honorary President, Medical Society of Salonika, 22 October 1952

Gold Medal of Athens, 31 October 1952

Freedom of Athens, 31 October 1952

Foreign Member, Academy of Athens, 31 October 1952

Honorary Citizen of Kastoria, October 1952

Honorary President of Greek Society of Microbiology and Hygiene, 7 November 1952

Honorary Member, French Society of Medical Biology, 1952

Foreign Member, Royal Netherlands Academy of Sciences and Letters, 1952

Honorary Member, Medical Society of Havana, 5 February 1953

Honorary Member, Cuban Society of Clinical Pathology, 10 April 1953

Honorary Member, Royal Society of British Sculptors, 16 April 1953

Honorary Member, Cuban Good Neighbour Foundation, 20 April 1953

Honorary Member, National Pharmaceutical College of Cuba, 21 April 1953

Honorary Member of Association of Medical Students, University of Havana, 23 April 1953

Grand Cross of Order of Honour and Merit of the Cuban Red Cross, 23 April 1953

Grand Commander, Order of Carlos Finlay, Cuba, 23 April 1953

Honorary Professor, University of Havana, 28 April 1953

Honorary Member, National Medical College of Cuba, 28 April 1953

Honorary Member, National College of Pharmacists, Cuba, April 1953

Grand Lodge Medal for distinguished achievement, Grand Lodge of Free and Accepted Masons of the State of New Jersey, 5 May 1953

Honorary Chairman of Medical Committee for Orphans in Greece, 28 May 1953 (awarded jointly with Amalia Fleming)

Honorary Member, Academy of José de Alencar, Brazil, 7 June 1953

Honorary Member, Botanical Society of Cuba, 29 September 1953

Honorary Member, Brazilian Association of Ex-combatants, 24 October 1953

Honorary DCL, University of Edinburgh, November 1953

Honorary Member, Copenhagen Medical Society, 1953

Honorary Citizen of Mikonos, 1953

Foreign Associate, Academy of Sciences of the Institute of France, 15 February 1954

Honorary D.Sc, University of Utah, 27 March 1954

Honorary Member, American Academy of General Practice, March 1954

Commissioned Kentucky Colonel, 7 April 1954

Award for Merit, University of Louisville, Kentucky, 13 April 1954

Honorary Member, Alpha Omega Alpha Fraternity, University of Oklahoma, April 1954

Honorary Member, Medical Society, Ribeirao Preto, 4 May 1954

Honorary Member, Academy of Medicine, São Paolo, 11 May 1954

Order of the Catapult (Ordem de Estilingue), Ribeirao Preto, 11 May 1954

Honorary Citizen of City of São Paolo, 11 May 1954

Honorary Citizen of Ribeirao Preto, 11 May 1954

Honorary Member of Central Academy XXV, Rio de Janeiro, 13 May 1953

Honorary MD, University of São Paolo, 13 May 1954

Honorary Member, Medical Association of Santos, 14 May 1954

Honorary Member, Paulista School of Medicine, May 1954

Honorary Citizen of State of São Paolo, May 1954

Honorary Member, Academy of Pharmacology and Odontology, São Paolo, May 1954

Honorary Member, Central Academy, Pereiro Barretto, May 1954

Citation from University of São Paolo, May 1954

Honorary Fellow, Royal Society of Medicine, 20 July 1954

Honorary Citizen, Bordeaux, 15 November 1954

Honorary MD, University of Bordeaux, 15 November 1954

Honorary Councillor, St Emilion, November 1954

Commander, 'Compagnons du Bontemps Medoc', November 1954

Freeman of Company of Barbers of London, 7 December 1954

Diploma , International Federation of Arts, Letters and Sciences, 1954

Vice-President Emeritus, Royal Sanitary Society, 1954

Honorary doctorate in veterinary medicine, University of Vienna, 10 March 1955

Glossary

6-APA (6-aminopenicillanic acid) molecular nucleus of penicillin molecule

acetone inflammable clear liquid used as solvent

acridine antiseptic

actinomycetes family of fungus-like bacteria from which many modern antibiotics are derived

adsorbent a solid that binds gases or dissolved substances to its surface, such as charcoal, which adsorbs gases, or kaolin, which adsorbs bacterial toxins

aerobe bacteria requiring oxygen to survive

agar a gelatine derived from seaweed used as a nutrient in solid bacterial culture media

amoxycillin antibiotic used against respiratory tract infections

amyl acetate inflammable solvent smelling of pears used in penicillin production process

anaerobe bacteria that will not grow in the presence of oxygen

antibiotic substance produced by one living micro-organism, such as a mould or bacterium, which kills or prevents the growth of other living micro-organisms, such as infection-causing bacteria

antibody protein that stimulates immunity against a particular infection

antiseptic chemical substance that destroys or inhibits the growth of micro-organisms

antitoxin an antibody that neutralises a toxic substance, produced either by the body as a response to invasion by toxin-producing bacteria or by the injection of a toxoid

Aspergillus family of fungi found in soil, manure and on grains

assay test chemically the purity of a substance

autoclave equipment for sterilisation using steam pressure

bacillus (plural bacilli) aerobic, Gram-positive, rod-shaped bacteria

bacteriophage a virus that acts as a parasite on bacteria

bacterium (plural bacteria) single-celled micro-organism

beta-lactam ring molecule that fuses with a thiazolidine ring to form the nucleus of penicillin

beta-lactamase enzyme capable of inactivating penicillin

benzyl also known as phenylmethyl, a radical or group of atoms in a chemical compound used in the production of benzyl penicillin

benzyl penicillin also known as 'penicillin G', one of the first penicillins to be developed

blood serum fluid that is exuded when blood clots

broad spectrum antibiotic antibiotic that acts against a wide range of infections

Carrel–Dakin solution antiseptic

carbolic acid antiseptic

carotid artery principal artery in neck

cellular theory of immunity idea developed by Elie Metchnikoff whereby bacteria were swallowed by the white blood cells in the process of phagocytosis

cephalosporin group of antibiotics initially discovered by Giuseppe Brozu in sewage off the coast of Sardinia

chemotherapy the use of specific chemical agents to treat disease in the human body

clavulanate substance used in connection with the antibiotic amoxycillin to inhibit the enzyme penicillinase produced by penicillin-resistant bacteria

clostridium welchii Gram-positive anaerobic bacillus that can cause gas gangrene

coccus spherical-shaped bacteria

complement fixation test specific blood test for the diagnosis of sexually transmitted infections

corn-steep liquor by-product of corn wet-milling process that was found to be an effective culture medium for the growth of penicillin

Corynebacterium acnes bacillus that causes acne

culture growth of bacteria in laboratory conditions

culture medium nutritive jellies used to grow bacteria in a petri dish

culture plate round dish used for the growth of bacteria, also known as petri dish

Czapek–Dox medium culture medium containing salts and glucose

endocarditis inflammation of inner lining of heart

enzyme soluble protein produced by living cells that acts as a catalyst

erysipelas infectious disease with streptococcal inflammation of the skin and fever

eusol antiseptic

ferment older name for enzyme

flagellum (plural **flagellae**) fine hair-like appendage of some bacteria capable of lashing movements

flavine antiseptic

gas gangrene wound infection caused by the bacillus *clostridium welchii*

gentian violet antiseptic

glucose dextrose or grape sugar

gonococcus bacterium that causes gonorrhoea

Gram stain a stain or dye developed by H.C.J. Gram and used to differentiate between bacteria with differing characteristics. Gram-positive bacteria retain the blue dye but Gram-negative strains are unaffected by it.

haemolysis disintegration of red blood cells

Haemophilus influenzae bacillus also known as Pfeiffer's bacillus after its discoverer Richard Pfeiffer, bacterium once thought to be the cause of influenza

humoral theory of immunity idea supported by Robert Koch, Emil Adolph von Behring and Paul Ehrlich that blood serum had bactericidal power

immunology study of immune system

inoculation injection of vaccine into human body; **or** introduction of micro-organisms into a culture medium

iodine antiseptic

iodoform antiseptic

lactose milk sugar, used in baby foods

leucocyte white blood corpuscles

lobar pneumonia pneumonia with inflammation of the lung

lysis dissolving of cells or bacteria

lysozyme an enzyme that dissolves bacteria, discovered by Fleming in November 1921

M and B 693 popular name for sulphapyridine manufactured by the firm of May and Baker

MRSA (methicillin-resistant *Staphylococcus aureus*) superbug resistant to most antibiotics

Malta Fever now known as brucellosis, infection causing fever in man transmitted through contact with cattle and goats, studied by David Bruce in Malta

medical flat flat-bottomed flask in which bacteria or fungi were grown

meningococcus bacterium that causes meningitis

methicillin a semi-synthetic penicillin

Micrococcus lysodeikticus bacterium discovered by Fleming against which lysozyme is most effective, now known as *Micrococcus luteus*

mycologist mould specialist

nucleus inner part of a cell

Opsonic Index a measurement of the ability of phagocytes to swallow up bacteria and other foreign bodies, devised by Almroth Wright

opsonin an antibody that makes cells more susceptible to phagocytosis

osteomyelitis inflammation in marrow of bone

Oxford unit standard measurement for estimating the purity and strength of penicillin devised by Norman Heatley at the University of Oxford

para-aminobenzoic acid chemical compound similar to sulphanilamide that acts as nutrient for certain bacteria

pathogen agent that causes disease

pathogenic disease-producing

penicillin the first antibiotic

penicillinase enzyme that destroys penicillin

penicillium genus of moulds, including *Penicillium notatum* and *Penicillium chrysogenum*, that produce penicillin

peptone agar type of solid culture medium used for growing fungi

peritonitis inflammation of the membrane lining the abdomen and pelvic cavities

petri dish round plate used for the culture of bacteria, devised by R.J. Petri, also known as a culture plate

Pfeiffer's bacillus bacterium named after its discoverer Richard Pfeiffer, also known as *Haemophilus influenzae bacillus*, and once thought to be the cause of influenza

phagocyte a cell capable of engulfing bacteria

phagocytosis swallowing up of bacteria by phagocytes

phenylacetic acid a chemical used to produce a precursor of penicillin

picric acid a chemical that precipitates proteins

pneumococcus a bacterium arranged in pairs that causes lobar pneumonia

polysaccharide carbohydrate such as starch and cellulose

precursor a substance that acts as a forerunner from which another is formed by chemical processes

prontosil sulphonamide drug originating in the red dye prontosil

Sabouraud's medium a culture medium used for the growth of fungi

salvarsan drug developed by Paul Ehrlich, also known as Compound 606, which was the first effective modern treatment for syphilis

Seitz filter used to filter liquids through a small disc of asbestos fibres

semi-synthetic penicillins artificially modified penicillin where the original side chain has been detached from the nucleus and a new side chain added

septicaemia blood-poisoning

serum fluid that is exuded when blood clots

side chain part of chemical structure of molecule attached to the nucleus

slide cell technique for studying bacteria under the microscope devised by Almroth Wright allowing for easy comparison between the contents of each compartment in the space between two microscopic slides divided by strips of Vaseline-smeared paper into four very thin cells

spirochaete spiral-shaped bacterium; *Spirochaeta pallida* (now known as *Treponema pallidum*) causes syphilis

staphylococcus bacteria that cluster together and can cause abscesses and boils

streptococcus bacteria that form chains and can cause scarlatina, erysipelas, tonsillitis, endocarditis and wound infections

streptomycete fungus mainly found in the soil

streptomycin second of the major antibiotics to be developed by Selman Waksman and often used for the treatment of tuberculosis

Streptothorix thread-like bacterium

sucrose a sugar derived from sugar cane, sugar beet and maple syrup

sulphanilamide antibacterial drug first developed by Gerhard Domagk

Sulphapyridine sulphonamide drug also known as M and B 693

sulphonamides group of antibacterial drugs derived from sulphanilamide

sychosis barbae infection of beard follicles

thiazolidine ring molecule made up of a ring of one nitrogen, one sulphur, three carbon and five hydrogen atoms; it fuses with a beta-lactam ring to form the nucleus of penicillin

titration analysis of strength of concentration of a solution by volume

toxin product of a bacterium that kills or damages cells

toxoid a toxin altered in such a way that it has lost its poisonous properties but can still stimulate the production of antibodies

vaccine therapy method of treatment developed by Almroth Wright to treat disease with vaccines as well as prevent them

vancomycin strong antibiotic used to treat staphylococcal infections in which other antibiotics have been rendered ineffective

Wassermann Reaction test complement fixation blood test for detection of syphilis developed by Augustus Wassermann

Wright's capsules devised by Almroth Wright to separate blood cells from serum

Notes

Chapter One

1 F. Johnson, 'Going into Science', *IMLS Gazette* (December 1991), 655.
2 V.D. Allison, 'Personal Recollections of Sir Almroth Wright and Sir Alexander Fleming', *Ulster Medical Journal*, 43 (1974), 89.
3 Private information from John Crawford Adams, remembering a conversation with Merlin Pryce. Pryce was to emphasise in correspondence with Ronald Hare in St Mary's Hospital Archives that Fleming was responsible for the discovery.
4 BL Add. MS 56215, D.M. Pryce.
5 A. Fleming, 'Penicillin', *Journal of the Royal Naval Medical Service*, 31/2 (April 1945), 75.
6 BL Add. MS 56218, D.M. Pryce.
7 BL Add. MS 56209, original penicillin culture plate, 1928.
8 R. Hare, *The Birth of Penicillin* (1970), pp. 54–5.
9 BL Add. MS 56215, Frederick Ridley.
10 E.B. Chain, 'A Short History of the Penicillin Discovery, from Fleming's Observations in 1929 to the Present Time', in J. Parascandola (ed.), *History of Antibiotics* (1980), p. 17.
11 G. Macfarlane, *Alexander Fleming, the Man and the Myth* (1984), p. 115, quoting from his own correspondence with Vivian Pitchford.
12 R. Cruickshank, 'Sir Alexander Fleming', *Dictionary of National Biography* (1971).
13 BL Add. MS 56217, Anthony M. Ritchie.
14 Hare, *The Birth of Penicillin*, pp. 54–5.
15 Biomedical Research Centre Alexander Fleming, Vari, Greece, Fleming's passport, no. 46827, issued 20 October 1944.
16 BL Add. MS 56217, Anthony M. Ritchie.
17 BL Add. MS 56217, James Jackson; Biomedical Research Centre Alexander Fleming, Vari, Greece, Fleming's press cuttings, Sheila Wood, 'Whose Who and Why' (source of cutting otherwise unrecorded): 'When Britain's small, studious, soft-spoken scientist, whose searching blue eyes seem to be looking into the invisible world about us, of which ordinary men are unaware, starts playing about in his laboratory, something which will work to the good of all mankind is likely to be discovered.'
18 BL Add. MS 56215, E.J.W. Todd.
19 BL Add. MS 56217, D.M. Pryce.
20 BL Add. MS 56217, V.D. Allison.
21 BL Add. MS 56217, Anthony M. Ritchie.
22 BL Add. MS 56215, John Cameron.

23 BL Add. MS 56216, Dan Stratful.

24 BL Add. MS 56215, E.J.W. Todd (widow of E.W. Todd).

25 Johnson, 'Going into Science', 654–5.

26 BL Add. MS 56216, Dan Stratful.

27 K. Brown, 'The Clarence Wing Story', *St Mary's Hospital Gazette*, 98/3 (October 1992), 40–2.

28 BL Add. MS 56215, John McKeen.

29 A. Fleming in *Remarks Made at the Dinner for Sir Alexander Fleming, Mayo Foundation House* (16 July 1945), pp. 9–10.

30 A. Fleming, 'The Staphylococci', in Medical Research Council, *A System of Bacteriology in Relation to Medicine* (1929), vol. 2, pp. 11–26.

31 A.E. Wright, quoted in J. Freeman, 'Almroth Wright, Philosopher and Pathologist', *St Mary's Hospital Gazette*, 58/4 (1952), 94.

32 BL Add. MS 56162, notebook, 1924–32.

33 J.W. Bigger, C.R. Boland and R.A.Q. O'Meara, 'Variant Colonies of *Staphylococcus aureus*', *Journal of Pathology and Bacteriology*, 30 (1927), 260–9.

34 A. Fleming, 'Penicillin', 75.

35 Hare, *The Birth of Penicillin*, pp. 65–80.

36 *Smiths Weekly*, 29 November 1941.

37 *Evening Standard*, 3 March 1943.

38 'As my laboratory window overlooks a public house it may well be that a country traveller brought it along', Fleming quoted in *Daily Mirror*, 18 May 1945.

39 BL Add. MS 56217, Arthur Hayward.

40 Hare, *The Birth of Penicillin*, pp. 83–7; see also D.B. Colquhoun, *World Medicine*, 29 January 1975,

p. 41, in support of the idea that the culture plate had not been incubated.

41 A.W. Frankland, 'Perspective: Penicillin History and Allergy', *Immunology and Allergy Practice*, 14 (October 1992), 367–9.

42 Examples at random include Macfarlane, *Alexander Fleming: the Man and the Myth*; D.B. Kell, 'Forces, Fluxes and the Control of Microbial Growth and Metabolism: the Twelfth Fleming Lecture', *Journal of General Microbiology*, 133 (1987), 1651–5; N. Russell, 'A Scientist's Personality Can Be the Key to his Work', *Times Higher Education Supplement*, 25 September 1987; J. Waller, *Fabulous Science* (2002).

43 A. Fleming, 'Success, Rectorial Address', *Student* (Edinburgh University Magazine), 47/8 (1952), 330.

44 'Dans les champs de l'observation le hazard ne favorise que les esprits préparés', address given at the inauguration of the Faculty of Science, University of Lille, 7 December 1854.

Chapter Two

1 A. Fleming, 'Louis Pasteur', lecture delivered at the Science Museum, 10 April 1947 to inaugurate the Pasteur Exhibition, *British Medical Journal*, 1 (19 April 1947), 517.

2 René Vallery-Radot, *La Vie de Pasteur* (1906); R.J. Dubos, *Louis Pasteur: Freelancer of Science* (1951); Patrice Debré, *Louis Pasteur* (1994).

3 W.D. Foster, *History of Medical Bacteriology and Immunology*

(1970); F.C. Cartwright, *Development of Modern Surgery* (1967).

4 *Lancet* (8 August 1896), 429. See also F.B. Smith, *The People's Health 1830–1910* (1979), for a consideration of infection and the experience of patients in nineteenth-century Britain.

5 e.g. John Rowland, *The Penicillin Man* (1957).

6 Census returns, 1881, 1891.

7 Robert Fleming, *Sir Alexander Fleming* (1957), pp. 6–7, in the possession of Dr Robert Fleming. Further copies are deposited at the British Library, National Library of Scotland and Dick Institute, Kilmarnock.

8 *Ibid.*, pp. 4, 6.

9 BL Add. MS 56121, biographical information for the Pontifical Academy, *c.* 1946.

10 Robert Fleming, *Alexander Fleming*, p. 8.

11 BL Add. MS 56218, William Morton.

12 Robert Fleming, *Alexander Fleming*, p. 17.

13 *Ibid.*, p. 12,

14 *Ibid.*, p. 16.

15 L.J. Ludovici, *Alexander Fleming, Discoverer of Penicillin* (1952), p. 24.

16 BL Add. MS 56222, letter from Marion Stirling, 12 November 1945.

17 BL Add. MS 56218, William Morton.

18 Robert Fleming, *Alexander Fleming*, p. 13.

19 *Ibid.*, pp. 20–1.

20 BL Add. MS 56121, biographical information for the Pontifical Academy, *c.* 1946.

21 Ludovici, *Alexander Fleming*, pp. 22–4; A. Maurois, *The Life of Sir Alexander Fleming, Discoverer of Penicillin* (1959), p. 24.

22 BL Add. MS 56217, James Jackson (the boy who collided with Alec Fleming and fractured his nose); Robert Fleming, *Alexander Fleming*, pp. 22–3; Maurois, *Life of Fleming*, p. 23.

23 Kilmarnock Academy Admissions Register, 28 August 1894.

24 BL Add. MS 56215, Agnes Smith.

25 BL Add. MS 56218, Revd Hamilton Dunnett.

26 Robert Fleming, *Alexander Fleming*, p. 22.

27 G. Macfarlane, *Alexander Fleming: the Man and the Myth* (1984), p. 17.

28 Robert Fleming, *Alexander Fleming*, pp. 34–8.

29 *Ibid.*, p. 33.

30 *Ibid.*, pp. 35–6.

31 *Ibid.*, pp. 36–7.

32 *Ibid.*, pp. 38–9.

33 *Ibid.*, pp. 39–40.

34 *London Scottish Regimental Gazette*, 5 (1900), 164.

35 *London Scottish Regimental Gazette*, 13 (1908), 148. In a territorial army reorganisation of 1908, Fleming's regimental number changed from 6392 to 37 but he remained in H Company.

36 *London Scottish Regimental Gazette*, 49 (1944), 132.

37 *London Scottish Regimental Gazette*, 18 (1913), 88.

38 BL Add. MS 56216, G.W.B. James.

39 *London Scottish Regimental Gazette*, 52 (1947), 60.

40 BL Add. MS 56215, Sandy Ross.

41 *London Scottish Regimental Gazette*, 49 (1944), 132; *London*

Scottish Regimental Gazette (1947), 60.

42 Robert Fleming, *Alexander Fleming*, pp. 40–1.

43 *Philadelphia Inquirer*, 17 July 1945. This legend is one that will not go away, however often it is refuted.

44 BL Add. MS 56115, letter from A. Gratia, 9 November 1945; letter to A. Gratia, 14 November 1945.

45 Robert Fleming, *Alexander Fleming*, pp. 41–2.

46 *Ibid.*, pp. 42–3. Robert also refers to his brother's use of rhyme to help him remember facts: 'If you want the bowels to go | Try rhubarb, ginger MgO | But if you want a regular starter | try jalap, ginger, cream of tartar.'

47 St Mary's Hospital Archives, MS/AD20/2, roll of students.

48 A lithograph of 1853 shows the hospital in its full glory, although it was not until 1884 that the hospital as originally designed was completed. The lithograph sets it in an elegant milieu rather than among the warehouses and slums of the Paddington Basin.

49 Edmund Owen, 'An Address, Chiefly Retrospective', *St Mary's Hospital Gazette*, 8/10 (1902), 153. Meckel's ganglion was a difficult to find cyst.

50 D.W. Carmalt-Jones, 'Sir Almroth Edward Wright', *Lancet*, 1 (1947), 930.

51 BL Add. MS 56222. C.A. Pannett.

52 *St Mary's Hospital Gazette*, 15/1 (1909), 14.

53 University of London matriculation certificate, January examination 1902, placed in the first division,

26 February 1902, now at Biomedical Sciences Research Centre Alexander Fleming, Vari.

54 Maurois (*Life of Fleming*, p. 33) says that Fleming was taught anatomy by the flamboyant W.H. Clayton-Greene, who would illustrate his lectures with beautiful anatomical drawings in coloured chalk on the blackboard as he talked. However Clayton-Greene was only appointed to teach anatomy in 1905 after Fleming had finished attending anatomy classes.

55 First-year anatomy prize certificate of honour, 1901–2; senior prize in anatomy certificate, 1903–4, now at Biomedical Sciences Research Centre Alexander Fleming, Vari.

56 Certificate of honour for having held appointment of Prosector, 1903–4, now at Biomedical Sciences Research Centre Alexander Fleming, Vari.

57 First-year physiology prize certificate, 1901–2, now at Biomedical Sciences Research Centre Alexander Fleming, Vari.

58 Certificate of honour for prize in physiology, 1903–4, now at Biomedical Sciences Research Centre Alexander Fleming, Vari.

59 This microscope was donated to the Department of Bacteriology at St Mary's Hospital Medical School in 1978 and subsequently transferred to the Alexander Fleming Laboratory Museum in 1993.

60 A.P. Laurie, 'Roentgen Rays', *St Mary's Hospital Gazette*, 2/3 (1896), 33.

61 St Mary's Hospital Archives, prospectuses and Dean's reports of

St Mary's Hospital Medical School 1897, 1898, 1900, 1901, 1902.

62 St Mary's Hospital Archives, SM/AD 28/1, Minutes of subcommittee set up to examine financial state of the medical school, 13 December 1901–18 June 1902.

63 Certificate of honour for prize in biology, 1901–2; certificate of honour for first-year prize in physiology, 1902–3; certificate of honour for first-year prize in anatomy, 1902–3; certificate of honour for prize in organic chemistry, 1903–4; certificate of honour for senior prize in anatomy, 1903–4; certificate of honour for prize in histology, 1903–4; certificate of honour for having gained General Proficiency Scholarship in Anatomy and Physiology (including histology), 1903–4; all now at Biomedical Sciences Research Centre Alexander Fleming, Vari.

64 V.Z. Cope, *History of St Mary's Hospital Medical School* (1954), p. 179.

65 A.W. Dickson Wright, 'St Mary's Sisters of 50 year ago', *St Mary's Hospital Past and Present Nurses' League Journal*, 8 (1971), 22–7. In her memoirs of her training as a nurse at St Mary's during the First World War, Princess Arthur of Connaught recalled that Granny Casualty always left any cases she considered disgusting to the probationer nurses and that she herself had delivered her first baby in Casualty while Sister Colbeck was telling the mother that she could not give birth at St Mary's but must go to Queen Charlotte's Hospital half a mile away on Marylebone Road. See Alexandra, Duchess of Fife (Princess Arthur of Connaught), *A Nurse's Story* (1954). See also K. Brown, 'Contact with the Seamy Side of Life: a Nurse's Story', *St Mary's Hospital Gazette*, 96/10 (1990), 38–9.

66 Macfarlane (*Alexander Fleming*, p. 45) writes of medical students gaining their first experience of obstetrics on the well-equipped labour wards before being sent out on the district. He was referring to the situation when he himself trained at St Bartholomew's in the 1930s and assumed that St Mary's in 1906 was the same, which it was not, rather than looking at the available sources, which would have told him what the actual situation was at that time. St Mary's opened labour wards only in 1921 and it was not until 1961 that they could be considered well equipped for the first time, in the opinion of the obstetrician Aleck Bourne.

67 Certificate of honour for pathology, 1904–5; certificate of honour awarded for general proficiency in midwifery, pharmacology, pathology and medical jurisprudence, 1905; now at Biomedical Sciences Research Centre Alexander Fleming, Vari. Second and third general proficiency prizes and psychological medicine prizes held by the Hellenic Foundation for Basic Medical Research Alexander Fleming, Athens.

68 BL Add. MS 5616, G.W.B. James.

69 Leonard Colebrook, 'Alexander Fleming', *Biographical Memoirs of Members of the Royal Society* (1956), vol. 2, pp. 117–18.

70 University of London MB, BS degree certificate, with distinction in medicine, pathology, forensic medicine and hygiene, bracketed equal for the University of London Gold Medal, 17 June 1908, now at Biomedical Sciences Research Centre Alexander Fleming, Vari.

71 *London Scottish Regimental Gazette*, 13 (1908), 109, 114.

72 *London Scottish Regimental Gazette*, 47 (1942), 190.

Chapter Three

1 Wright's earliest biographers had both known him and were accordingly less inclined to give a full portrait of such a controversial figure, though their personal relationships with him make their books invaluable first-hand accounts in many sections: Leonard Colebrook, *Almroth Wright, Provocative Doctor* (1954); V.Z. Cope, *Almroth Wright, Founder of Modern Vaccine Therapy* (1966). Much fuller and better researched is the first independent assessment of Wright, Michael Dunnill, *The Plato of Praed Street: the Life and Times of Almroth Wright* (2000).

2 Colebrook, *Almroth Wright*, p. 56.

3 A. Maurois, *The Life of Sir Alexander Fleming, Discoverer of Penicillin* (1959), p. 36.

4 *St Mary's Hospital Gazette*, 15/6 (1909), 77.

5 Colebrook, *Almroth Wright*, p. 123.

6 *Ibid.*, p. 138.

7 *Ibid.*, p. 46.

8 J. Freeman, 'Almroth Edward Wright', *British Medical Journal*, 1 (1947), 659; Colebrook, *Almroth Wright*, p. 60.

9 A.E. Wright, 'The World's Greatest Problem', *Liverpool Daily Post*, 30 August 1905.

10 J. Freeman, 'Almroth Wright, Philosopher and Pathologist', *St Mary's Hospital Gazette*, 58/4 (1952), 94.

11 Obituary of A.E. Wright, *Lancet*, 1 (1947), 656.

12 Colebrook, *Almroth Wright*, p. 5.

13 L. Colebrook, 'Almroth Edward Wright', *Obituaries of Notable Fellows of the Royal Society* (1947), p. 297.

14 P. Hoare, *Spike Island: the Memory of a Military Hospital* (2001), pp. 164–70.

15 Wright, 'On the Application of the Serum Test to the Differential Diagnosis of Typhoid and Malta Fever', *Lancet*, 1 (1897), 656.

16 Colebrook, *Almroth Wright*, p. 30.

17 Wright, 'On Vaccination against Typhoid Fever', *British Medical Journal*, 1 (1897), 256.

18 *Lancet*, 2 (1900), 952.

19 Colebrook, *Almroth Wright*, p. 38.

20 Colebrook, 'Obituary of Almroth Edward Wright', *Lancet*, 1 (1947), 654.

21 L. Colebrook, 'Almroth Edward Wright', *British Medical Journal*, 19 September 1953.

22 Report of Advisory Board for Army Medical Services, 25 September 1902, published in *Journal of Royal Army Medical Corps*, 5 (1905), 242.

23 Karl Pearson, Letter to the Editor, *British Medical Journal*, 1 (1904), 1243, 1259, 1614, 1667.

24 St Mary's Hospital Archives, SM/AD2/4, pp. 467–8.

25 Wright, Letter to the Editor, *Lancet*, 1 (1901), 783–5, 786, 857–8.

26 A.I. Tauber and L. Chernyak, *Metchnikoff and the Origins of Immunology* (1991).

27 A.M. Silverstein, *A History of Immunology* (1989).

28 A.E. Wright, *Studies on Immunisation* (1903), p. 83.

29 G.B. Shaw, *The Doctor's Dilemma* (1913).

30 Wright, *Studies in Immunisation*, p. 102; *St Mary's Hospital Gazette*, 10/6 (1904), 89–91.

31 A.E. Wright, *Brief Survey of the History and Development of the Inoculation Department, St Mary's Hospital, W2* (1945), p. 4; Colebrook, *Almroth Wright*, p. 47.

32 St Mary's Hospital Archives, SM/AD2/5, Board of Management, 11 December 1905.

33 *Ibid.*, 22 February 1906.

34 St Mary's Hospital Archives, minutes of Inoculation Department Committee, April 1908.

35 St Mary's Hospital Archives, WF/MX/9/5, annual report of Inoculation Department, 1912; Wright, *Brief Survey*.

36 Parke Davis and Co., *Pharmacal Notes*, 9/2 (1908), 35; *Catalogue* (1911–12), pp. 215–17.

37 W.F. Bynum, *Science and the Practice of Medicine in the Nineteenth Century* (1994), pp. 158–9, 167.

38 Wai Chen ('The Laboratory as Business, Sir Almroth Wright's Vaccine Programme and the Construction of Penicillin', in A. Cunningham and P. Williams (eds), *The Laboratory Revolution in Medicine* (1992)) argues that all the research work done in the Inoculation Department, including the discovery of penicillin, was conditioned by the commercial production and sale of vaccines. The relationship is perhaps not as simple as Wai Chen suggests.

39 Shaw, *The Doctor's Dilemma*.

40 J. Freeman, 'Almroth Wright, Philosopher and Pathologist', *St Mary's Hospital Gazette*, 58/4 (1952), 94; A.D. Wright, Obituary of Sir Almroth Wright, *St Mary's Hospital Gazette*, 53/5 (1947), 112–13.

41 K. Brown, 'The Doctor's Dilemma: a Play for Today?' *St Mary's Hospital Gazette*, 104/2 (1998), 49–52.

42 A.E. Wright, *Alethetropic Logic* (1953), pp. 222–33; L. Colebrook, 'Sir Almroth Wright', *Listener*, 4 December 1947, p. 963; Colebrook, *Almroth Wright*, p. 216.

43 A.E. Wright, *The Unexpurgated Case against Woman Suffrage* (1913).

44 *St Mary's Hospital Gazette*, 12/1 (1906), 6.

45 A. Maurois, *Life of Sir Alexander Fleming* (1959), p. 105. See also James Stuart Garner, 'The Great Experiment: the Admission of Women Students to St Mary's Hospital Medical School, 1916–1925', *Medical History*, 42/1 (1998), 68–88.

46 St Mary's Hospital Archives, MS/AD3/3, Medical School Committee, 3 June 1904.

47 Freeman, 'Almroth Wright, Philosopher and Pathologist', 54.

48 D.W. Carmalt-Jones, 'Almroth Edward Wright', *Lancet*, 1 (1947), 930.

49 V.Z. Cope, *Almroth Wright*, p. 164.

50 'Wright's Lab Thirty Years Ago by a Former Assistant', reprinted from the *New Zealand Medical Journal* (December 1936).

51 W.H. Howard Hughes, *Alexander Fleming and Penicillin* (1974), p. 21.

52 J. Freeman, 'Leonard Noon', *International Archives of Allergy and Applied Immunology*, 4/4 (1953), 282–4.

53 *St Mary's Hospital Gazette*, 14/6 (1908), 65.

54 Obituary of John Herbert Wells, *St Mary's Hospital Gazette*, 15/9 (1909), 123–4.

55 Maurois, *Life of Fleming*, pp. 55–6.

56 A.E. Wright, *Technique of the Teat and Capillary Glass Tube* (1912).

57 Personal information, Miss Hayden.

58 A.E. Wright, S.R. Douglas, J. Freeman, J.H. Wells and A. Fleming, 'Therapeutic Immunisation', *Lancet*, 2 (1907), 1217.

59 L. Noon and A. Fleming, 'The Accuracy of Opsonic Estimations', *Lancet*, 1 (1908), 1203.

60 A. Fleming, 'Some Observations on the Opsonic Index, with Especial Reference to the Accuracy of the Method, and to Some of the Sources of Error', *Practitioner*, 80 (1908), 607.

61 A. Fleming, 'The Diagnosis of Acute Bacterial Infection', *St Mary's Hospital Gazette*, 15/6 (1909), 67–9, 72–7.

62 Robert Fleming, *Alexander Fleming* (1955), p. 47.

63 A. Fleming, 'On the Aetiology of Acne Vulgaris and its Treatment by Vaccines', *Lancet*, 1 (1909), 1035.

64 St Mary's Hospital Archives, minutes of Inoculation Department House Committee, 28 May 1909. This honorarium was worth £5,818 at 1998 values (calculated using table of cost of living and inflation rates given in *Whitaker's Almanack* (London, HMSO, 2001), p. 618).

65 BL Add. MS 56218, C.A. Pannett.

66 Personal information, A.W. Frankland.

67 H.M. Bateman, cartoon, *The only FRCS never to have done an operation.*

68 A. Fleming, Shattuck Lecture, 'Twentieth-Century Changes in the Treatment of Septic Infections', *New England Journal of Medicine*, 248 (1953), 1038.

69 Michael Worboys, 'Vaccine Therapy and Laboratory Medicine in Edwardian Britain', in John V. Pickstone (ed.), *Medical Innovations in Historical Perspective* (1992), pp. 92–3.

70 Peter Keating, 'Vaccine Therapy and the Problem of Opsonins', *Journal of the History of Medicine*, 43 (1988), 281–2.

71 Its importance can be shown by the fact that Hollywood chose to make a film version of Ehrlich's quest for a magic bullet. However, *Dr Ehrlich's Magic Bullet* never actually mentions the disease against which it was so effective other than to discuss in the vaguest of terms an illness so terrible in its consequences that it could blight whole families with its effects!

72 A Fleming and L. Colebrook, 'On the Use of Salvarsan in the Treatment of Syphilis', *Lancet*, 1 (1911), 1631–4.

73 Ronald Gray, cartoon, *Private 606*, given to Almroth Wright and the

Inoculation Department in 1936 and subsequently taken by Amalia Fleming to Athens, where it is now at the Basic Medical Research Centre Alexander Fleming, Vari, Greece.

74 J. Bettley, 'Post Voluptatem Misericordia: the Rise and Fall of the London Lock Hospitals', *London Journal*, 10/2 (1984), 167–75. David Innes Kerr, *The London Lock, a Charitable Hospital for Venereal Disease 1746–1952* (1999).

75 Carey Combes, 'Pulmonary Disease due to Acquired Syphilis', *St Mary's Hospital Gazette*, 10/3 (1904), 45.

76 A. Fleming, 'A Simple Method of Serum Diagnosis of Syphilis', *Lancet*, 1 (1909), 1512–15.

77 For the criticisms of Fleming, see *Lancet*, 1 (1912), 1752–4; *Lancet*, 2 (1912), 48, 183–5, 258–9, 336, 408, 558. For Fleming's response, see A. Fleming, 'Hecht's Modification and the Wassermann Test', *Lancet*, 2 (1912), 115–17; letter to *Lancet*, 2 (1912), 258–9.

78 Fleming, 'Hecht's modification and the Wassermann Test', 115–17.

79 St Mary's Hospital Archives, DP46/1. An album of personal photographs taken by Leonard Colebrook was unearthed in the attic of a house in which his widow had later lived and was donated to St Mary's Hospital Archives in 1994. See K. Brown, 'Almroth Wright and Alexander Fleming *en déshabille*', *St Mary's Hospital Gazette*, 100/3 (1994), 51–2.

80 L.J. Ludovici, *Fleming, Discoverer of Penicillin* (1952), pp. 55–6.

81 BL Add. MS 56216, Marjorie Pegram.

82 BL Add. MS 56215, L. Jennings.

83 BL Add. MS 56215, B. Davis.

84 BL Add. MS 56216, Marjory Pegram.

85 BL Add. MS 56215, Josephine Thomson; BL Add. MS 56215, E. Storer.

86 BL Add. MS 56215, E. Storer.

87 BL Add. MS 56215, L. Jennings.

88 BL Add. MS 56218, B. Davis.

89 BL Add. MS 56215, Gerald Willcox. On New Year's Eve 1925, Fleming went to the Chelsea Arts Club Ball dressed as an Arab chieftain.

90 Robert Fleming, *Sir Alexander Fleming*, p. 51.

91 *Sancta Maria Lodge, no. 2682: Fiftieth Anniversary* (1947), p. 6.

92 R.M. Handfield-Jones, *History of the Sancta Maria Lodge, no. 2682, 1897–1960* (1960).

93 J.L.W. Wright, *Sancta Maria Lodge, no. 2682: a Short Centenary History* (1997), p. 20.

94 Some of Fleming's masonic regalia were donated by his son to the Alexander Fleming Laboratory Museum. It has been identified by John Wright, consulting ENT Surgeon to St Mary's Hospital and Assistant Secretary of Sancta Maria Lodge (1996) as including his Master Mason's Apron, Sancta Maria Collar, 18th Degree Rose Croix Apron and Collar and 30th Degree Rose Croix collar.

95 BL Add. MS 56216, G.W.B. James.

Chapter Four

1 *London Scottish Regimental Gazette*, 19 (1914), 61.

2 *Ibid.*, p. 78.

3 St Mary's Hospital Annual Report, 1934.

4 St Mary's Hospital Archives, SM/MX4/16, brochure *Who Won the Great War?*, *c.* 1931.

5 Leonard Colebrook, *Almroth Wright, Provocative Doctor and Thinker* (1954), p. 42.

6 *Ibid.*, p. 72.

7 BL Add. MS 56214, William Claydon.

8 Fleming, 'Some Notes on the Bacteriology of Gas Gangrene', *Lancet*, 2 (1915), 376–8; 'On the Bacteriology of Septic Wounds', *Lancet*, 2 (1915), 638–43; S.R. Douglas, A. Fleming and L. Colebrook, 'On the Question of Bacterial Symbiosis in Wound Infections, *Lancet*, 1 (1917), 604–7; S.R. Douglas, L. Colebrook and A. Fleming, 'On the Growth of Anaerobic Bacilli in Fluid Media under Apparently Aerobic Conditions', *Lancet*, 2 (1917), 530–2.

9 A.E. Wright and A. Fleming, 'Further Observations on Acidaemia in Gas Gangrene and the Conditions which Favour the Growth of its Infective Agent in the Blood Serum', *Lancet*, 1 (1918), 205–10; 'The Aerobic Infections of War Wounds', *Medical Research Council Special Report Series*, no. 39 (1919), 70–8.

10 A. Fleming and F.J. Clemenger, 'A Simple Method of Recording Automatically the Gas Produced by Bacteria in a Culture and of the Oxygen Absorbed by Aerobic Non-Gas-Forming Bacteria', *British Journal of Experimental Pathology*, 1 (1920–1), 66–9.

11 A.E. Wright, A. Fleming and L. Colebrook, 'The Conditions under which the Sterilisation of Wounds by

Physiological Agency can be Obtained', *Lancet*, 1 (1918), 831–7.

12 A.E. Wright, *British Medical Journal*, 2 (1915), 629, 670, 717; W.W. Cheyne, *British Journal of Surgery*, 3 (1917), 427.

13 'The Physiological and Antiseptic Action of Flavine (with Some Observations on the Testing of Antiseptics', *Lancet*, 2 (1917), 341–5; Letter to *Lancet*, 2 (1917), 508–9.

14 A. Porritt, 'Treatment of War Wounds', in *History of the Second World War, United Kingdom Medical Services, Surgery* (1953), p. 927.

15 A.E. Wright, *Lancet*, 2 (1915), 629, 670, 717.

16 Contemporary Medical Archives Centre, RAMC 365/4, A.E. Wright, 'Memorandum on the Necessity of Creating at the War Office a Medical Intelligence and Investigation Department to get the Best Possible Treatment for the Wounded, Diminish Invaliding and Return Men to the Ranks in the Shortest Time'.

17 PRO, FD/97.

18 Contemporary Medical Archives Centre, RAMC 365/4.

19 BL Add. MS 56216, Roger Lee.

20 Colebrook, *Almroth Wright*, p. 71.

21 BL Add. MS 56216, H.B. Day.

22 BL Add. MS 56216, Norman Keith.

23 BL Add. MS 56216, A.B. Porteous.

24 Robert Fleming, *Sir Alexander Fleming* (1958), p. 53.

25 Colebrook, *Almroth Wright*, p. 70.

26 BL Add. MS 56216, G.W.B. James.

27 St Mary's Hospital Archives, SM/AD35/6, no. 16, Report of Medical Committee on proposals for

the establishment of a Special Department for the diagnosis and treatment of Venereal Diseases, 11 December 1916. Fleming's salary of £250 would have been worth £11,635 at 1998 values (calculated using table of cost of living and inflation rates given in *Whitaker's Almanack*, London, HMSO, 2001, p. 618).

28   St Mary's Hospital Archives, SM/AD35/6, no. 24, Report of Venereal Diseases Department Committee, 23 March 1917.

29   A. Fleming and A.B. Porteous, 'Streptococcal Infections of Septic Wounds at a Base Hospital', *Lancet*, 2 (1919), 49–52.

30   A. Fleming and A.B. Porteous, 'Blood Transfusion by the Citrate Method: a Report on 100 Cases of Blood Transfusion at a Base Hospital, *Lancet*, 1 (1919), 973–5.

31   A. Fleming and F.J. Clemenger, 'An Experimental Research into the Specificity of the Agglutinins Produced by Pfeiffer's Bacillus', *Lancet*, 2 (1919), 869–71.

32   The results of this work were: A.E. Wright, *Prolegomena to the Logic which Searches for Truth* (1941); A.E. Wright, *Alethetropic Logic* (1953).

33   'The Action of Chemical and Physiological Antiseptics in a Septic Wound', *British Journal of Surgery*, 7 (1919–20), 99–129.

34   Marriage certificate in the possession of Dr Robert Fleming.

35   Baptism certificate in the possession of Dr Robert Fleming. See *The Discovery of Penicillin and its Kilfilian Connection*, booklet published to mark the *Unveiling of a memorial to Lady Sarah and Sir Alexander Fleming, Kilfian Ballina, County Mayo, Monday 6 August 2001*, for an account of Sareen Fleming's family background. There are inaccuracies in the references to Alexander Fleming.

36   Marriage certificate and death certificate in the possession of Dr Robert Fleming. Robert learned of this subterfuge only in 2001 when he visited Ireland to unveil a memorial to his parents at his mother's birthplace and was presented by the parish priest with a copy of his mother's baptism details.

37   Nursing diploma of Sarah Marion McElroy, trained at Richmond Whitworth and Hardwicke Hospitals, Dublin, 25 March 1903–25 March 1907, awarded 19 July 1907, among Fleming papers at Biomedical Sciences Research Centre Alexander Fleming, Vari, Attica, Greece.

38   BL Add. MS 5616, Mrs McKinnon.

39   BL Add. MS 56218, Gerald Willcox.

40   BL Add. MS 56217, Mollie Ritchie.

41   Personal information, Dr Robert Fleming.

42   Robert Fleming, *Sir Alexander Fleming*, p. 55.

43   Personal information, Dr Robert Fleming.

44   BL Add. MS 56216, Norah Hanbury Kelk Risby.

45   Personal information, Phyllis French, née Norton, whose childhood was spent at Barton Mills.

46   BL Add. MS 56218, Gerald Willcox; personal information, Dr Robert Fleming.

47   V.D. Allison, 'Personal Recollections of Sir Almroth Wright and Sir

Alexander Fleming', *Ulster Medical Journal*, 43/2 (1974) 97.

48 The finances of the Inoculation Department as an independent self-financing unit within the curtilage of St Mary's were messy and kept deliberately obscure by Almroth Wright, who had no desire for any interference with his empire. Nor was it in the interests of St Mary's Hospital for the public to be aware of income accruing from such commercial activities as the sale of vaccines. Financial accounts of the department have not survived. Fleming's salary from the Inoculation Department would have been worth *c*. £23,270 in 1919 (calculated using table of cost of living and inflation rates given in *Whitaker's Almanack*, London, HMSO, 2001, p. 618).

49 Michael Dunnill, *The Plato of Praed Street* (2000), pp. 207–11. Wright did retain his salary of £2,000 p.a. as director of bacteriology as part of a generous deal with the MRC, though it was now a personal grant payable until the age of 65. He rarely acknowledged this largesse from the MRC.

50 Wellcome Library, PP/COL, Leonard Colebrook's Diary, 13 November 1919.

51 V.Z. Cope, *Almroth Wright* (1966), p. 164.

52 St Mary's Hospital Archives, minutes of House Committee for Therapeutic Inoculation, 23 February 1921.

53 Better known as Lord Moran, Winston Churchill's physician and President of the Royal College of Physicians.

54 Ronald Hare, *The Birth of Penicillin*, (1970), p. 30.

55 This series continues to this day as the Almroth Wright Lecture series.

56 SM/AD 2/9, 60–5. The application was signed by Wright, the Dean and the Chairmen of the Hospital, Inoculation and Medical Committees. It may never have been sent, as there is no record of it at the Rockefeller Foundation Archives.

57 Hare, *The Birth of Penicillin*, p. 35.

58 A. Fleming, 'Antiseptics: the Lister Memorial Lecture', delivered in Edinburgh, 9 November 1944, *Chemistry and Industry*, 3 (20 January 1945), 18–23.

59 R.J. Goodlee, *Lord Lister* (1917).

60 Fleming, 'Antiseptics', 18.

61 BL Add. MS 56219, V.D. Allison. V.D. Allison, 'Personal recollections of Sir Almroth Wright and Sir Alexander Fleming', *Ulster Medical Journal*, 43/2 (1974), 90–2.

62 Bacteriophage had been discovered by F.W. Twort in 1915. F.H. D'Herelle in 1921 suggested the link with natural immunity and claimed to have treated intestinal infections with a bacteriophage.

63 BL Add. MS 56154, Fleming's notebook, 21 November 1921.

64 *Ibid.*, 23 November 1921.

65 *Ibid.*, 23 November 1921–December 1921.

66 *Ibid.*, April 1922.

67 *Ibid.*, 21 November 1921; Allison, 'Personal Recollections', 91–2.

68 BL Add. MS 56154, Fleming's notebook, 16 February 1922, 3 March 1922. It is now known as *Micrococcus luteus*.

69 L.H. Collier (ed.), *The History of the Medical Research Club,*

1891–1991 (1991), privately printed
for members of the Medical
Research Club.

70   BL Add. MS 56219, H.H. Dale.
71   G.H. Buttle, 'The First Sixty Years',
     in Collier, *History of the Medical
     Research Club* (1991), p. 34.
72   BL Add. MS 56220, Dan Stratful.
73   J.H. Dowd, *Punch*, 28 June 1922.
     The original artwork of the cartoon
     was acquired by Fleming and is now
     in the collections of the Alexander
     Fleming Laboratory Museum.
74   BL Add. MS 56154, Fleming's
     notebook, 12 January 1922.
75   Allison, 'Personal Recollections', 93.
76   A. Fleming, 'On a Remarkable
     Bacteriolytic Element Found in
     Tissues and Secretions', *Proceedings
     of the Royal Society*, B, 93, (1922),
     306.
77   Royal Society Fellowship records.
78   Allison, 'Personal Recollections', 92.
79   A. Fleming and V.D. Allison,
     'Further Observations on a
     Bacteriolytic Element Found in
     Tissues and Secretions', *Proceedings
     of the Royal Society*, B, 94 (1922),
     p. 142.
80   A. Fleming, 'Arris and Gale Lecture
     on Lysozyme, a Bacteriological
     Ferment Found Normally in Tissues
     and Secretions', *Lancet*, 1 (1929),
     217.
81   Fleming and Allison, 'On the
     Antibacterial Power of Egg White',
     Lancet, 1 (1924), 1303.
82   A.E. Wright, L. Colebrook and
     E.J. Storer, 'New Principles in
     Therapeutic Inoculation', *Lancet*, 1
     (1923), 365, 417, 473.
83   A. Fleming, 'A Comparison of the
     Activities of Antiseptics on Bacteria
     and on Leucocytes', *Proceedings of*

the Royal Society, B, 96 (1924),
171.
84   A. Fleming and V.D. Allison, 'On
     the Development of Strains of
     Bacteria Resistant to Lysozyme
     Action and Relation of Lysozyme
     Action to Intracellular Digestion',
     *British Journal of Experimental
     Pathology*, 8 (1927), 214.
85   Fleming, 'Arris and Gale Lecture',
     217.
86   A. Fleming, *Proceedings of the
     Royal Society of Medicine*, 26
     (1932) (Pathology Section), 1.
87   A. Fleming, 'Lysozyme, President's
     Address', *Proceedings of the Royal
     Society of Medicine*, 26 (1931),
     71–84.
88   Personal information from H.M.
     Queen Elizabeth the Queen Mother
     (President of St Mary's Hospital,
     1930–2002), April 1994 and June
     1995.
89   It was Ernst Chain and Robert
     Robinson at Oxford who a decade
     later were to take lysozyme further.
     E.F. Osserman, R.E. Canfield and
     S. Beychock (eds), *Lysozyme* (1974).
     The proceedings of a 50th-
     anniversary conference held in 1972
     contained 2,586 references to papers
     on the subject.

Chapter Five

1   *Bacillus coli.*
2   The bacterium meant by 'hay'
    remains unidentified.
3   BL Add. MS 56162, notebook,
    30 October 1928.
4   The bacteriologist J.M.C. Gram had
    devised a method for differentiating
    different types of micro-organisms
    using a crystal violet stain. The
    division into Gram-positive, which

are stained by the dye, and Gram-negative bacteria remains important, as some antibiotics attack only one species or the other and some are broad spectrum and attack both kinds.

5   BL Add. MS 56162, notebook, 22 November 1928, 28 November 1928, 29 November 1928. The bacteria Fleming found to be inhibited by penicillin were streptococcus, staphylococcus, pneumococcus, gonococcus, meningococcus and the diphtheria bacillus. It had no effect on typhoid, para-typhoid, enterococci, *haemophilus influenzae* or coliform bacilli.

6   BL Add. MS 56162, notebook, November 1928; 11 December 1928.

7   R. Biourge, *Des moissures du group Penicillium Link* (1923), p. 172.

8   BL Add. MS 56220, C.J. La Touche; La Touche also recorded Fleming's original thoughts in an inscription in the copy of Biourge that he used to identify the mould. Donated to the Department of Bacteriology at St Mary's Hospital Medical School, it is now in St Mary's Hospital Archives.

9   A. Fleming, 'The Story of Penicillin', *Medical Annals of the District of Columbia*, 14/9 (September 1945), 397.

10 Psalm 51: 7; quoted in A. Maurois, *Life of Sir Alexander Fleming* (1959), p. 127.

11 Craddock erroneously believed that Wright was responsible for naming penicillin, BL Add. MS 56218, Stuart Craddock.

12 M. Wainwright, 'Fleming's Early

Search for Antibiotics Other than Penicillin', *Society of General Microbiology Quarterly*, 18 (1991), 46–7.

13 BL Add. MS 56217, Arthur Hayward.

14 These were *Eidamia viridiscens, Botyris cineria, Aspergillus fumigatus, Sporotrichum, Cladosporium, Penicillium;* A. Fleming, 'On the Antibacterial Action of Cultures of a Penicillium with Special Reference to their Use in the Isolation of *B. influenzae*', *British Journal of Experimental Pathology*, 10 (1929), 227.

15 R. Hare, 'New Light on the Discovery of Penicillin', *Medical History*, 26 (1982), 1–24.

16 BL Add. MS 56162, notebook, 24 September 1929.

17 *Ibid.*, 9 September 1929, 1 October 1929.

18 *Ibid.*, 20 January 1932.

19 A. Fleming, 'Arris and Gale Lecture on Lysozyme: a Bacterial Ferment Found Normally in Tissues and Secretions', *Lancet*, 1 (1929), 217.

20 BL Add. MS 56218, Frederick Ridley.

21 BL Add. MS 56218, Stuart Craddock.

22 BL Add. MS 65218, Frederick Ridley; R. Hare, *The Birth of Penicillin* (1970), p. 94.

23 BL Add. MS 56224, Stuart Craddock's notebook, 6 February 1929.

24 *Ibid.*, 13 March 1929: 'active principle extracted more effectively with alcohol'.

25 A. Fleming, 'On the Specific Antibacterial Properties of Penicillin and Potassium Tellurite –

Incorporating a Method of
Demonstrating Some Bacterial
Antagonisms', *Journal of Pathology
and Bacteriology*, 35 (1932), 831.

26 BL Add. MS 56218, Stuart
Craddock.

27 BL Add. MS 56218, Frederick
Ridley.

28 Fleming, 'On the Antibacterial
Action of Cultures of a Penicillium',
228.

29 BL Add. MS 56224, Stuart
Craddock's notebook, 6 February
1929, 14 February 1929, 20
February 1929, 12 March 1929,
13 March 1929.

30 Fleming, 'On the Antibacterial
Action of Cultures of a Penicillium',
232.

31 BL Add. MS 56224, Stuart
Craddock's notebook, 29 March
1929: 'inhibitor does not remain free
in serum for many minutes.'

32 BL Add. MS 56218, Stuart
Craddock.

33 BL Add. MS 56162, notebook,
9 January 1929.

34 BL Add. MS 56220, R.M.
Handfield-Jones.

35 BL Add. MS 56224, Stuart
Craddock's notebook, 2 April 1929.

36 Fleming, 'On the Antibacterial
Action of Cultures of a Penicillium',
236.

37 'Mortality from Influenza', *Lancet*,
1 (1929), 903.

38 Wai Chen, 'The Laboratory as
Business, Sir Almroth Wright's
Vaccine Programme and the
Construction of Penicillin', in
A. Cunningham and P. Williams
(eds), *The Laboratory Revolution in
Medicine* (1992), pp. 245–92. While
the role of penicillin in aiding the

vaccine production programme in
Wright's laboratory was important
and did encourage Fleming, who was
responsible for ensuring the
profitability of this enterprise on
which the department depended, to
pursue its role in the isolation of *B.
influenzae*, Wai Chen overstates his
case that Fleming failed to construct
an identity for penicillin as an
antibiotic but succeeded in
developing its identity as a laboratory
'weedkiller for bacterial farming' in
pursuit of the commercial goals of
vaccine production. What Fleming
did do was examine the various
possibilities for his discovery and
explore various avenues before
finding a role for his discovery. It was
this role as a laboratory agent which
initially indicated the most successful
road, though Fleming did not
eliminate the other possibility of
therapeutic potential in his 1929
paper. It was the success of penicillin
as an agent for selective culture of
resistant strains of bacteria that
interested other scientists without any
commercial motives.

39 BL Add. MS 56229, Sir Henry Dale.

40 BL Add. MS 56217, H.J. Parish.

41 G. Macfarlane, *Alexander Fleming:
the Man and the Myth* (1984),
pp. 133–6.

42 M. Wainwright, 'Fleming did
Discover Penicillin', *Society for
General Microbiology Quarterly*,
15/2 (1988), 30–1.

43 Fleming, 'On the Antibacterial
Action of Cultures of a Penicillium',
226–36.

44 I.H. Maclean, 'A Modification of
the Cough Plate Method of
Diagnosis in Whooping Cough',

Journal of Pathology and Bacteriology, 45 (1937), 472–3.

45 B. Sokoloff, *Penicillin: a Dramatic Story* (1946), pp. 105–6.

46 Quoted in *ibid.*, p. 105.

47 S.A. Waksman, *Microbial Antagonisms and Antibiotic Substances* (1945). Waksman coined the term antibiotic in 1943 following Vuillemin's 1889 coinage.

48 J. Burdon-Sanderson, *The Thirteenth Report of the Medical Officer of the Privy Council, 1870* (1871), Appendix 5, pp. 56–66.

49 J. Tyndall, 'The Optical Department of the Atmosphere in Relation to the Phenomena of Putrefaction and Infection', *Philosophical Transactions of the Royal Society*, 164 (1876), 27–74.

50 J. Lister, *Commonplace Books* (1871), vol. 1, pp. 31–45, quoted in Lord Webb-Johnson, *Annals of the Royal College of Surgeons*, 6 (1950), 140–1.

51 W. Fraser-Moodie, *Proceedings of the Royal Society of Medicine*, 64 (1971), 87.

52 Letter from Alexander Fleming to Lord Webb-Johnson, President of Royal College of Surgeons, quoted in Lord Webb-Johnson, *Annals of the Royal College of Surgeons*, pp. 140–1.

53 G. Papagostas and J. Gaté, *Les Associations microbiennes* (1928).

54 L. Pasteur and M.J. Joubert, 'Chimie physiologique – Charbon et septicémie', *Comptes rendus de l'Académie des sciences*, 85 (1877), 101–15.

55 C. Garré, *Korrespondenzblatt für Schweize Ärtate*, 17 (1887), 385.

56 V. Tiberio, 'Sugli estratti di alcune muffe', *Annali d'Igiene*, 5 (1895), 91.

57 E.A. Duchesne, *Contribution à l'étude de la concurrence vitale chez les microorganismes: antagonisme entre les moissures et les microbes* (1897); R.A. Kyle and M.A. Shampo, 'Ernest Augustin Clement Duchesne', *Journal of American Medical Association*, 240/9 (1978), 847.

58 See, for example, *Daily Mail*, 30 July 1999, reporting on a claim by Richard Barry that Duchesne was the 'Frenchman who found penicillin before Fleming' and a refutation of that claim by the author of this book.

59 Wainwright, 'Fleming Did Discover Penicillin', 30–1; M. Wainwright, 'A Response to Some Criticisms of Fleming's Role in the Discovery of Penicillin', *St Mary's Hospital Gazette*, 103/3 (1997), 31–4.

60 BL Add. MS 56115, letter from A.D. Gratia to Alexander Fleming, 21 November 1945. Gratia also repeated this claim in a letter to Robert Fulton, 28 January 1946, now in the Fulton Collection at Yale University, quoted by Gladys Hobby, *Penicillin: Meeting the Challenge* (1985), pp. 4–5.

61 BL Add. MS 56173, notebook, 19 November 1931, December 1931; BL Add. MS 56168, notebook, 4 March 1932.

62 Hellenic Foundation for Basic Medical Research Alexander Fleming, Athens, Greece, letter from Fleming to A.D. Gratia, 5 November 1944; Biomedical Sciences Research Centre, Alexander Fleming, Vari, Greece, letter from A.D. Gratia to Fleming, 11 November 1944.

63 BL Add. MS 56118, letter from Fleming to Professor Liljestrand, 21 March 1949.

64 BL Add. MS 56219, Stuart Craddock.

65 BL Add. MS 56224, Stuart Craddock's notebook.

66 BL Add. MS 56218, Stuart Craddock; personal information, Iain Craddock.

67 A. Fleming, 'Penicillin, its Discovery, Development and Uses in the Field of Medicine and Surgery: the Harben Lectures', *Journal of the Royal Institute of Public Health and Hygiene*, 8 (1945), 93.

68 A. Fleming, with L. Colebrook, E.E. Lewis and R. Mowlem, 'Discussion on Chemotherapy and Wound Infection', *Proceedings of the Royal Society of Medicine*, 36 (1941), 45. See also A. Fleming, 'On the Specific Antibacterial Properties of Penicillin and Potassium Tellurite – incorporating a Method of Demonstrating Some Bacterial Antagonisms', *Journal of Pathology and Bacteriology*, 35 (1932), 831.

69 BL Add. MS 56217, Keith Rogers; personal information, Dr K.B. Rogers.

70 A. Fleming, 'Penicillin', *Journal of the Royal Naval Medical Service*, 31/2 (April 1945), 76.

71 A. Fleming, 'Some Problems in the Use of Antiseptics', *British Dental Journal*, 52 (1931), 105.

72 M. Wainwright and H.T. Swan, 'C.G. Paine and the Earliest Surviving Clinical Records of Penicillin Therapy', *Medical History*, 30 (1996), 42–56; M. Wainwright, 'St Mary's Other Man of Penicillin', *St Mary's Hospital Gazette*, 103/2 (1997), 41–3; D. Masters, *Miracle Drug* (1946), pp. 57–60.

73 A. Fleming, 'Penicillin: the Robert Campbell Oration', *Ulster Medical Journal*, 13 (October 1944), 95.

74 BL Add. MS 56218, H. Berry.

75 BL Add. MS 56218, T.S. Carswell, Vice-President Commercial Solvents.

76 C. Thom, 'Mycology Presents Penicillin', *Mycologia*, 37/4 (1945), 460–75.

77 BL Add. MS 56217, Reginald Lovell.

78 BL Add. MS 56220, Professor Lovell.

79 P.W. Clutterbuck, R. Lovell and H. Raistrick, 'Studies in the Biochemistry of Micro-Organisms, no. 26, the Formation from Glucose by Members of the *Penicillium chrysogenum* Series of a Pigment, an Alkali-soluble Protein and Penicillin – the Antibacterial Substance of Fleming', *Biochemical Journal*, 26 (1932), 1907–18.

80 Masters, *Miracle Drug*, p. 53.

81 A. Fleming (ed.), *Penicillin* (1946), p. 14.

82 Royal Society HF1/3/2/12/25, letter from Fleming to Florey, 7 February 1946.

83 Maurois, *Life of Fleming*, pp. 148–56. Maurois was quoting C.B. Dyson out of context. When Dyson wrote that 'It seemed to me that he had a secret sorrow or was too repressed', he was actually referring to Fleming's general demeanour, BL Add. MS 56217, C.B. Dyson.

84 A. Fleming, 'Lysozyme', *Proceedings of the Royal Society of Medicine*, Section of Pathology, 26 (1932), 71–84.

85 St Mary's Hospital Archives, SM/AD 46/12, St Mary's Hospital Annual Report, 1928.

86 St Mary's Hospital Archives, minutes of SM/AD 2/9 Board of Management, 30 May 1929, 24 July 1929.

87 V.Z. Cope, *History of St Mary's Hospital Medical School* (1954), p. 67.

88 St Mary's Hospital Archives, minutes of Inoculation Department Committee, 22 October 1931, 18 February 1932, and December 1933.

89 'Foundation Stone Ceremony', *St Mary's Hospital Gazette*, 37/10 (1931), 73–5; *The Times*, 1 July 1931.

90 Information from Giles J. Romanes, August 1995.

91 The Biomedical Sciences Research Centre Alexander Fleming, Vari, Greece has examples: bird, The Dhoon, guardsman in sentry box, ballerina, girl's head, girl and dog, man chopping wood, lady's head with shingled bob, flower, life guardsman, and a Union Jack and steamship in a diagram illustrating the 'permanence of bacterial pigments'.

92 BL Add. MS 56217, H.J. Bunker; BL Add. MS 56216, Mrs Portuoli.

93 Personal information, Andrew Matthews.

94 BL Add. MS 56219, W.D.W. Brooks.

95 BL Add. MS 56221, Philip Willcox.

96 BL Add. MS 56220, R. May.

97 BL Add. MS 56221, Dr Ogilvie.

98 BL Add. MS 56216, Weldon-Dalrymple-Champney.

99 BL Add. MS 56217, D.M. Pryce.

100 BL Add. MS 56217, C.B. Dyson.

101 At that time non-medically qualified scientists working in a medical school like St Mary's were looked down upon by their doctor colleagues, who may in fact have been academically less well qualified. Fleming, however, made no distinction. Another non-medical doctor to whom he was friendly, if characteristically unforthcoming, was Charles Foster, appointed lecturer in biology in 1948. Personal information from Professor C.L. Foster and Anne Maddocks Foster.

102 BL Add. MS 56220, L.B. Holt; R. Hare, *The Birth of Penicillin* (1970), pp. 103–4.

103 R.D. Reid, 'Some Observations on the Ability of a Mold, or its Metabolic Products to Inhibit Bacterial Growth', *Journal of Bacteriology*, 27 (1934), 28; R.D. Reid, 'Some Properties of a Bacterial-Inhibitory Substance Produced by a Mold', *Journal of Bacteriology*, 29 (1935), 215–21; M. Wainwright, 'Roger Reid's Early Contribution to the Study of Penicillin', *Journal of Medical Biography*, 4/1 (1996), 14–17.

104 BL Add. MS 56217, Roger D. Reid.

105 BL Add. MS 56170, notebook, 12 July 1934.

106 *Ibid.*, February 1935.

107 BL Add. MS 56172, notebook, 29 May 1935.

108 BL Add. MS 56173, notebook, 18 December 1939.

109 BL Add. MS 56170, notebook, 24–5 May 1935, June 1935.

110 BL Add. MS 56172, notebook, 23 June 1936.

111 BL Add. MS 56173, notebook, 11 February 1938.

112 Milton Wainwright of the University of Sheffield, adopting from the field of musicology the idea of a composer completing an unfinished symphony, has written the paper that Fleming never published: M. Wainwright, 'Fleming's Unfinished', *Perspectives in Biology and Medicine*, 45/4 (2002), 529–38. Wainwright postulates that Fleming may have written a paper on his work on penicillin after 1929 but that it probably wasn't accepted for publication because it would have had nothing new to say on purification. However, since the therapeutic use of penicillin did not become a major issue for anyone until the 1940s, it is unlikely that this would have stopped a journal from publishing a paper. Fleming did not have any trouble in having articles accepted for publication nor in expressing what he wished to communicate in either a scientific paper or a lecture. Wainwright supports Maurois's idea of Fleming's frustration at not having his views on penicillin accepted in the 1930s.

113 G.C. Haslam, 'Fleming and the Development of Penicillin', *Daily Telegraph*, 8 April 1984; G.C. Haslam, 'The Fleming Saga', *St Mary's Hospital Gazette*, 96/1 (1990), 6; A.W. Frankland, 'Perspective: Penicillin History and Allergy', *Immunology and Allergy Practice*, 14/10 (1992), 21.

114 H.H. Dale, 'Sir Alexander Fleming', *British Medical Journal*, 1 (1955), 732, 795.

115 Maurois, *Life of Fleming*, pp. 137–8.

116 Royal Society membership records.

117 Hare, *The Birth of Penicillin*, p. 115.

118 L. Colebrook, 'Treatment of Human Puerperal Infections and of Experimental Infections in Mice with Prontosil', *Lancet*, 1 (1936), 1279.

119 L. Colebrook, 'Gerhard Domagk, 1895–1964', *Biographical Memoirs of Fellows of the Royal Society* (1964), vol. 10, p. 39; G. Domagk, 'Ein Beitrag zur Chemotherapie der bacteriellen Infektionen', *Deutsche Medizinische Wochenschrift*, 61 (1935), 250; G. Domagk and C. Hegler, *Chemotherapie bakterieller Infektionen* (1944).

120 Hare, *The Birth of Penicillin*, pp. 138–9.

121 BL Add. MS 56172, 23 October 1936.

122 A. Fleming, 'The Antibacterial action *in vitro* of 2-(p-amino-benzenesulphonamido) Pyridine on Pneumococci and Streptococci', *Lancet*, 2 (1938), 74–8; A. Fleming, 'The Antibacterial Power of the Blood of Patients Receiving 2-(p-amino-benzesulphonamido) Pyridine', *Lancet*, 2 (1938), 564–7; I.H. Maclean, K.B. Rogers and A. Fleming, 'M & B 693 and Pneumococci', *Lancet*, 1 (1939), 562–8; A. Fleming, 'Serum and Vaccine Therapy in Combination with Sulphanilamide or M & B 693', *Proceedings of Royal Society of Medicine*, 32 (1939), 911–20.

123 Robert Fleming, *Alexander Fleming* (1957), p. 61.

124 BL Add. MS 56220, Mrs Marshall (housekeeper, 1932–55).

125 Personal information, Dr Robert Fleming.

126 Personal information, Phyllis French, née Norton.

127 L.J. Ludovici, *Fleming, Discoverer of Penicillin* (1952), pp. 131–2.

128 BL Add. MS 56217, D.M. Pryce.

129 BL Add. MS 56215, E.J.W. Todd.

130 e.g. A. Fleming, 'Success, Rectorial Address', *Student* (Edinburgh University Magazine), 47/8 (1952), 325.

131 Maurois, *Life of Fleming*, p. 233.

132 BL Add. MS 56217, D.M. Pryce.

133 Personal information, Dr Robert Fleming.

134 Letter from Dorothy Wilson to Geoffrey Maurice, 23 January 1936, quoted in R. Lovell, *Churchill's Doctor: a Life of Lord Moran* (1992), p. 115.

135 Personal information, Dr Robert Fleming.

136 BL Add. MS 56219, Helen Buckley.

137 St Mary's Hospital Archives, minutes of Inoculation Department House Committee, 6 February 1924, 20 February 1936. In terms of 1998 purchasing power, his salary of £1,200 in 1924 was worth £39,096 and his 1936 salary of £1,600 the equivalent of £65,152 (calculated using table of cost of living and inflation rates given in *Whitaker's Almanack*, London, HMSO, 2001, p. 618).

138 BL Add. MS 56217, Anthony M. Ritchie.

139 BL Add. MS 56184, diary, 6 January–4 February 1935.

140 BL Add. MS 56217, V.D. Allison.

141 A. Fleming, 'Selective Bacteriostasis: Opening Paper of a Discussion on the Inhibitory Action on the Growth of Bacteria and Fungi of Substances of Known Constitution and Products of the Growth of Micro-Organisms', *Proceedings of Second International Congress of Microbiology, 1936* (1937), p. 33.

142 *Abstracts of Third International Congress of Microbiology, New York, 1939* (1940), p. 587.

143 BL Add. MS 56219, Allan W. Downie.

144 'Et si j'associe à cet admirable exemple de sérénité et d'équilibre les paroles que Mrs Fleming devait prononcer en nous quittant, le regard songeur et perdu dans le lontain: "Ce sera dur, ce sera long, mais nous vaincrons."' A. Gratia, *Revue médicale de Liège*, 2/3 (1947), 66.

Chapter Six

1 E. Chain, H.W. Florey, A.D. Gardner, N.G. Heatley, M.A. Jennings, J. Orr-Ewing and A.G. Sanders, 'Penicillin as a Chemotherapeutic Agent', *Lancet*, 2 (24 August 1940), 226–8.

2 BL Add. MS 56216, E.B. Chain.

3 Wellcome Library, GC/48/B5, Heatley's diary, 2 September 1940.

4 L. Bickel, *Rise up to Life: a Biography of Howard Florey* (1972); G. Macfarlane, *Howard Florey: the Making of a Great Scientist* (1979); T.I. Williams, *Howard Florey: Penicillin and After* (1984).

5 S.R. Douglas, 'Georges Dreyer', *Obituary Notices of Fellows of the Royal Society* (1932–5), vol. 1, p. 569; Obituary notice, 'Georges Dreyer', *Journal of Pathology and Bacteriology*, 39 (1934), 707.

6 E.P. Abraham, 'Howard Walter Florey', *Biographical Memoirs of*

Fellows of the Royal Society (1971), vol. 17, pp. 255–302.

7   Royal Society, HF/1/1/2, Florey's notebook, 17 January 1929, recording that organs and tissues from dead rats had been sent to Fleming.

8   H.E. Florey and N.E. Goldsworthy, 'Some Properties of Mucus, with Special Reference to its Antibacterial Functions', *British Journal of Experimental Pathology*, 11 (1930), 192.

9   A. Fleming, 'Lysozyme', *Proceedings of the Royal Society of Medicine*, 26 (December 1932), Section of Pathology, p. 7.

10 E.P. Abraham and R. Robinson, 'Lysozyme', *Nature*, 140 (1937), 24.

11 R.W. Clark, *The Life of Ernst Chain, Penicillin and Beyond* (1985).

12 L.A. Epstein later changed his name to L.A. Falk.

13 L.A. Epstein and E.B. Chain, 'Lysozyme', *British Journal of Experimental Pathology*, 21 (1940), 339.

14 Wellcome Library, PP/EBC/B68, draft appreciation of Florey by Chain, 1967.

15 BL Add. MS 56216, E.B. Chain.

16 E.B. Chain, 'The Early Years of the Penicillin Discovery', edited version of paper given at the symposium 'Penicillin 1928–1978' at St Mary's Hospital Medical School, *TIPS, inaugural issue* (1979), 9.

17 BL Add. MS 56216, E.B. Chain.

18 Chain, 'The Early Years of the Penicillin Discovery', p. 9.

19 Wellcome Library, PP/EBC/B63, letter from Chain to Professor Burn, 6 January 1945. Heatley disputed

that any serious work had started before mid-1939 at the earliest, but Florey's report to the Medical Research Council in January 1939 mentions work having been started.

20 Wellcome Library, PP/EBC/B16, Chain's draft for grant application to Rockefeller Foundation, submitted November 1939.

21 Rockefeller Archive Center, North Tarrytown, NY, RF R.G. 1–1, Project Series 401D England, Box 36, F 457. Application to Rockefeller Foundation from H.W. Florey, Sir William Dunn School of Pathology, University of Oxford, 20 November 1939, received 11 December 1939.

22 Rockefeller Archive Center, North Tarrytown, NY, RF R.G. 1–1, Project Series 40D England, Box 36, F 458, Grant-in-aid to Department of Pathology, University of Oxford, under Professor H.W. Florey, 21 February 1940; Grant-in-aid, 30 December 1941; Trustees' Bulletin, October 1943.

23 E.B. Chain, 'Thirty Years of Penicillin Therapy', *Proceedings of the Royal Society of London*, B, 179 (1971), 293.

24 Wellcome Library, PP/EBC/B65, letter from Chain to *Evening Standard*, September 1953.

25 Wellcome Library, PP/EBC/ B109, letter from Chain to Joseph Trueta, 15 June 1973.

26 Personal information, N.G. Heatley.

27 Interview with Boyd Woodruff at Rutgers University, New Jersey, 7 October 2002.

28 Wellcome Library, GC 48/B3, notes by Norman Heatley on his relations with Chain.

29 Wellcome Library, PP/EBC/B109, letter from Chain to Joseph Trueta, 15 June 1973.

30 'The Oxford Unit', *British Medical Bulletin*, 2/1 (1944), 26.

31 Wellcome Library, GC/48/A1, Heatley's notebook, 20 July 1939– 29 March 1940; E.P. Abraham, E. Chain, C.M. Fletcher, H.W. Florey, A.D. Gardner, N.G. Heatley and M.A. Jennings, 'Further Observations on Penicillin', *Lancet*, 2 (16 August 1941), 177–88.

32 H.T. Clarke, J.R. Johnson and R. Robinson, *The Chemistry of Penicillin* (1949).

33 Royal Society, HF/1/3/12/2, Heatley's diary, 5 April 1940, 6 April 1940.

34 Wellcome Library, GC/48/B5, Heatley's diary, 25 May 1940, 26 May 1940.

35 Wellcome Library, PP/EBC/B41, 'What is Penicillin?'

36 Personal information, Norman Heatley.

37 Wellcome Library, GC/48/B5, Heatley's diary, 20 May 1940, 15 June 1940.

38 Wellcome Library, GC/48/B5, Heatley's diary, 15 July 1940.

39 A. Fleming, 'Chemotherapy for War Wounds: Comparisons and Combinations', *British Medical Journal*, 2 (1940), 715.

40 Royal Society, HF1/3/2/12/1, letter from Fleming to Florey, 15 November 1940.

41 Wellcome Library GC/48/B1, Heatley's notes.

42 Wellcome Library, GC/48/B5, Heatley's diary, 3 June 1940, 4 June 1940. He scoured Oxford grocers' shops for biscuit tins and then obtained 100 from Huntley and Palmer in Reading.

43 Wellcome Library, GC/48/B5, Heatley's diary, 30 May 1940, 18 October 1940, 31 October 1940, 18 November 1940, 23 December 1940.

44 Wellcome Library, PP/EBC/B104.

45 PRO, FD 1/3331, Medical Research Council, file on grants to Professor H.W. Florey.

46 Abraham *et al.*, 'Further Observations on Penicillin', 177–88.

47 C.M. Fletcher, 'First Clinical Use of Penicillin', *British Medical Journal*, 289 (1984), 22–9.

48 H. Ellis, 'Penicillin Forty Years On', St Mary's Hospital Archives, Audio-Visual Department files, undated cutting.

49 Abraham *et al.*, 'Further Observations on Penicillin', 177–88.

50 Fletcher, 'First Clinical Use of Penicillin', 22–9.

51 Abraham *et al.*, 'Further Observations on Penicillin', 177–88.

52 Wellcome Library, PP/EBC/B41, 'What is Penicillin?'

53 *British Medical Journal*, 2 (30 August 1941), 310.

54 *British Medical Journal*, 2 (13 September 1941), 386.

55 *Daily Herald*, 4 September 1941; *Listener*, 9 October 1941; *Tit Bits*, 21 November 1941; *Smiths Weekly*, 29 November 1941; *Nursing Times*, 4 October 1941; *Pharmaceutical Journal*, 25 October 1941; *Veterinary Record*, 4 October 1941.

56 Rockefeller Archive Center, North Tarrytown, NY, RF R.G. 1–1,

Project Series 40D England, Box 37, F 481, grant-in-aid to Howard Florey, 19 June 1941.

57 Royal Society, HF1/3/12/4, letter from Florey to Heatley, 9 October 1941.

58 Royal Society, HF1/3/2/18, Florey to Mellanby, 11 December 1942.

59 C. Kennedy, *ICI, the Company that has Changed our Lives* (1993), p. 122.

60 Pfizer Records Centre, Sandwich, Kent, Kemball Bishop Records, Box 96B-2E, file 1, letter from J.E. Whitehall, Managing Director, to Florey, 20 August 1942.

61 Pfizer Records Centre, Sandwich, Kent, Kemball Bishop Records, Box 96B–2E, file 1, letter from Whitehall to Florey, 23 February 1942.

62 Pfizer Records Centre, Sandwich, Kent, Kemball Bishop Records, Box 96B–2E, file 7, J.G. Barnes, 'Early Work on Penicillin in England with Special Reference to Bromley', May 1971.

63 M.E. Florey and H.W. Florey, 'General and Local Administration of Penicillin', *Lancet*, 1 (27 March 1943), 387–97.

Chapter Seven

1 Royal Society, HF/1/1/11, Florey's notebook, 13 August 1942.

2 Royal Society, HF/1/3/2/12/3, letter from Fleming to Florey, 16 August 1942.

3 BL Add. MS 56183, Harry Lambert case notes; A. Fleming, 'Streptococcal Meningitis Treated with Penicillin: Measurement of the Bacteriostatic Power of Blood and Cerebrospinal Fluid', *Lancet*, 2 (9 October 1943), 434–8.

4 C.L. Dunn, *The Emergency Medical Services* (1952), p. 44.

5 BL Add. MS 56219, Helen Buckley.

6 Personal information, Phyllis French, née Norton.

7 BL Add. MS 56216, Peggy McMillan.

8 BL Add. MS 56216, Dan Stratful.

9 BL Add. MS 56217, Anthony M. Ritchie.

10 BL Add. MS 56216, Peggy McMillan; BL Add. MS 56217, Mollie Ritchie.

11 BL Add. MS 56219, V.D. Allison.

12 BL Add. MS 56221, Henry Nash.

13 BL Add. MS 56219, Helen Buckley.

14 BL Add. MS 56217, Reginald Hudson; BL Add. MS 56219, V.D. Allison.

15 Personal information, Dr Robert Fleming.

16 BL Add. MS 56113, letter from Fleming to Duncan, 24 March 1942, letter from Duncan to Alex [Fleming], 26 March 1942.

17 BL Add. MS 56113, letter from Fleming to Davidson Pratt, 28 April 1942.

18 BL Add. MS 56113, letter from Fleming to Andrew [Duncan], 30 May 1942, report by Fleming on Dr Wiesner's work.

19 BL Add. MS 56113, letter from J. Davidson Pratt to Fleming, 9 June 1942, letter from Fleming to Davidson Pratt, 10 June 1942.

20 BL Add. MS 56113, letter from Dr F.H.K. Green of Medical Research Council, on behalf of Major-General Poole of the War Office, to Fleming, 24 July 1942, Fleming's report on Marfanil, 11 August 1942.

21 BL Add. MS 56112, minutes of first meeting of General Penicillin

Committee, 25 September 1942.

22 R.P.T. Davenport-Hines and Judy Slinn, *Glaxo: a History to 1962* (1992), pp. 138–9.

23 BL Add. MS 56112, minutes of General Penicillin Committee, 25 September 1942.

24 BL Add. MS 56112, minutes of General Penicillin Committee, 15 March 1943.

25 BL Add. MS 56113, letter from Dr L.T. Clark of Parke Davis, Detroit, 29 November 1940; letter from J. Stanley White of Parke Davis to Fleming, 7 February 1941.

26 C. Kennedy, *ICI: the Company that Changed our Lives* (1993), p. 122; 'The Production of Penicillin – a Short Account of Imperial Chemical Industries Plant', *Industrial Chemist* (November 1944), 592–4.

27 Pfizer Records Centre, Sandwich, Kent, Kemball Bishop Records, Box 96B–2E, file 1, letter from J.E. Whitehall, Managing Director, to Florey, 20 August 1942.

28 Davenport-Hines and Slinn, *Glaxo: a History*, pp. 144–6

29 W. Howard Hughes, *Alexander Fleming and Penicillin* (1974), p. 73.

30 R. Hare, *The Birth of Penicillin* (1970), p. 31.

31 Royal Society, HF/1/3/2/12/2, letter from Florey to Fleming, 24 February 1941.

32 Royal Society, HF/1/3/2/10/5, Fleming to Florey, 25 April 1941.

33 BL Add. MS 56221, R.J.V. Pulvertaft.

34 Combined Intelligence Objectives report, file xxiv-16, 'Pharmaceutical Targets Visited in Southern Germany, 19–26 May 1945', pp. 4–5. Gilbert Schama of Loughborough University brought this reference to my attention.

35 *Evening News*, 26 January 1945.

36 BL Add. MS 56112, minutes of General Penicillin Committee, 25 September 1942.

37 Pfizer Records Centre, Sandwich, Kent, Kemball Bishop Records, Box 96B–2E, file 2, letter from Whitehall to L. Theodore Hann, Ministry of Supply, 15 August 1944.

38 BL Add. MS 56112, minutes of General Penicillin Committee, 13 October 1942.

39 Pfizer Records Centre, Sandwich, Kent, Kemball Bishop Records, Box 96B–2E, file 1, letter from Florey to Whitehall, 23 September 1942.

40 *Ibid.*, file 2, letter from Whitehall to Arthur Mortimer, 13 May 1943.

41 *Ibid.*, letter from Mortimer to Whitehall, 16 May 1943.

42 *Ibid.*, file 1, letter from Florey to Whitehall, 12 May 1943; file 2, letter from Whitehall to Mortimer, 24 September 1943.

43 BL Add. MS 56112, minutes of General Penicillin Committee, 25 September 1942.

44 Pfizer Records Centre, Sandwich, Kent, Kemball Bishop Records, Box 96B–2E, file 7, report by John Gray Barnes, 'Early Work on Penicillin Production in England, with Special Reference to Bromley', May 1971.

45 *Ibid.*, file 1, letter from Whitehall to Florey, 4 November 1942, letter from Whitehall to Florey, 11 May 1943.

46 BL Add. MS 56112, minutes of General Penicillin Committee, 22 December 1943.

47 *Ibid.*, 5 April 1944.

48 *Ibid.*, 11 May 1944.

49 *Ibid.*, 5 April 1944, 11 May 1944.

50 *Ibid.*, speech by John Wilmot, Minister of Supply, at press conference on penicillin, 1 May 1946.

51 *Ibid.*, minutes of General Penicillin Committee, 15 March 1943.

52 R.J.V. Pulvertaft, 'Local Therapy of War Wounds with Penicillin', *Lancet*, 2 (18 September 1943), 341–6.

53 Hellenic Foundation for Basic Medical Research Alexander Fleming, Athens, letter from Lord McGowan to Fleming, 30 June 1943; Royal Society, HF/1/3/2/1/28, letter from Lord McGowan to Florey, 30 June 1943.

54 Personal information, John Liddell, who donated the camera in 1996 to the Alexander Fleming Laboratory Museum.

55 H.W. Florey and H. Cairns, *A Preliminary Report to the War Office and Medical Research Council on Investigations Concerning the Use of Penicillin in War Wounds* (October 1943); L.P. Garrold, 'The Treatment of War Wounds with Penicillin', *British Medical Journal*, 2 (11 December 1943), 755–6; H.W. Florey and H. Cairns, 'Penicillin in Warfare', *British Journal of Surgery*, 32 (1944), 110–224.

56 J. Howie, 'Gonorrhoea: a Question of Tactics', *British Medical Journal*, 2 (1979), 1631.

57 *Sunday Chronicle*, 19 September 1943.

58 BL Add. MS 56112, minutes of General Penicillin Committee, 8 July 1943.

59 *Ibid.*, speech by John Wilmot, Minister of Supply, at press conference on penicillin, 1 May 1946.

60 *Ibid.*, minutes of General Penicillin Committee, 22 December 1943.

61 BL Add. MS 56114, letter from H.R.H. Princess George of Greece to Fleming, 29 January 1945.

62 *Daily Telegraph*, 14 February 1944.

63 *Evening Standard*, 21 September 1944.

64 *Evening News*, 19 October 1944.

65 PRO, FO 370/926, requests for penicillin from abroad, 1944–5.

66 PRO, FO 370/926, Foreign Office note on case of Señor Moral Figuerres, 13 August 1944.

67 BL Add. MS 56114, letter from 'Giles' [Stuart Craddock] to Fleming, 16 February 1945; letter from Fleming to Craddock, 26 February 1945.

68 Personal information from Iain Craddock. See also D. Hillebrandt, 'The Circle of Medical History', *Lancet*, 355/9215 (6 May 2000). This article by a Holsworthy GP says that the dog belonged to one of his patients, but Iain Craddock has corrected the story and said that the dog was his, not a neighbour's.

69 *Smiths Weekly*, 29 November 1941.

70 BL Add. MS 56220, Arthur Mortimer.

71 BL Add. MS 56116, letter from Dennis Dooley to Fleming, 13 March 1947, letter from Fleming to Dooley, 14 March 1947.

72 Quoted in L.J. Ludovici, *Fleming, Discoverer of Penicillin* (1952), p. 196.

73 Personal information, John Ballantyne.

74 Personal information, George Bonney; St Mary's Hospital

Archives, interview with Jack Litchfield, 27 November 1996.

75 Interview at Science Museum with Jessie Carter, 4 September 2002.

76 Personal information, Margaret Child (née Bray).

77 Professor Sir Stanley Peart, and quoted by A.W. Frankland, interview 7 May 2003.

78 St Mary's Hospital Archives, interview with Tom Kemp, 22 January 1997.

79 Gwyn Macfarlane asserts that apart from his approach to Sir Andrew Duncan and membership of the Penicillin Committee, 'Fleming had taken no part in the production or the clinical use of penicillin' (G. Macfarlane, *Alexander Fleming: the Man and the Myth* (1984), p. 198). In fact he was very involved in its clinical use and even in production through the testing of batches for Glaxo.

80 BL Add. MS 56113, letter from Hurran of Glaxo to Fleming, 10 May 1944; letter from Hurran to Fleming, 17 May 1944.

81 A. Fleming, M.Y. Young, J. Suchet and A.J.E. Rowe, 'Penicillin Content of Blood Serum after Various Doses of Penicillin by Various Routes', *Lancet*, 2 (1944), 621.

82 *The Times*, 27 August 1942.

83 *The Times*, 31 August 1942.

84 *The Times*, 2 September 1942.

85 L. Bickel, *Rise up to Life: A Biography of Howard Walter Florey who Gave Penicillin to the World* (1972), pp. 173–4.

86 T.I. Williams, *Howard Florey: Penicillin and After* (1984), pp. 45–6.

87 *News Chronicle*, 5 September 1942.

88 *Evening Standard*, 31 August 1942; *Tit Bits*, 9 October 1942.

89 *Glasgow Herald*, 1 September 1942; *Kilmarnock Standard*, 24 July 1943.

90 *Dublin Sunday Independent*, 20 September 1942.

91 Royal Society, HF/1/3/15/1, *Marching on*, script for *BBC*, 15 October 1942.

92 W.S. Churchill, *The Second World War: Closing the Ring* (1952), vol. 5, p. 373.

93 *Daily Telegraph and Morning Post*, 21 December 1943.

94 See Chapter 2 for a refutation.

95 BL Add. MS 56217, Lord Beaverbrook.

96 Royal Society, HF/1/3/2/12, letter from Fleming to Florey, 29 August 1942.

97 *Ibid.*, letter from Fleming to Florey, 2 September 1942.

98 Royal Society, HF/1/3/2/12/5, letter from Fleming to Florey, 7 September 1942.

99 BL Add. MS 56112, minutes of General Penicillin Council, 25 September 1942, 13 October 1942, 15 March 1943, 8 July 1943.

100 Royal Society, HF/1/3/15/1–4, Florey's press cuttings books; Biomedical Sciences Research Centre Alexander Fleming, Vari, Greece, Fleming's press cuttings, July–August 1943.

101 BL Add. MS 56112, minutes of General Penicillin Committee, 6 October 1943.

102 Royal Society, HF/1/3/4/3/1, letter from Florey to Dale, 11 December 1942.

103 *Ibid.*, HF/1/3/4/3/2, letter from Dale to Florey, 17 December 1942.

104 Royal Society, EC/1943/07, election

certificate for Alexander Fleming, 18 March 1943. The proposers were Almroth E. Wright, J.C.G. Ledingham, James Walter McLeod, Charles J. Martin, Harold Raistrick, C.H. Andrews, Paul Fildes, Joseph A. Arkwright and H.W. Florey.

105 BL Add. MS 56218, Douglas MacLeod.

106 *The Recorder*, 27 November 1943.

107 BL Add. MS 56110, address of Norman T. Kirk, 13 December 1943.

108 *News Chronicle*, 10 December 1943.

109 *Picture Post*, 8 January 1944.

110 *Time*, 15 May 1944.

111 BL Add. MS 56110, letter from Eric Hodgkins, Editorial Vice-President of *Time*, to Fleming, 1 August 1944.

112 National Academy of Sciences, Washington DC, Committees on Military Medicine, penicillin correspondence, penicillin, file 1, letter from J.F. Fulton to Chester S. Keefer, 7 July 1944.

113 *Ibid.*, letter from J.F. Fulton to Chester S. Keefer, 14 July 1944.

114 Royal Society, HF/1/3/2/18/107, letter from Florey to Mellanby, 19 June 1944.

115 PRO, PREM 4/88/7, Prime Minister's papers, speech of Churchill at Royal College of Physicians, 2 March 1944.

116 Royal Society, HF/1/3/2/18/108, letter from Mellanby to Florey, 30 June 1944.

117 PRO, FD1/6668, letter from Howard Jones, Medical Department of British Council, to F.H.K. Green, Medical Research Council, 26 February 1944.

118 Royal Society, HF/1/3/2/11/4, notes to Basil Wright, 1944.

119 Royal Society, HF/1/3/2/11/20, letter

from Florey to Basil Wright, 30 May 1944.

120 Royal Society, HF/1/3/2/11/59, letter from Florey to Alexander Shaw, Realist Film Unit, 10 February 1945.

121 Personal information, Wolfgang Suschitzky, cameraman on the ICI film.

122 *Daily Mail*, 11 February 1944.

123 *Hansard*, 24 February 1944.

124 Letter from D'Arcy W. Thompson, *The Times*, 7 March 1944.

125 Quoted in *Daily Sketch*, 12 June 1944; *The Times*, 12 June 1944.

126 *Daily Herald*, 15 June 1944.

127 *Sunday Express*, 9 July 1944.

128 Private information from Barbara Gammon (née Parry).

129 Private information from Margaret Parfitt (formerly Mant née Cummins), Sister at the Base Hospital, Basingstoke in 1944.

130 *St Mary's Hospital Gazette*, 51/8 (1945), 113–14; personal information, John Hofmeyr.

131 St Mary's Hospital Archives, minutes of Inoculation Department House Committee, 17 May 1944.

132 *Ibid.*, 16 May 1945.

133 'Centenary of the Hospital', *St Mary's Hospital Gazette*, 51/6 (1945), 85–6.

134 'Exhibition of Penicillin and Modern Medicine', *St Mary's Hospital Gazette*, 51/8 (1945), 120–1.

135 St Mary's Hospital Archives, SM/AD 46/16, Annual Report of St Mary's Hospital (1947), p. 33. The hospital still awaits the complete rebuilding that was the hoped-for outcome of the appeal. The planned new Queen Elizabeth Wing was eventually opened in 1987 as the Queen Elizabeth the Queen Mother Wing.

Chapter Eight

1 BL Add. MS 56115, A. Fleming, report on visit to USA and Canada, [1945].

2 *Ibid.*

3 BL Add. MS 56215, John Cameron, November 1956.

4 Some of their comments he noted down in his diary; for example: 'Lord B. Talked about the Queen. Great admirer. Frightened of getting fat. No use for Edward. Baldwin great job. Wonders whether Elizabeth will give way to a male' (BL Add. MS 56187, diary, 24 May 1945).

5 Fleming made frequent applications to finance work at the Wright Fleming Institute and shortly before his death it was agreed that the Fund should be used to grant him a pension of £1,000 p.a. to supplement his pension of £2,000 from the Institute (St Mary's Hospital Archives, WF 1/1, minutes of Council of Wright Fleming Institute, 17 December 1953). By 1959 the Trustees of the University of Pennsylvania funded his widow to sort out his papers (St Mary's Hospital Archives, WF 1/2, minutes of Council of Wright Fleming Institute, 9 December 1959, 20 January 1960). Amey Hutchins of the University of Pennsylvania Archives has been unable to trace any reference to the Alexander Fleming Memorial Fund in the records of the Office of Treasurer or the accounts of either the University of Pennsylvania or the University Hospital. Staff in the Gift Planning Department of the Office of the Development and Alumni Relations and in the Trust Administration Department have also been unable to find any trace of the Fund (communication to the author, 25 July 2002).

6 Biomedical Sciences Research Centre Alexander Fleming, Vari, Athens, Fleming's diary of North American tour 1945.

7 *New Haven Register*, 11 March 1962.

8 BL Add. MS 56216, Roger Lee.

9 BL Add. MS 56115, report by Fleming on visit to USA and Canada [1945].

10 *Times* (Chicago), 17 July 1945.

11 BL Add. MS 5615, John Cameron, 1956.

12 Rockefeller Archive Center, North Tarrytown, NY, record group 1.1, series 401, box 37, file 481, grant-in-aid from Rockefeller Foundation of $6,000 to provide travel funds and living expenses to Professor H.W. Florey and Dr Norman G. Heatley, 19 June 1941.

13 Royal Society, HF/1/3/12/2, extract from personal diary of Norman Heatley, 25 April 1941.

14 Wellcome Library, PP/EBC, B104, Chain's comments on penicillin.

15 Royal Society, HF/1/3/12/2, extract from personal diary of Norman Heatley, 26 June 1941.

16 *Ibid.*, 3 July 1941.

17 *Ibid.*, 4 July 1941.

18 *Ibid.*, 9 July 1941.

19 L.J. Ludovici, *Alexander Fleming, Discoverer of Penicillin* (1952), p. 178.

20 *Daily Pantograph* (Bloomington, Illinois), 2 October 1939; United States Department of Agriculture,

National Center for Agricultural Utilization Research, Peoria, Illinois, programme for Cornerstone ceremonies at Northern Regional Research Laboratory, 18 October 1939; *Peoria Star*, 19 October 1939; *Cedar Rapids Gazette*, 8 January 1941.

21 *Technical Association of the Pulp and Paper Industry Bulletin*, 55 (30 June 1945).

22 National Archives, College Park, Maryland, Record Group 97, Bureau of Agricultural and Industrial Chemistry, series 41, Northern Regional Research Laboratory, file 1, telegram from P.A. Wells to O.E. May, 9 July 1941.

23 *Ibid.*, telegram from O.E. May to P.A. Wells, 10 July 1941.

24 *Ibid.*, memorandum of conference on 'Pilot Scale Production of Bacteriostatic Material from Fleming's Penicillium in Connection with Medical Defence Plans', 9 July 1941; memorandum from P.A. Wells to Dr May, 10 July 1941.

25 *Ibid.*, conference on production of penicillin, 15 July 1941.

26 Royal Society, HF/1/3/2/15, letters from Heatley to Florey, 7 December 1941, 2 May 1942.

27 Wellcome Library GC/48, notes made by N. Heatley on board clipper between Lisbon and New York, notes made from memory because Heatley's notebooks had been sealed by the UK censors, 1–2 July 1941.

28 National Archives, College Park, Maryland, Record Group 97, Bureau of Agricultural and Industrial Chemistry, series 40, notebook of Charles Thom, notes of

cultures of penicillin received, '5112 = 5112.1. A. Raistrick, *P. rubrum* isolated by Fleming', 14 May 1930; '5767 = 5112.1 culture brought by and received from Heatley of Oxford', 14 July 1941.

29 Wellcome Library, GC/48, statement on research conducted by A.J. Moyer.

30 Personal information given to author, after delivering the 2001 Andrew J. Moyer Lecture, 'Penicillin in Peace and War, 1928–1945', National Center for Agricultural Utilization Research, 12 July 2001.

31 Royal Society, HF/1/3/2/15, letter from Heatley to Florey, 10 November 1941; letter from Florey to Heatley, 3 December 1941.

32 Florey could not resist surmising after the Japanese attack on Pearl Harbor, 'It will be very interesting to know the reaction of people like Moyer' (Royal Society, HF/1/3/2/15, letter from Florey to Heatley, 8 December 1941). Heatley too was curious about the reaction in Peoria to the outbreak of war: 'The Japanese blow came as a terrific surprise to everyone here, and I only wish I could have been in Peoria during this last week!' (Royal Society, HF/1/3/2/15, letter from Heatley to Florey, 14 December 1941).

33 Royal Society, HF/1/3/2/15, letter from Heatley to Florey, 10 November 1941.

34 National Archives, College Park, Maryland, Record Group 97, Bureau of Agricultural and Industrial Chemistry, series 41, Northern Regional Research Laboratory, file 2, report by Coghill on nutritional requirements of *Penicillium notatum*,

11 October 1941; letter from O.E. May to G.E. Hilbert, 24 November 1941; report on contract M-838, 26 August 1942.

35 Kenneth B. Raper, 'The Penicillin Saga Remembered', *American Society for Industrial Microbiology News*, 44/12 (1978), 645–53; National Archives, College Park, Maryland, Record Group 97, Bureau of Agricultural and Industrial Chemistry, series 41, Northern Regional Research Laboratory, file 5, letter from K.B. Raper to Alexander Fleming, 30 November 1945.

36 *Ibid.*, file 2, report on cooperative work on penicillin by A.J. Moyer and N.G. Heatley, 2 December 1942.

37 *Ibid.*, 'Improved Methods for Production of Penicillin', manuscript of unpublished paper by Moyer and Heatley, 2 December 1941.

38 F. H. Stodola, J.L. Wachtel, A.J. Moyer and R.D. Coghill, 'Penitrinic Acid: a New Pigment from *Penicillium notatum*', *Journal of Biological Chemistry*, 159/1 (June 1945), 67–70; A.J. Moyer and R.D. Coghill, 'Penicillin: production of Penicillin by Surface Cultures', *Journal of Bacteriology*, 1/1 (January 1946), 57–77; A.J. Moyer and R.D. Coghill, 'Penicillin: the Laboratory Scale Production of Penicillin in Submerged Culture by *Penicillium notatum Westling* (NRRL 832)', *Journal of Bacteriology*, 51/1 (January 1946), 79–93; W.H. Schmidt and A.J. Moyer, 'Penicillin: Methods of Assay', *Journal of Bacteriology*, 47/2 (February 1946), 199–208.

39 US Department of Agriculture National Center for Agricultural Utilization Research, Peoria, Illinois, NRRL 832.

40 Raper, 'The Penicillin Saga Remembered', 650.

41 M. Scoutaris, 'Moldy Mary and the Illinois Fruit and Vegetable Company', *Pharmacy in History*, 38/4 (1996), 175–7.

42 *Scottish Daily Express*, 22 August 1947; 'Mouldy Mary Brought in a Decayed Antelope', *Press and Journal*, 22 August 1947. The reporter had obviously misheard cantaloupe as antelope.

43 National Center for Agricultural Utilization Research, mycology register of accessions, NRRL 1951.

44 R.D. Coghill and R.S. Koch, 'Penicillin: a Wartime Accomplishment', *Chemical and Engineering News*, 23/24 (25 December 1945), 2311–12.

45 *Utica Nebraska Sun*, 26 August 1943.

46 Royal Society, HF/1/3/2/31, report from Florey to Dr Warren Weaver, Rockefeller Foundation, 9 September 1941.

47 I. Stewart, *Organising Scientific Research for War: the Administrative History of the Office of Scientific Research and Development* (1948).

48 G.P. Zachary, *Endless Frontier: Vannevar Bush, Architect of the American Century*, 1997.

49 Royal Society, HF/1/3/2/31, report from Florey to Dr Warren Weaver, Rockefeller Foundation, 9 September 1941.

50 National Archives, College Park, Maryland, Record Group 227,

Office of Scientific Research and Development, series E-162, Committee for Medical Research, meeting 6, p. 2, minutes, 2 October 1941.

51 *Ibid.*, series E-165, Committee for Medical Research, minutes of Penicillin Conference, 8 October 1941.

52 *Ibid.*, Series E-162, Committee for Medical Research, meeting 12, p. 6, minutes, 19 November 1941.

53 *Ibid.*, Series E-165, Committee for Medical Research, minutes of Penicillin Conference, 17 December 1941.

54 National Archives, College Park, Maryland, Record Group 97, Bureau of Agricultural and Industrial Chemistry, series 41, Northern Regional Research Laboratory, file 2, Memorandum by R.D. Coghill on Penicillin Conference and visit to various industrial companies in New York City, 16–23 December 1941.

55 T. Mahoney, *The Merchants of Life: an Account of the American Pharmaceutical Industry* (1959), p. 197.

56 Interview with Boyd Woodruff, 7 October 2002.

57 'Penicillin Data Exempted from Antitrust Laws', *Oil, Paint and Drug Reporter*, 20 December 1944.

58 National Archives, College Park, Maryland, Record Group 227, Office of Scientific Research and Development, series E-165, Committee for Medical Research, general records, letter from J.T. Connor to Oscar Cox, Solicitor General, requesting assistance of anti-trust expert to work out contractual arrangements over collaboration of commercial firms in synthesis programme to avoid 'monopolistic control . . . contrary to the public interest', 5 October 1943.

59 *Ibid.*, penicillin file, sample letter from A.N. Richards to W.J. McManus, War Production Board, endorsing requests for priorities in allocation of materials, 18 March 1943.

60 R.D. Coghill, 'The Development of Penicillin Strains', in A. Elden (ed.), *The History of Penicillin Production*, American Institute of Chemical Engineers, Chemical Engineering Progress Symposium, 66/100 (1970), 14–15; P. Neushul, 'Science, Government and the Mass Production of Penicillin', *Journal of the History of Medicine and the Allied Sciences*, 48 (1993) 371–95.

61 W.H. Helfand, H.B. Woodruff, K.M.H. Coleman and D.L. Cowen, 'Wartime Industrial Development of Penicillin in the United States', in J. Parascandola (ed.), *History of Antibiotics: a Symposium* (1980), pp. 31–56.

62 National Archives, College Park, Maryland, Record Group 227, Office of Scientific Research and Development, series E-165, Committee on Medical Research, general records, letter from A.N. Richards to C.H. Matthews junior, Chief of Bureau of Priorities, War Production Board, 28 February, 1942; letter from Harrop of Squibb to A.N. Richards, 20 May 1942.

63 A. Elder, 'The Role of the Government in the Penicillin

Program', in Elder, *The History of Penicillin Production*, pp. 10–11.

64 National Archives, College Park, Maryland, Record Group 227, Office of Scientific Research and Development, series E-1, General records, special project on penicillin, letter from Vannevar Bush to Elihu Root, junior, 27 April 1943.

65 S. Mines, *Pfizer: an Informal History* (1978), p. 73.

66 National Archives, College Park, Maryland, Record Group 227, Office of Scientific Research and Development, series E-162, Committee on Medical Research, minutes of 65th meeting, 27 May 1943.

67 National Archives, College Park, Maryland, Record Group 97, Bureau of Agricultural and Industrial Chemistry, series 41, Northern Regional Research Laboratory, file 2, letter from Coghill to Richards, 6 March 1943: 'I feel that they will shortly be able to produce more penicillin than any other company with the exception of Merck and Squibb.' National Archives, College Park, Maryland, Record Group 227, Office of Scientific Research and Development, series E-165, Committee on Medical Research, general records, letter from A.N. Richards to W.J. McManus, 18 March 1943.

68 Pfizer, New York, Pfizer Penicillin papers, Gladys Hobby records, series 5, Pfizer history, box 38, folder 6, letter from John L. Smith to John Powers, 16 October 1941.

69 *Ibid.*, report by Jasper Kane on third penicillin conference held on 17 December 1941 at University

Club, New York City, 24 December 1941.

70 *Ibid.*, folder 7, letter from J.L. Smith to A.N. Richards, 14 December 1942.

71 *Ibid.*, report by Jasper Kane to J.L. Smith on expansion of penicillin submerged fermentation, 27 August 1943.

72 Mines, *Pfizer: an informal history*, p. 75.

73 Pfizer, New York, Pfizer Penicillin papers, Gladys Hobby records, series 5, Pfizer history, box 38, folder 7, note in pay packets of all contractors, 22 November 1943.

74 *Ibid.*, folder 8, annual report of Works Committee to Board of Directors, 7 March 1945.

75 *Ibid.*, folder 8, letter from Major General Lull to J.F. Smith, 4 July 1944.

76 J.E. McKeen, 'The Production of Penicillin', *Transactions of American institute of Chemical Engineers*, 40/6 (25 December 1944), 747–58.

77 Pfizer, New York, Pfizer Penicillin papers, Gladys Hobby records, series 5, Pfizer history, box 38, folder 8, report on penicillin by a visitor from Squibb, 30 March 1944.

78 Personal communication, Dr Elmer Gaden, 9 November 2002.

79 Personal communication, Dr Thomas Lees, 28 September 2002.

80 Interview with Boyd Woodruff, 7 October 2002.

81 National Archives, College Park, Maryland, Record Group 227, Office of Scientific Research and Development, series E-165, Committee on Medical Research, general papers, letter from A.N. Richards to Cutter, Ben Venue,

Cheplin, Schenley and Heyden, 9 October 1943.

82 R. Hare, *The Birth of Penicillin and the Disarming of Microbes* (1970), p. 177.

83 BL Add. MS 56112, General Penicillin Committee, memorandum from Sir Henry Dale, 12 August 1944.

84 R.P.T. Davenport-Hines and J. Slinn, *Glaxo: a History to 1962* (1992), pp. 147–8.

85 National Archives, College Park, Maryland, Record Group 227, Office of Scientific Research and Development, series E-162, Committee on Medical Research, minutes of 68th meeting, 1 July 1943; Record Group 227, Office of Scientific Research and Development, series E-165, Committee on Medical Research, general records, report by Chester Keefer on visit to Bushnell General Hospital, May 1943.

86 *Ibid.*, general papers, letter from Colonel Robert M. Hardaway to A.N. Richards, 1 June 1943.

87 *Ibid.*, letter from Champ Lyons to A.N. Richards, 1 April 1943.

88 *Ibid.*, E-163 contractors' reports, OEM cmr-275, L4, C. Lyons, F.B. Queen, H. Hollenberg, J.S. Sweeney and A.J. Ingram, *Penicillin Therapy for Septic Compound Fractures in a Military Hospital: a Report of the Investigative Unit of the Committee on Medical Research at the Bushnell General Hospital*, n.d.

89 National Archives, College Park, Maryland, Record Group 227, Office of Scientific Research and Development, series E-165,

Committee on Medical Research, general papers, letter from A.N. Richards to Major-General Norman T. Kirk, 5 June 1943.

90 J.B. Coates, *Surgery in World War II: Activities of the Surgical Consultants* (1962), vol. 1, pp. 20–1.

91 National Archives, College Park, Maryland, Record Group 227, Office of Scientific Research and Development, series E-165, Committee on Medical Research, general papers, letter from A.N. Richards to Major-General Norman T. Kirk, 5 June 1943.

92 The impact of penicillin on military medicine was dramatic. In 1944, only 4.5 per cent of wounds in the US army proved fatal and 3.2 per cent in the US navy. An American soldier's chances of dying in the Second World War were 1 in 100, a third of the First World War rate and a tenth of the Civil War rate. This was thanks to improvements in blood transfusion as well as the availability of penicillin, but it was penicillin that hit the headlines (M. Clodfelter, *Warfare and Armed Conflicts: a Statistical Reference to Casualty and Other Figures, 1618–1991* (1992), pp. 962–3).

93 National Archives, College Park, Maryland, Record Group 179, War Production Board, document no. 533.8134, letter from J.N. McDonnell to Fred J. Stock, 4 June 1943.

94 P. Neushul, 'Fighting Research: Army Participation in the Clinical Testing and Mass Production of Penicillin during the Second World War', in R. Cooter, M. Harrison and

S. Sturdy (eds), *War, Medicine and Modernity* (1998), pp. 203–24.

95 A. Elder, 'The Role of the Government in the Penicillin Program', in Elder, *The History of Penicillin Production*, pp. 3–11.

96 *Ibid.*, p. 4.

97 Royal Society, HF/1/3/2/9, letter from Florey to Coghill, 4 November 1941.

98 e.g. BL Add. MS 56112, minutes of General Penicillin Committee, 25 September 1942, 22 December 1943, 20 March 1944.

99 BL Add. MS 56112, minutes of General Penicillin Committee, 13 October 1942, 15 March 1943.

100 BL Add. MS 56112, minutes of General Penicillin Committee, 22 February 1944.

101 National Archives, College Park, Maryland, Record Group 227, Office of Scientific Research and Development, series E-162, Committee on Medical Research, minutes of 78th meeting, 30 December 1943; minutes of 105th meeting, 15 February 1945. National Archives, College Park, Maryland, Record Group 227, Office of Scientific Research and Development, series E-165, Committee on Medical Research, general papers, letter from Sir Edward Mellanby to Vannevar Bush, 24 March 1944; letter from Vannevar Bush to Sir Ronald Campbell, British Embassy, 28 August 1944.

102 PRO, FD 1/7049, minutes of Penicillin Synthesis Committee, 1 November 1944.

103 National Academy of Sciences, Washington, DC, National Research Council Archives, Institute of Medicine, Committees on Military Medicine, correspondence, penicillin, file 1, letter from J.F. Fulton to Captain C.S. Stephenson, Bureau of Medicine and Surgery, Naval Department, 18 March 1942.

104 *Yale Medicine* (1999–2000); *New York Times*, obituary, 9 June 1999.

105 M.H. Dawson, G.L. Hobby, K. Meyer and E.J. Chafee, *Journal of Clinical Investigation*, 20 (1941), 434.

106 *New York Times*, 30 November 1942; *Time*, December 1942; *Harper's*, February 1943.

107 D.C. Bodenham, 'Infected Burns and Surface Wounds: the Value of Penicillin', *Lancet*, 2 (11 December 1943), 725–8.

108 C. Lyons, 'Problems of Infection and Chemotherapy', *Annals of Surgery*, 117 (1943), 99–100; J.C. Aub, H.K. Beecher, B. Cannon, S. Cobb, O. Cope, N.W. Faxon, C. Lyons, T. Mallory and R. Schatzki, *Management of the Cocoanut Grove Burns at the Massachusetts General Hospital* (1943).

109 *New York Journal-America*, 12 August 1943; *Milwaukee Sentinel*, 20 August 1943, 12 September 1943, 22 September 1943; *Newsweek*, 30 August 1943.

110 *Liberty, the Magazine of a Free People*, 22 July 1944.

111 *Sun Chicago*, 18 August 1943; *Tribune Chicago*, 18 August 1943.

112 National Archives, College Park, Maryland, Record Group 227, Office of Scientific Research and Development, series E-1, General records, special project on penicillin,

letter from Chester Keefer to
A.N. Richards, 8 February 1944.

113 *Ibid.*, Series E-165, Committee on
Medical Research, general papers,
memoranda on civil distribution of
penicillin, 27 April 1944, 28 April
1944.

114 D.P. Adams, *The Greatest Good for
the Greatest Number: Penicillin
Rationing on the American Home
Front, 1940–1945* (1991).

115 P. de Kruif, *Life among the Doctors*
(1949), pp. 210–51.

116 *New York World-Telegram*, 2 May
1946; *Nation's Business*, January
1949.

117 Coghill and Koch, 'Penicillin: a
Wartime Accomplishment', 2310.

118 *New York Times*, 15 March 1945.

119 J.C. Sheehan, *The Enchanted Ring:
the Untold Story of Penicillin*
(1982), p. 1. There were more than
39 major laboratories and over
1,000 chemists involved in the
synthetic penicillin project.

120 Coghill, 'The Development of
Penicillin Strains', in Elder, *The
History of Penicillin Production*,
p. 15.

Chapter Nine

1 BL Add. MS 56214, letter from
W.H. Howard Hughes.

2 BL Add. MS 56219, Victor Craxton.

3 BL Add. MS 56218, Lady Thomson.

4 BL Add. MS 56122; K. Brown,
'Alexander Fleming – Beyond
Penicillin', *Society for General
Microbiology Quarterly*, 22/1
(1995), 4–5.

5 BL Add. MS 56187, diary,
10 October 1946.

6 Alexander Fleming Laboratory
Museum: Freedom of Paddington,

17 May 1945; Freedom of Darvel,
26 October 1946; Freedom of
Chelsea, 16 March 1949.

7 BL Add. MS 56219, Bebe Daniels
and Ben Lyon.

8 A. Maurois, *The Life of Sir
Alexander Fleming, Discoverer of
Penicillin* (1959), p. 206.

9 BL Add. MS 56185, diary,
3–8 September 1945.

10 *Ibid.*, 5 September 1945.

11 BL Add. MS 56114, Report on
French trip [September, 1945].

12 'Saw Prince Regent. Ordinary young
man and apparently rather anxious
to please' (BL Add. MS 56185,
diary, 19 September 1945).

13 *Ibid.*, 19 September 1945.

14 Personal information, Denis Dooley.

15 BL Add. MS 56115, letter to Lee
Smith, British representative to the
Vatican, 5 November 1945.

16 A.L. Stalker, quoted in G.
Macfarlane, *Alexander Fleming: the
Man and the Myth* (1984),
pp. 219–20.

17 BL Add. MS 56186, diary,
30 September 1945, 1 October
1945.

18 BL Add. MS 56816, diary,
29 November 1945. Fleming's
assessment of the Italian Regent at
the time was very similar; see
n. 12.

19 BL Add. MS 56115, letter to
Physician in Charge of SAR the
Prince Regent of the Belgians,
6 December 1945.

20 BL Add. MS 56123, speech,
Louvain, 30 November 1945.

21 See Nanna Svartz, '1945 års
nobelpris I fysiologi och medicin',
Nordisk Medicine, 28/44
(2 November 1945), 2283–5.

22 e.g. *Daily Mail*, 17 October 1944;
    Times Herald, 18 October 1944;
    Boston Globe, 19 October 1944; see
    also Royal Society, HF/1/3/15/4 for
    a collection of press cuttings
    detailing news of the award and its
    subsequent refutation by the press.

23 BL Add. MS 56110, letter from
    Captain Maurice Welsch, US Army,
    8 December 1944; Letter to Captain
    Maurice Welsch, 18 December
    1944.

24 Nobel Archives, Karolinska Institute
    Stockholm, report by G. Liljestrand,
    20 November 1943, referred to in
    report by Anders Kristenson,
    27 August 1945.

25 On this occasion one of the
    examiners, Professor Svartz, came to
    the conclusion that while Fleming
    was eminently deserving of the
    Nobel Prize and Chain and Florey's
    input was also sufficiently valuable
    to merit consideration, their input
    was not of the same high calibre as
    Fleming's. Her colleague Professor
    Liljestrand thought that a way
    around the problem of differing
    degrees of merit would be to award
    50 per cent of the Prize to Fleming
    and to share the other half between
    Florey and Chain: 'Professor Svartz
    kom till resultatet, att Fleming var i
    eminent grad förtjänt av Nobelpris;
    Chains och Floreys insatser ansåg
    hon värda att belönas med
    Nobelpris, dock menade hon, att
    deras prestationer icke voro av
    samma höga klass som Flemings'
    ('Professor Svartz came to the
    conclusion that Fleming was
    eminently worthy of the Nobel Prize;
    the contributions by Chain and
    Florey were, in her view, also worthy

of being rewarded with the Nobel
Prize. However, it was her opinion
that their input was not of the same
magnitude as that of Fleming'),
Nobel Archives, Karolinska Institute,
Stockholm, report by G. Liljestrand,
20 August 1945.

26 Nobel Archives, Karolinska
    Institute, Stockholm, register of
    nominations, entries for Alexander
    Fleming, Howard Florey and Ernst
    Chain. Fleming received twenty
    nominations in all, while Florey
    received thirteen, all but one of
    which were jointly with Fleming,
    while Chain received one
    nomination jointly with Fleming and
    Florey. However, Chain's was an
    influential nomination coming from
    Liljestrand, Professor of
    Pharmacology at the Karolinska
    Institute and a member of the 1945
    Committee for Medicine or
    Physiology. There was also one
    nomination for A.N. Richards on
    account of his great contribution to
    the development of penicillin
    production from one of his
    colleagues, W.N. Bradley, at
    Philadelphia, but this was not
    pursued as his was not an original
    scientific or medical achievement as
    laid down by the Nobel statutes,
    Nobel Archives, Karolinska
    Institute, Stockholm, letter of
    nomination from W.N. Bradley,
    1944. A.N. Richards himself had
    nominated Fleming and Florey as
    joint recipients, letter of nomination
    from A.N. Richards, 14 November
    1944.

27 Seventeen additional nominations
    for Fleming, of which ten were
    jointly with Florey, were entered in

the registers under nominations received for 1946; Fleming also received a further nomination in 1952; Nobel Archives, Karolinska Institute, Stockholm, register of nominations, report of G. Liljestrand, 20 August 1945.

28 Letter from J.W. Fulton to P.J. Hennius, Swedish Legation, New York, 7 October 1944; cable to G. Liljestrand, Stockholm, 25 October 1944; letter to G. Liljestrand, 7 November 1944; cited in Gladys Hobby, *Penicillin: Meeting the Challenge* (1985), p. 303.

29 Nobel Archives, Karolinska Institute, Stockholm, reports of G. Liljestrand, 20 August 1945; Anders Kristenson, 27 August 1945; and Sven Hallerström, 31 August 1945. The reports by Liljestrand and Hellerström gave a general overview of the discovery, development, properties, production, therapeutic use and effects of penicillin and a summary of the views expressed in the nominations. Kristenson concentrated on the clinical impact of penicillin on dermatology and the venereal diseases.

30 BL Add. MS 56114, letter from Cecil Weir, 27 October 1945.

31 BL Add. MS 56186, diary, 8 December 1945.

32 BL Add. MS 56115, letter to John Campbell; 'Nobel Lecture on Penicillin, 11 December 1945', *Les Prix Nobels en 1945* (1947).

33 BL Add. MS 56117, letter from B. Kratochvil, Czechoslovak ambassador, 18 February 1948; invitation from Rector of Charles University, 19 February 1948.

34 BL Add. MS 56118, letter to Czechoslovak ambassador, 23 February 1948.

35 BL Add. MS 56118, letter to Ernest Bevin, Foreign Secretary, 23 February 1948; letter from B.C. MacDermot of Foreign Office, 25 March 1948.

36 BL Add. MS 56117, letter to Czechoslovak ambassador, 30 March 1948.

37 SMHA, Honorary doctorate awarded to Alexander Fleming by Univerzita Karlova, Praha, 8 April 1948, 7 April 1993.

38 K. Brown, 'Better Late than Never: a New Honour for Alexander Fleming', *St Mary's Hospital Gazette*, 99/3 (October 1993), 25–6.

39 BL Add. MS 56215, Stuart Craddock.

40 Personal information, Dr A.W. Frankland.

41 BL Add. MS 56190, diary, 31 May 1947. The trials were at West Dean, Sussex, and Fleming seems to have enjoyed the task.

42 BL Add. MS 56187, diary, 13 October 1946.

43 BL Add. MS 56216, G.E. Breen.

44 *Ibid.*

45 BL Add. MS 56187, diary, 9 October 1946.

46 BL Add. MS 56115, letter to Roger Lee.

47 PRO, BW 83/3, letter from C.R. Hiscocks to Lectures department, British Council, 15 May 1947.

48 Maurois, *Life of Fleming*, p. 199.

49 BL Add. MS 56115, John Cameron, 1956.

50 BL Add. MS 56115, report on visit to USA and Canada [1945].

51 BL Add. MS 56118, report on visit to Spain [June 1948].

52 Maurois, *Life of Fleming*, p. 229.

53 'Sir Alexander Fleming y su penicilina 26 May 1948', *La Vanguardia*, 23 August 1999.

54 BL Add. MS 56191, diary, 1 June 1948.

55 *Anales de Medicina y Cirugia, Barcelona*, 39 (September 1949), 139–52; *Real Academia de Medecina de Barcelona, sesión inaugural* (1949), pp. 18–20.

56 Ignasi M. Fossas, 'El Dr. Fleming a Montserrat', *Serra del Or* (1948), pp. 50–6. I am indebted to Lluis Martinez, sub-director of *Avui*, Barcelona for his great kindness in translating this article in the magazine of the Monastir de Montserrat from Catalan into Spanish for me.

57 *Fotos*, 5 June 1948.

58 BL Add. MS 56118, report on visit to Spain [June 1948].

59 BL Add. MS 56191, diary, 27 May 1948.

60 BL Add. MS 56191, diary, 3 June 1948. He had met the entertainer Josephine Baker previously and commented that he 'did not find her at all good looking', BL Add. MS 56118, report on visit to Spain, 1948.

61 BL Add. MS 5691, diary, 5 June 1948.

62 *Informaciones*, 8 June 1948.

63 Archivo General, Universidad Complutenses Madrid, personal file of Florencio Bustinza, 1942–72, copy made available by Carlos Flores Varela, Director.

64 E. Martinez Alonso, *Adventures of a Doctor* (1962), p. 164.

65 F. Bustinza Lachiondo, *De Pasteur à Fleming* (1945).

66 F. Bustinza Lachiondo, *Diez años de amistad con Sir Alexander Fleming* (1961), p. 56: 'Su escritura clara, elegante, como dibujada, me impresionó grandemente. En ella se reflejaban: orden, pulchritud, exactitud, rectitud, lógica, bondad, modestia, generosidad, buen gusto, aficines artísticas, extraordinaria penetración, serenidad y armonía mental; en resumen: su Aristocracia Espirituel. . . . a quien admiraba por su genio.' ('His clear handwriting, elegant, like a drawing, greatly impressed me. In it he is reflected: orderly, neat, accurate, upright, logical, kind, modest, generous, of good taste, artistically inclined, amazing insight, serenity and mental harmony; in short his spiritual nobility . . . whom I admire for his genius'.)

67 *Ibid*., p. 59: 'Tiene aire de distinción, dulzura, bondad, sinceridad, lo cual, unido a su encantadora modestia y a su sencillez, me cautivan immediatemente.'

68 *Ibid*., pp. 87–114.

69 A. Fleming and G. Smith, 'Some Methods for the Study of Moulds', *Transactions of the British Mycological Society*, 27 (1944), 13–19; K. Brown and D.E. Eveleigh, 'Preservation of Fungal Herbarium Cultures: the Sale of an Alexander Fleming *Penicillium notatum* Preserved Medallion', *Society for Industrial Mycology News*, 47/3 (May/June 1997), 116–18.

70 Personal information, H.M. Queen Elizabeth the Queen Mother, April 1994.

71 This particular specimen, dated
7 January 1952, was donated by
Edgar Lawley's daughter, Marjorie
Heath, to the Alexander Fleming
Laboratory Museum in 2003 after
she had repurchased the item that
had been stolen from her house
fourteen years previously. She was
alerted to its forthcoming sale at
Sothebys by a letter to *The Times*
from the present author correcting
a report that Edgar Lawley had
been Fleming's laboratory assistant.
See K. Brown, letters to *The Times*,
12 May 2003 and 1 July 2003.

72 Robert Fleming, *Sir Alexander
Fleming* (1958), pp. 70–1.

73 St Mary's Hospital Archives,
minutes of Inoculation Department
House Committee, 25 June 1946,
18 December 1946, 29 January
1947. At 1998 values this would
have had the spending value of
£66,030 in 1946, but by 1955 was
equivalent to only £43,620 as a
result of postwar inflation rates
(calculated using table of cost of
living and inflation rates given in
Whitaker's Almanack, London,
HMSO, 2001, p. 618).

74 BL Add. MS 56188, diary,
17 February 1947.

75 *Ibid.*

76 BL Add. MS 56217, Howard
Hughes; BL Add. MS 56219,
A.W. Frankland.

77 See BL Add. MS 56116, letter from
Dr Lins of Rio de Janeiro asking for
a fellowship at the Wright Fleming
Institute, 20 November 1946, for an
example of such an application.

78 BL Add. MS 56215, R. Borghi.

79 BL Add. MS 56217, W. Howard
Hughes.

80 BL Add. MS 56217, C.B. Dyson.

81 BL Add. MS 56217, W. Howard
Hughes.

82 BL Add. MS 56219, Victor Craxton.

83 BL Add. MS 56217, W. Clayden.

84 A. Fleming and C. Smith,
'Estimation of Penicillin in Serum',
Lancet, 1 (1947), 140; A. Fleming,
'The Role of Penicillin in Surgical
Practice', *Journal International de
Chirurgie*, 7 (1947), 184; A. Fleming
and E.W. Fish, 'Influence of
Penicillin on the Coagulation of the
Blood with Especial Reference to
Certain Dental Operations', *British
Medical Journal*, 2 (1947), 242;
A. Fleming, W.H. Hughes and
J.R. Kramer, 'Morphological
Changes in Some Bacteria Grown in
the Presence of Penicillin', *Journal of
General Microbiology*, 3 (1949),
p. xxiii.

85 Hellenic Foundation for Basic
Medical Research Alexander
Fleming, Athens, file of Fleming's
correspondence relating to the
treatment of patients, 1943–55.

86 A. Fleming, A. Voureka,
I.R.H. Kramer and W.H. Hughes,
'The Morphology and Motility of
Proteus vulgaris and Other
Organisms Cultured in the Presence
of Penicillin', *Journal of General
Microbiology*, 4 (1950), 257;
A. Fleming, 'Further Observations
on the Motility of *Proteus vulgaris*
Grown on Penicillin Agar', *Journal
of General Microbiology*, 4 (1950),
457.

87 BL Add. MS 56120, letter from
Fleming to A. Pijper, 12 January
1951.

88 BL Add. MS 56188, diary,
21 February 1947.

89 *Ibid.*, 18 February 1947, 28 February 1947.
90 BL Add. MS 56217, Merlin Pryce.
91 BL Add. MS 56188, diary, 1 July 1947.
92 BL Add. MS, 56219, W.D. Brooks.
93 BL Add. MS 56190, diary, 26 August 1947.
94 BL Add. MS 56205, diary, 26 February 1953; Maurois, *Life of Fleming*, pp. 256–7.
95 Interview with Dr A.W. Frankland. Transcript in St Mary's Hospital Archives.
96 At St Mary's, as at many other voluntary hospitals, it was customary to refer to ward sisters by the name of their wards rather than by their surnames.
97 BL Add. MS 56219, A.W. Frankland. The sister on Almroth Wright ward was also highly regarded by the hospital authorities and was sent as night nurse to Winston Churchill at Chartwell and Chequers when he was recovering from a stroke when Prime Minister in 1953.
98 BL Add. MS 56192, diary, 12 June 1948.
99 Private information, Dr Robert Fleming.
100 BL Add MSS 56216, G.W.B. James.
101 Maurois, *Life of Fleming*, 1959, p. 232; BL Add. MS 56196, notes on Oklahoma visit, 1949.
102 BL Add. MS 56195, diary, 22 June–14 July 1949; BL Add. MS 56110, letter to Fleming, award of honorary membership from the Kiowa, 3 July 1949.
103 BL Add. MS 56197, diary, 26–30 July 1949; Biomedical Research Centre Alexander Fleming,

Vari, Freedom of Verona, 12 July 1949.
104 BL Add. MS 56119, letter from Conte Giovanni Armenise, President of Industries Chimichie Farmaceutiche, to Fleming, 25 October 1949.
105 Death certificate of Sarah M. Fleming, 1949. The certificate gives her age as 68, although in fact she was 75.
106 BL Add. MS 56216, Peggy Marshall.
107 BL Add. MS 56220, Harold Montgomery.
108 BL Add. MS 56217, Mollie Ritchie.
109 Robert Fleming, *Alexander Fleming* (1957), p. 79.
110 Letter from Fleming to Bustinza, 17 January 1950, reproduced in facsimile in Bustinza Lachiondo, *Diez años de amistad con Sir Alexander Fleming*, p. 141.
111 BL Add. MS 56194, diary, 16 September 1950.
112 BL Add. MS 56197, diary, 29–31 January 1950, 17 February 1950; BL Add. MS 56198, diary, 14 March 1950–4 April 1950.
113 BL Add. MS 56198, diary, 1 April 1950.
114 BL Add. MS 56200, diary, 6 June 1950.
115 BL Add. MS 56108, letter from Fleming to Olympio O.R. da Fonseca, president of the Congress, 8 May 1950.
116 BL Add. MS 56108, report by Fleming to the University of London on the International Congress of Microbiology, 17–24 August 1950.
117 BL Add. MS 56218, Gladys Hobby.
118 BL Add. MS 56203, diary, 30 October 1951.

119 BL Add. MS 56120, letter from Denis Dooley to Fleming, 10 November 1951.

120 BL Add. MS 56202, diary, 8 April 1951.

121 BL Add. MS 56202, diary, 15 April 1951.

122 Biomedical Research Centre Alexander Fleming, Vari, Fleming's diary, 16 March 1951, 17 March 1951; BL Add. MS 56203, diary, 29 September 1951, e.g. the Chairman he described as 'a good chairman. Allows people to talk (perhaps too much) but keeps things within bounds.'

123 BL Add. MS 56121, letter from Dorothy E. Snavely, project Director of WHO. Visiting team to Dr D.L. Schistava, Central Drug Research Institute, Lucknow, 24 February 1953.

124 Biomedical Research Centre Alexander Fleming, Vari, Fleming's diary, 14 March 1953.

125 BL Add. MS 56218, Mrs B. Davis.

126 e.g. BL Add. MS 56186, diary, 28 September 1945, 'very beautiful young woman. Very blond, very vivacious.' BL Add. MS 56192, diary, 7 June 1948, notes that reporters greeting him in Madrid included an 'attractive English girl' representing the *New York Herald Tribune*.

127 Personal information, A.W. Frankland.

128 BL Add. MS 56217, Vera Allison.

129 Personal information from Dr Robert Fleming.

130 Amalia Fleming, *A Piece of Truth: Lady Fleming on the Colonels' Greece* (1972), pp. 13–14, 23–4, 197, 202; P.C. Zetridou and H.P. Psemenou, *Ελλήνιδες* (*Women of Greece in World War II*) (1950).

131 Maurois, *Life of Fleming*, p. 223.

132 Biomedical Sciences Research Centre Alexander Fleming, Vari, diary, 26 November 1950.

133 *Ibid.*, 10 December 1950.

134 BL Add. MS 56222, George Joakimogolou.

135 E. Alonso Martinez, *The Adventures of a Doctor* (1962), p. 164.

136 Hellenic Foundation for Basic Medical Research Alexander Fleming, Athens, 'Observations on Greece after a Month's Visit, 1952'.

137 BL Add. MS 56204, diary, 30 October 1952.

138 BL Add. MS 56204, diary, 9 November 1952.

139 Personal information, A.W. Frankland.

140 Bustinza Lachiondo, *Diez años de amistad con Sir Alexander Fleming*, p. 150.

141 The marriage was covered after the event in the newspapers. One cutting now at the Biomedical Research Centre Alexander Fleming, Vari, showed photographs of the weddings of Alexander Fleming and Amalia Coutsouris and of Prince Jean and Princess Josephine Charlotte of Luxembourg on the same day, 9 April 1953, both being love matches, 'l'un et l'autre étaient des marriages d'amour'. *Samedi-Soir*, 14 April 1953, used the headline, 'Après la penicilline Fleming découvre l'amour'.

142 Private information.

143 BL Add. MS 56221, Alec L. Zaiger of E. and R. Garrould.

144 Personal information, Mrs Edith Dee (formerly Mrs Wehden), a

patient on Almroth Wright ward, St Mary's Hospital, 1949–53.

145 Personal information, Barbara Gammon, Sister Almroth Wright, 1947–55.

146 BL Add. MS 56216, Ernst Chain.

147 BL Add. MS 56222, papers on Nice visit, 1953.

148 BL Add. MS 56221, Dr Ogilvie.

149 BL Add. MS 56111, letter from Fleming to John McKeen, Pfizer, 19 January 1954.

150 *St Mary's Hospital Gazette*, 60/5 (August 1955), 77–8. The tureens were donated to the Alexander Fleming Laboratory Museum by Dr Robert Fleming.

151 Personal information, A.W. Frankland.

152 *St Mary's Hospital Gazette*, 60/8 (December 1954), 162–5.

153 St Mary's Hospital Archives, WF/AD3/1, minutes of Council of Wright Fleming Institute, 17 December 1953, 3 December 1954.

154 BL Add. MS 56220, Thomas Hunt.

155 BL Add. MS 56222, account of burglary, March 1955.

156 BL Add. MS 56107, letter from R.H. Jardine Willoughby, British Council, to Fleming, 18 February 1955.

157 BL Add. MS 56220, Thomas Hunt.

158 e.g. messages of condolence received by the Foreign Office on the death of Fleming are in the following files: PRO, FO 371/114070 (Argentina); PRO, FO 371/114105; PRO, FO 371/114238; PRO, FO 117709; PRO, FO 371/117987 (Italy); PRO, FO 371/117912 (Spain).

159 PRO/FO 371/114140, Foreign Office copy of decree declaring 14 March a day of national mourning in Dominican Republic.

160 A. Papadopolou, *Girton Review* (Easter 1955).

161 Bustinza Lachiondo, *Diez años de amistad con Sir Alexander Fleming*, pp. 215–19.

Chapter Ten

1 In his will dated 15 April 1953, except for one legacy of £500 to a niece, Fleming divided his estate equally between his wife Amalia and son Robert. Probate was granted on 21 June 1955, when the estate was valued at £28,931 14s 8d net. In 1998 this would have had a purchasing power of approximately £420,657 (calculated using table of cost of living and inflation rates given in *Whitaker's Almanack*, London, HMSO, 2001, p. 618).

2 *Daily Telegraph*, 4 May 1959.

3 H.A. Lechevalier, 'The Waksman Institute of Microbiology, 1954–1984', *Journal of Rutgers University Libraries*, 50 (June 1988), 20–45.

4 Personal information, David Pramer (graduate student of Waksman's and later Director of Waksman Institute), October 2002.

5 G.T. Stewart, letter to Editor, *Glasgow Herald*, 7 July 1979.

6 Wellcome Library, PP/EBC, B69, letter from Chain to Martin Ware, Editor of *British Medical Journal*, 4 March 1968.

7 US Patents 2423873, 2399840, 2573741, 2504161, 2476107, 2443989, 2442141, 2432638.

8 UK Patents 618415, 618416; PRO, FD1/6845, letter from Vannevar

Bush to Edward Mellanby, 30 January 1945.

9 PRO, FD1/2175, letter from C.M. Scott to Landsborough Thomson, 18 May 1950.

10 Library of Congress, Vannevar Bush papers, container 27, report of John T. Connor to Vannevar Bush, 28 October 1952.

11 Harold Wilson, Parliamentary debates, 451, HC Deb. (Series 5) col. 2682, 11 June 1948.

12 PRO, FO 371/58556, letter from Houston-Boswell in Sofia to Foreign Office, 22 January 1946.

13 PRO, FO 943/156, note by C.B.J. Gledhill, 25 October 1946.

14 PRO, FO 938/90, note by John Simpson, 14 January 1947.

15 PRO, FO 371/87185, notes on export of Podbielniak extractors to Eastern Europe, 30 December 1949, 8 January 1950, 25 January 1950; PRO, MH 79/416, report by Joint Intelligence Committee on sale of penicillin plant, 6 March 1948.

16 Rutgers University Archives, New Brunswick, New Jersey, R-MC 003, box 5, folder 8, 'Streptomycin Odyssey' (diary), 31 October 1945.

17 Rutgers University Archives, New Brunswick, New Jersey, R-MC 003, box 5, folder 7, letter from Waksman to Russell Watson, Rutgers Endowment Foundation, 10 November 1947.

18 A. Fleming, 'Nobel Lecture on Penicillin, 11 December 1945', *Les Prix Nobel en 1945* (1947), p. 164.

19 M. Barber, 'Coagulase-Positive Staphylococci Resistant to Penicillin', *Journal of Pathology and Bacteriology*, 59 (1947), 373–84.

20 S. Cannon, *Nature's Revenge, Why Antibiotics can Breed Disease* (1995).

21 A.W. Frankland, 'Aerobiology and Allergy – an Autobiography', *Aerobiologia*, 12 (1996), 58.

22 A.W. Frankland, 'Penicillin sensitivity', in A. Fleming (ed.), *Penicillin* (1950).

23 H.W. Florey, 'Penicillin, Nobel Lecture, December 11, 1945', *Les Prix Nobel en 1945* (1947), pp. 165–75.

24 S.A. Waksman, *Microbial Antagonisms and Antibiotic Substances* (1945); S.A. Waksman, *My Life with the Microbes* (1958); H. Lechevalier, *The Development of Applied Microbiology at Rutgers* (1982); F. Ryan, *Tuberculosis, the Greatest Story Never Told* (1992).

25 E.M. Tansey and L.A. Reynolds (eds.), *Post Penicillin Antibiotics, from Acceptance to Resistance?* (2000), pp. 16, 19, 21.

26 E.P. Abraham, 'A Glimpse of the Early History of the Cephalosporins', *Reviews of Infectious Diseases*, 1 (1979), 99.

27 Streptomycin (1944), chloramphenicol (1947), cephalosporin (1948), chlortetracycline (1948), erythromycin (1952), vancomycin (1956) and gentamycin (1963) are some of the main antibiotics developed in this period. See L. Garrod and F. O'Grady, *Antibiotics and Chemotherapy* (1971).

28 Rutgers University Archives, New Brunswick, New Jersey, R-MC 003, box 6, folder 5, Waksman's agreements with Merck, 1939–47 and notes by Waksman on his

connection with Merck, 1970.

29 Wellcome Library, PP/EBC B28, letter from Florey to Chain, 14 September 1945.

30 Wellcome Library, PP/EBC F49, letter from Chain to Sir Charles Dodds, medical consultant to Beecham, 24 September 1955.

31 H.T. Clarke, J.R. Johnson and R. Robinson, *The Chemistry of Penicillin* (1949).

32 E.P. Abraham, E.B. Chain, W. Baker and R. Robinson, *Pen 103*, 23 October 1943; J.C. Sheehan, *The Enchanted Ring* (1982), p. 114.

33 G. Ferry, *Dorothy Hodgkin: A Life* (1998), pp. 190–217.

34 Sheehan, *The Enchanted Ring.*

35 H.G. Lazell, *From Pills to Penicillin: the Beecham Story* (1975), pp. 137–50; G. Rolinson, 'Forty Years of beta-lactam Research', *Journal of Antimicrobial Chemotherapy*, 41/61 (1998), 589–603; Tansey and Reynolds, *Post Penicillin Antibiotics*, pp. 25–31.

36 Lazell, *From Pills to Penicillin, the Beecham Story*, pp. 165–70.

37 Personal information, Dr Bill Smith.

38 M. Weatherall, 'An End to the Search for New Drugs', *Nature*, 296 (1982), pp. 387–90; M. Tischler, 'Drug Discovery, Background and Foreground', *Clinical Pharmacology and Therapeutics*, 14 (1973), 479–86; Editorial, 'Bigger Companies for Better Drugs', *Lancet*, 346 (1995), 585.

39 C. Kennedy, *ICI: the Company that Changed our Lives* (1993).

40 G.A. Gambardella, *Science and Innovation, the American Pharmaceutical Industry during the*

1980s (1995); R.P. Bauman, P. Jackson and J.T. Lawrence, *From Promise to Performance a Journey of Transformation at SmithKline Beecham* (1997); J.L. Rodengen, *The Legend of Pfizer* (1999).

41 M.P. Jevons, 'Celbenin-Resistant Staphylococci', *British Medical Journal*, 1 (1960), 124–5.

42 e.g. 'New Superbug at Hospital Renders Antibiotics Useless', *Independent*, 27 May 2002.

43 House of Lords, *Select Committee on Science and Technology*, 7th report: *Resistance to Antibiotics and Other Antimicrobial Agents*, HL Paper (1988) no. 81.

Chapter Eleven

1 *St Paul's Cathedral Order of Service for the burial of Sir Alexander Fleming, F.R.S., M.B., B.Sc., F.R.C.S., F.R.C.P., Commander of the Legion of Honour*, 18 March 1955.

2 Personal information, Elsa Rokofillou.

3 Wellcome Library, PP/EBC K79, letter from Amalia Fleming to Ernst Chain, 25 March 1955.

4 Amalia Fleming, *A Piece of Truth* (1972), p. 21.

5 BL Add. MS 56217, W. Howard Hughes. Fleming's collection of press cuttings is at the Biomedical Research Centre Alexander Fleming, Vari, Greece and at the Hellenic Foundation for Basic Medical Research, Athens, Greece.

6 BL Add. MS 56118, report on visit to Spain [June 1948].

7 *Pueblo*, 7 June 1948: 'un rotundo y laconico "no"'. Despite that he was happy to give his impressions of Spain to the paper's readers: 'sus

impresiones de España son inmejorables – "they have been very nice to me."'

8 BL Add. MS 56187, diary, 9 October 1946: 'Mayor short, stout pugnacious-looking communist (might be Al Capone) . . . Mayor made a speech. I was apparently a representative of the working man. I had to reply so I argued I was a good workman and that was the only way to success (or his or communists).'

9 BL Add. MS 56187, diary, 10 October 1946.

10 BL Add. MS 56119, letter from Henry J. Klaunberg, Washington Institute of Medicine, 25 August 1950.

11 BL Add. MS 56118, letter from Dr Zollschain Jozsef of Budapest, 28 April 1949.

12 BL Add. MS 56116, letter from Carlos Bilbao Gama, Rio de Janeiro, 6 September 1946

13 BL Add. MSS 56116, letter from José Gonzalvo, 11 February 1947; Letter from Fleming to José Gonzalvo, 6 March 1947.

14 M. Mariotti, 'Una nuova applicazione della penicillina', *Patologia Tropicale, nota preventita* 3 (1945).

15 BL Add. MS 56115, letter from dottor Maurizio Mariotti, Ancona, 22 November 1945: 'Chi Le scrive e un giovane medico, che ha attentamente seguito con enthusiasmo la Sua scoperta e tutti i successivi lavori sinora uscita sulla penicillina.'

16 BL Add. MS 56120, letter to Dr Munawar Ali, Pakistan Medical Conference, 8 March 1951.

17 BL Add. MS 56120, letter from Dr S.S. Bhatnagar, Ministry of Natural Resources and Scientific Research, Government of India, 22 February 1951.

18 BL Add. MS 56120, letter to Dr Munawar Ali, Pakistan Medical Association, Karachi, 2 April 1951.

19 BL Add. MS 56120, programme of 'Visit of Sir Alexander Fleming under the auspices of the Pakistan Medical Association, Karachi', 15–17 April 1951.

20 BL Add. MS 56121, World Health Organisation Press Release, 26 January 1953. Inevitably, Fleming was again in demand to give lectures and take part in seminars throughout India, but all such requests were declined on his behalf by the organisers of the visit, since Fleming was there as part of a team to carry out a specific programme in medical schools in India and was restricted to such activities (BL Add. MS 56121, letter from Dorothy E. Snavely, Administrative Director of the World Health Organisation Visiting Team to Dr D.L. Schivastava of the Central Drug Institute, Lucknow, 24 February 1953).

21 BL Add. MS 56120, letter from Owen Waller, Editor of *The Chemist and Druggist*, 21 December 1951. Gwyn Macfarlane has said (*Alexander Fleming: the Man and the Myth* (1984), p. 274), that, by being fêted and given all the credit for penicillin, Fleming gave Florey the space to develop as a great scientist. This may be true, but, on the other hand, it is difficult to imagine Florey taking on Fleming's

role as the acceptable face of medicine.

22 BL Add. MS 56117, letter from A.H. Cook of Imperial College, 21 May 1947.

23 Royal Society HF/1/3/3/8, Festival of Britain file, 1 November 1948–24 February 1951.

24 See R. Bud, 'Penicillin and the New Elizabethans', *British Journal for the History of Science*, 31 (1998), 305–33; R. Weight, *Patriots, National Identity in Britain 1940–2000* (2002).

25 BL Add. MS 56114, 10 September 1945.

26 BL Add. MS 56118, report on visit to Spain [June 1948].

27 BL Add. MS 56118, letter from H.G. Petty, on behalf of Senores Veres and Rodriguez, 14 June 1949; Letter to H.G. Petty, 17 June 1949.

28 BL Add. MS 56118, letter to British Red Cross Society Cadet Units, Urmstone, 17 June 1949.

29 BL Add. MS 56118, Letter to A. Bernay, 21 June 1949.

30 e.g. D. Masters, *Miracle Drug: the Inner History of Penicillin* (1946); B. Sokoloff, *Penicillin: a Dramatic story* (1946).

31 BL Add. MS 56120, letter from Fleming to Mary G. Milne, 30 April 1951.

32 BL Add. MS 56120, letter from Fleming to L.J. Ludovici, 10 May 1951.

33 BL Add. MS 56120, letter from Fleming to C.A. Pannett, Robert Fleming, Robin Bailes and Leonard Colebrook, 17 May 1951.

34 BL Add. MS 56120, letter from R.J. Fleming to Miss Hunter, 22 October 1952.

35 André Maurois, *Life of Sir Alexander Fleming* (1959), pp. 9–10; *Les Silences de Colonel Bramble*.

36 Maurois, *Life of Fleming*, pp. 11–12.

37 W. Howard Hughes, 'The Invention of Alexander Fleming', *St Mary's Hospital Gazette*, 77 (January 1970), 1–2.

38 Macfarlane, *Alexander Fleming*, p. x.

39 e.g. R.J. Unstead, *People in History: from Caractacus to Fleming* (1957), p. 493. Bud ('Penicillin and the New Elizabethans', 331) points out that the juxtaposition of colourful images of Francis Drake and Fleming on the cover of this book was a parallel between the geographical expansion of the age of Elizabeth I and the scientific spirit of the age of the New Elizabethans of the 1950s.

40 Royal Society, HF/1/3/2/11/22, letter from Myron Selznick to Florey, 12 June 1944; HF/1/3/2/11/24, letter from Florey to David Henley of Myron Selznick, 17 July 1944.

41 J.D. Ratcliffe, *Yellow Magic: the Story of Penicillin* (1945).

42 *New York Journal-America*, 24 August 1945; *Hartford Connecticut Times*, 27 August 1945.

43 *Star*, 20 July 1945.

44 BL Add. MS 65110, letter from Boris Sokoloff to Fleming, 2 November 1948.

45 BL Add. MS 65110, letter from Fleming to Sokoloff, 23 November 1948.

46 Ian Curteis, *Biography of Sir Alexander Fleming*, broadcast 1970; *St Mary's Hospital Gazette*, 76 (October 1970) 2–4.

47 *The Third Man* (1949); Graham Greene, *The Third Man* (1950). The

story is based on a penicillin ring
operating in the Berlin black market
in 1946.

48   G. Chappell, 'Adventure in Stained
     Glass: a Window with a Message',
     St Mary's Hospital Gazette, 58/2
     (December 1952) 208–10;
     information from Godard Gibbs,
     stained glass makers.

49   St Mary's Hospital Archives, MS/AD
     85/1, 1981.

50   BL Add. MS 56121, letter from
     W.G. Chapman, Fellow in Spanish,
     Queen's College, Oxford, 9 January
     1955.

51   F. Bustinza Lachiondo, *Diez años de
     amistad con Sir Alexander Fleming*
     (1961), p. 162.

52   Personal information, Lluis
     Martinez, *Avui*, Barcelona.

53   I am indebted to Maria Luisa Messa
     for this information. The streets are
     in Milan, Trezzano sul Naviglio and
     Bollate, and the clinics in Milan and
     Trezzano sul Naviglio.

54   *Brescia Oggi*, 26 May 1975, p. 13.
     See also *Voce del Popolo*, 16 June
     1972 on the commissioning of the
     statue.

55   Information from Dr Michele
     Francaviglia, Medical Director and
     Communications Manager, Fleming
     Labs, Brescia, Italy.

56   Biomedical Sciences Research Centre
     Alexander Fleming, Vari, Greece,
     Honorary Chairman of Medical
     Committee for Orphans in Greece,
     28 May 1953.

57   Personal information, Professor
     John Volankis, Dr George
     Panayotou and Dr Evi Kalodiki.

58   St Mary's Hospital Archives,
     WF/AD 1/2, minutes of Wright
     Fleming Institute Council,

     9 December 1959, 20 January 1960.

59   Amalia Fleming, *A Piece of Truth*;
     PRO, FCO 9/1389, FCO 9/1390,
     FCO 9/1391, Foreign Office files on
     the case of Lady Fleming,
     September–November 1971.

60   Wellcome Library, PP/EBC K81,
     letter from Amalia Fleming to Chain,
     19 February 1965, copy of
     government decree setting up the
     Hellenic Institute of Basic Biological
     Research, 19 February 1965.

61   Wellcome Library, PP/EBC K80,
     letter from Chain to Amalia
     Fleming, 11 May 1963.

62   Personal information, Elsa
     Rokofillou, President of Hellenic
     Foundation for Basic Medical
     Research.

63   Personal information, George
     Panayotou, Senior Investigator,
     BSRC A. Fleming.

64   St Mary's Hospital Archives, MS/AD
     80/1, minutes of meeting held
     1 April 1955; letter from Oliver
     Dawney to Sir Arthur Porritt,
     14 April 1955.

65   Weight, *Patriots: National Identity
     in Britain 1940–2000*, pp. 236–7.

66   PRO, FD 9/123, minutes of meeting,
     held at Buckingham Palace and
     chaired by HRH the Duke of
     Edinburgh, to discuss a memorial to
     Sir Alexander Fleming, 9 November
     1955.

67   PRO, FD 9/123, letter from Florey
     to Sir Harold Himsworth,
     28 November 1955; letter from
     Lord Adrian to Himsworth, 14
     February 1956.

68   PRO, FD 9/123, letter from Sir
     Harold Himsworth to Lieutenant-
     Commander Michael Parker, 3 May
     1956.

69   St Mary's Hospital Archives, MS/AD
      80/2, letter from Florey to Albert
      Neuberger, 8 October 1958.

70   Wellcome Library, PP/EBC E61,
      letter from Chain to Albert
      Neuberger, 2 February 1959.

71   St Mary's Hospital Archives, MS/AD
      80/2, minutes of Fleming Memorial
      Fund Joint Special meeting of
      Executive and Finance and Planning
      Committees to consider comments
      by Professor Neuberger on the
      future of the Fleming Appeal,
      4 November 1959.

72   Wellcome Library PP/EBC E62,
      Executive Committee decision to
      close down Appeal, 12 August 1963.
      The Wright Fleming Institute had
      received £79,000, the William Dunn
      School £54,000 and Chain £50,000
      for research with smaller amounts
      allocated to other institutions.

73   Wellcome Library, PP/EBC E61,
      letter from Chain to R.A. Paget-
      Cooke, 24 November 1959.

74   St Mary's Hospital Archives, WFI
      1/2, minutes of Wright Fleming
      Institute Council, 3 October 1958,
      11 January 1960, 21 September
      1961. The first holder of a new
      Chair of Immunology, funded by
      Pfizer, Rodney Porter, was destined
      to become the second Nobel Prize
      winner to have worked at St Mary's,
      winning the 1972 Prize for Medicine
      or Physiology for work done at
      St Mary's on the structure and
      functions of the immunoglobulins.

75   St Mary's Hospital Archives, WFI
      1/2, Wright Fleming Institute
      Council minutes, 27 June 1968.

76   Imperial College has also capitalised
      on past glories it has inherited from
      St Mary's. The name of the Wright
      Fleming Institute was revived for a
      centre for research into infectious
      diseases established in the former
      medical school premises. When
      Imperial College sought a name for
      its new Basic Medical Sciences
      Building at its South Kensington
      Campus, the name of Sir Alexander
      Fleming had more cachet than
      anything else.

77   *Scotsman*, 17 December 1999;
      Guardian, 'Top Scot', 18 December
      1999; letter from M. O'Donnell,
      21 December 1999; A.J. Tulloch,
      22 December 1999; K. Brown,
      23 December 1999; BBC Radio 4,
      Today, discussion between Michael
      O'Donnell and Kevin Brown.

78   Ned Heindel, 'Penicillin Celebrated',
      Chemical Heritage, 18/3 (2000),
      32.

79   *Mary's Matters*, 25 (October 2000).

80   Visitor figures to the Alexander
      Fleming Laboratory Museum
      illustrate the worldwide interest in
      Fleming: 38 per cent of visitors were
      from the UK, 29 per cent from USA
      and Canada, 15 per cent from
      Western Europe (excluding
      Scandinavia), 9 per cent from
      Scandinavia, 2 per cent from South
      America, 2 per cent from
      Australasia, 3 per cent from Asia,
      1 per cent from Eastern Europe
      and 1 per cent from Africa
      (2002).

Bibliography

PRIMARY ARCHIVAL SOURCES

British Library, London
Alexander Fleming papers, BL Add. MSS 56106–225
Papers relating to penicillin collected by Dr H.T. Swan, BL Add. MS 71717

Hellenic Foundation for Basic Medical Research Alexander Fleming, Athens (Greece)
Alexander Fleming papers retained by Amalia Fleming when the bulk of the papers were
  deposited in the British Library

Alexander Fleming Biomedical Sciences Research Centre, Vari, Attika (Greece)
Alexander Fleming papers retained by Amalia Fleming and museum artefacts collections
  transferred from Hellenic Foundation for Basic Medical Research Alexander Fleming

St Mary's Hospital Archives and Alexander Fleming Laboratory Museum, London
Archives of St Mary's Hospital, Paddington, SM/AD
Archives of St Mary's Hospital Medical School, MS/AD
Archives of Wright Fleming Institute, WF/AD
Alexander Fleming Laboratory Museum collections
Oral history interviews with Felix Eastcott, Bill Frankland, Tom Kemp, Jack Suchet
  (recordings and transcripts)

Royal Society, London
Howard Walter Florey papers, HF (formerly numbered 98HF)

Wellcome Library, London
Ernst Boris Chain papers, PP/EBC
Leonard Colebrook papers, PP/COL
Charles M. Fletcher papers, PP/CMF
Ronald Hare papers, PP/HAR
Norman George Heatley papers, GC48
Robert Gwyn Macfarlane papers, PP/RGM

National Archives (Public Records Office), Kew, London
Medical Research Council Archives, PRO, FD1
Cabinet papers, PRO, CAB
Prime Minister's papers, PRO/PREM
Foreign Office papers PRO, FO
Foreign and Commonwealth Office papers, PRO, FCO
Dominions Office papers, PRO/DO
Board of Trade papers, PRO, T
Ministry of Health papers, PRO, MH
Ministry of Supply papers, PRO, AVIA
British Council papers, PRO, BW

London Scottish Regiment HQ, London
London Scottish Regiment Gazette

Karolinska Institutet, Stockholm (Sweden)
Archives of the Nobel Committee for the award of the Nobel Prize for Medicine

Archivo General de la Universidad Complutense de Madrid (Spain)
File on Professor Florencio Bustinza Lachiondo

National Archives, Washington, DC (USA)
Office of Scientific Research and Development records, RG 227
War Production Board records, RG 179
Bureau of Agricultural and Industrial Chemistry records, RG 97
Northern Regional Research Laboratory records, RG 97, series 41

National Center for Agricultural Utilization Research, Peoria, Illinois (USA)
Mycology registers
Press cuttings collection

National Academy of Sciences, National Research Council Archives, Institute of Medicine, Washington, DC (USA)
Committee on Chemotherapeutic and Other Agents records
Committees on Military Medicine records
Venereal Diseases Bulletin

Rockefeller Archive Center, North Tarrytown, NY (USA)
Rockefeller Foundation archives, records of projects funded, RF, RG 1.1, projects series
  401, boxes 36–7, folders 457–70, 481–4

Rutgers University Libraries, Special Collections and University Archives, New Brunswick, NJ (USA)
Selman A. Waksman papers, R-MC 003

Pfizer Information Center, Corporate Affairs Division, New York (USA)
Pfizer penicillin papers, Gladys Hobby records, series 5, Pfizer history

Pfizer Records Centre, Sandwich, Kent
Kemball Bishop and Co. records, Box 96B–2E

Merck Archives, Whitehouse Station, New Jersey (USA)
Merck corporate archives

PAPERS WRITTEN BY ALEXANDER FLEMING

(with A.E. Wright, S.R. Douglas, J. Freeman, J.H. Wells), 'Studies in Connexion with Therapeutic Immunisation', *Lancet*, 2 (1907), 1217–36
(with Noon, L.), 'The Accuracy of Opsonic Estimations', *Lancet*, 1 (1908), 1203–4
'Some Observations on the Opsonic Index, with Especial Reference to the Accuracy of the Method, and to Some of the Sources of Error', *Practitioner*, 80 (1908), 607–34
'Demonstration of a Simple Method of Serum Diagnosis of Syphilis by the Complement Deviation Method', *Proceedings of the Royal Society of Medicine*, 2 (1908), 220–5
'Bacteriology and Vaccine Therapy of Acne Vulgaris', *British Medical Journal*, 2 (1909), 533–4
'The Serum Diagnosis of Syphilis', *British Medical Journal*, 2 (1909), 984–5
'On the Aetiology of Acne vulgaris and its Treatment by Vaccines', *Lancet*, 1 (1909), 1035
'A Simple Method of Serum Diagnosis of Syphilis', *Lancet*, 1 (1909), 1512–15
'The Diagnosis of Acute Bacterial Infections', *St Mary's Hospital Gazette*, 15 (1909), 67–9, 72–7
(with L. Colebrook), 'On the Use of Salvarsan in the Treatment of Syphilis', *Lancet*, 1 (1911), 1631–4
'Fleming's (Hecht's) Modification and the Wassermann Test', *Lancet*, 2 (1912), 115–25, 258–9
'Some Bacterial Observations Made in the Casualty Room', *St Mary's Hospital Gazette*, 18 (1912), 96–8
'Recent Work on Vaccine Therapy', *Practitioner*, 90 (1913), 591–7
'Some Notes on the Bacteriology of Gas Gangrene', *Lancet*, 2 (1915), 376–8
'On the Bacteriology of Septic Wounds', *Lancet*, 2 (1915), 638–43
'Fashions in Wound Treatment, a Reply', *St Mary's Hospital Gazette* (1916), 60–2
(with S.R. Douglas, L. Colebrook), 'On the Question of Bacterial Symbiosis in Wound

Infections', *Lancet*, 1 (1917), 604–7

(with S.R. Douglas, L. Colebrook), 'On Skin-Grafting: a Plea for its More Extensive Application', *Lancet*, 2 (1917), 5–12

'The Physiological and Antiseptic Reaction of Flavine', *Lancet*, 2 (1917), 341–5

(with S.R. Douglas, L. Colebrook), 'On the Growth of Anaerobic bacilli in Fluid Media under Apparently Anaerobic Conditions', *Lancet*, 2 (1917), 530–2

(with A.E. Wright), 'Further Observations on Acidaemia in Gas Gangrene and on the Conditions which Favour the Growth of its Infective Agent in the Blood Serum', *Lancet*, 1 (1918), 205–10

(with S.R. Douglas, L. Colebrook), 'A Case of Rat-Bite Fever', *Lancet*, 1 (1918), 253–5

(with A.E. Wright, L. Colebrook), 'The Conditions under which the Sterilisation of Wounds by Physiological Agency can be Obtained', *Lancet*, 1 (1918), 831–7

'On Some Simply Prepared Culture Media for B. *influenzae* with a Note Regarding the Agglutination Reaction of Sera from Patients Suffering from Influenza to this Bacillus', *Lancet*, 1 (1919), 138–9

(with A.B. Porteous), 'Blood Transfusion by the Citrate Method: a Report on 100 Cases of Transfusion at a Base Hospital', *Lancet*, 1 (1919), 973–5

(with A.B. Porteous), 'Streptococcal Infections of Septic Wounds at a Base Hospital', *Lancet*, 2 (1919), 49–51

(with F.J. Clemenger), 'An Experimental Research into the Specificity of the Agglutinins Produced by Pfeiffer's Bacillus', *Lancet*, 2 (1919), 869–71

'The Aerobic Infections of War Wounds', *Medical Research Committee, Special Report no. 39*, London, HMSO, 1919, pp. 70–84

'Influence of the Aerobic on the Anaerobic Infection of Wounds', *Medical Research Committee, Special Report no. 39*, London, HMSO, 1919, pp. 84–8

'The Action of Physiological and Chemical Antiseptics in a Septic Wound', *St Mary's Hospital Gazette* (1919), 44–9

'The Action of Chemical and Physiological Antiseptics in a Septic Wound', *British Journal of Surgery*, 7 (1919–20), 99–129

(with S.R. Douglas, L. Colebrook), *Studies in Wound Infection: Medical Research Committee, Special Report no. 57*, London, HMSO, 1920

(with F.J. Clemenger), 'A Simple Method of Recording Automatically the Gas Produced by Bacteria in a Culture and of the Oxygen Absorbed by Aerobic Non-Gas-Forming Bacteria', *British Journal of Experimental Pathology*, 1 (1920), 66–9

'Vaccine Therapy in Regard to General Practice', *British Medical Journal*, 1 (1921), 255–9

(with S.R. Douglas), 'On the Antigenic Properties of Acetone-Extracted Bacteria', *British Journal of Experimental Pathology*, 2 (1921), 131–40

'On a Remarkable Bacteriolytic Element Found in Tissues and Secretions', *Proceedings of the Royal Society of London*, B, 93 (1922), 306–17

(with V.D. Allison), 'Observations on a Bacteriolytic Substance "lysozyme" Found in Secretions and Tissues', *British Journal of Experimental Pathology*, 3 (1922), 252–60

(with V.D. Allison), 'Further Observations on a Bacteriolytic Element Found in Tissues and Secretions', *Proceedings of the Royal Society of London*, B, 94 (1922), 142–5 (with V.D. Allison), 'On the Antibacterial Power of Egg White', *Lancet*, 1 (1924), 1303–7

'On the Accuracy of the Measurement of Small Volumes of Fluid with a Capillary Pipette: Incorporating a Description of a Graduated Pipette for Rapidly and Accurately Making a Series of Dilutions of a Fluid', *British Journal of Experimental Pathology*, 5 (1924), 148–58

'A Comparison of the Activities of Antiseptics on Bacteria and on Leucocytes', *Proceedings of the Royal Society of London*, B, 96 (1924), 171–80

(with V.D. Allison), 'On the Specificity of the Protein of Human Tears', *British Journal of Experimental Pathology*, 6 (1925), 87–90

'On the Effect of Variations of the Salt Content of Blood on its Bactericidal Power *in vitro* and *in vivo*', *British Journal of Experimental Pathology*, 7 (1926), 274–81

'A Simple Method of Removing Leucocytes from Blood', *British Journal of Experimental Pathology*, 7 (1926), 281–6

'On Wright's Centrifuge Method of Estimating Phagocytosis and Rate of Opsonisation of Bacteria by Normal Serum', *British Journal of Experimental Pathology*, 8 (1927), 50–7

(with V.D. Allison), 'On the Development of Strains of Bacteria Resistant to Lysozyme Action and Relation of Lysozyme Action to Intracellular Digestion', *British Journal of Experimental Pathology*, 8 (1927), 214–18

'On the Influence of Temperature on Rate of Agglutination of Bacteria', *British Journal of Experimental Pathology*, 9 (1928), 231–5

'The Bactericidal Power of Human Blood and Some Methods of Altering it', *Journal of Laryngology and Otology*, 48 (1928), 385–97

'The Bactericidal Power of Human Blood and Some Methods of Altering it', *Proceedings of the Royal Society of London*, 21 (1928), 25–33

'On the Antibacterial Action of Cultures of a Penicillium, with Special Reference to their Use in the Isolation of *B. influenzae*', *British Journal of Experimental Pathology*, 10 (1929), 226–36

'Arris and Gale Lecture on Lysozyme, a Bacteriolytic Ferment Found Normally in Tissues and Secretions', *Lancet*, 1 (1929), 217–20

'The Staphylococci', in Medical Research Council, *A System of Bacteriology in Relation to Medicine*, vol. 2, London, HMSO, 1929, pp. 11–28

(with. I.H. Maclean), 'On the Occurrence of Influenza Bacilli in the Mouths of Normal People', *British Journal of Experimental Pathology*, 11 (1930), 127–34

'Tuberculin', in Medical Research Council, *A System of Bacteriology in Relation to Medicine*, vol. 5, London, HMSO, 1930, pp. 305–8

'Some Problems in the Use of Antiseptics', *British Dental Journal*, 52 (1931), 105–17

'Blood Transfusion', *British Medical Journal*, 2 (1931), 801–3

'Phagocytosis, Emigration of Leucocytes and the Bactericidal Power of Blood', in Medical Research Council, *A System of Bacteriology in Relation to Medicine*, vol. 9, London, HMSO, 1931, pp. 212–22

(with V.Z. Cope, P.H. Mitchiner, T.H.C. Benians), 'Discussion on the Indications for, and the Value of, the Intravenous Use of Germicides', *Proceedings of the Royal Society of Medicine*, 24 (1931), 805–26

'On the Specific Antibacterial Properties of Penicillin and Potassium Tellurite, Incorporating a Method of Demonstrating Some Bacterial Antagonisms', *Journal of Pathology and Bacteriology*, 35 (1932), 831–42

'Lysozyme, President's Address', *Proceedings of the Royal Society of Medicine*, 26 (1932), 71–84

(with H.L. Tidy and G.L Keynes), 'Blood Transfusion', *Transactions of the Medical Society of London*, 55 (1932), 15–38

'The Trend of Modern Research in Bacteriology', *Journal of State Medicine*, 41 (1933), 559–65

'Recent Advances in Vaccine Therapy', *Practitioner*, 133 (1934), 537–43

(with G.F. Petrie), *Recent Advances in Vaccine and Serum Therapy*, London, J. and A. Churchill, 1934

'Stewart Rankin Douglas, 1871–1936', *Journal of Pathology and Bacteriology*, 42 (1936), 515–22

'Selective Bacteriostasis', in R. St John-Brookes (ed.), *Second International Congress for Microbiology, 25 July–1 August 1936, Report of Proceedings*, London, 1937, pp. 33–4

(with I.H. Maclean), 'On the Use of Staphylococcus Antitoxin, Toxin, Toxoid and Vaccine', in R. St John-Brookes (ed.), *Second International Congress for Microbiology, 25 July–1 August 1936, Report of Proceedings*, London, 1937, p. 519

'The Growth of Micro-Organisms on Paper', in R. St John-Brookes (ed.), *Second International Congress for Microbiology, 25 July–1 August 1936, Report of Proceedings*, London, 1937, pp. 552–3

'The Treatment of Pneumonia', letter to *British Medical Journal*, 2 (1938), 37–8

'The Antibacterial Action *in vitro* of 2-(p-amino-benzenesulphonamido) Pyridine on Pneumococci and Streptococci', *Lancet*, 2 (1938), 74–8

'The Antibacterial Power of the Blood of Patients Receiving 2-(p-amino-benzenesulphonamido) Pyridine', *Lancet*, 2 (1938), 564–7

'Recent Advances in Vaccine Therapy', *British Medical Journal*, 2 (1939), 99–104

(with I.H. Maclean, K.B. Rogers), 'M & B 693 and Pneumonia', *Lancet*, 1 (1939), 562–8

'Serum and Vaccine Therapy in Combination with Sulphanilamide or M & B 693', *Proceedings of the Royal Society of Medicine*, 32 (1939), 911–20

(with W.H. Willcox, E. Holland, G.L.M. McGelligott), 'Sulphanilamide: its Use and Misuse', *Transactions of the Medical Society of London*, 62 (1939), 19–43

'Observations on the Bacteriostatic Action of Sulphanilamide and M & B 693 and the Influence thereon of Bacteria and Peptone', *Journal of Pathology and Bacteriology*, 50 (1940), 69–81

(with M.Y. Young), 'The Inhibitory Action of Potassium Tellurite on Coliform Bacteria', *Journal of Pathology and Bacteriology*, 51 (1940), 29–35

'Antiseptics and Chemotherapy', *Proceedings of the Royal Society of Medicine*, 33 (1940), 127–36

'Chemotherapy and Ophthalmology', in F. Ridley and A. Sorsby (eds), *Modern Trends in Ophthalmology*, London, Butterworth, 1940, pp. 493–8

'Chemotherapy for War Wounds: Comparisons and Combinations', *British Medical Journal*, 2 (1940), 715

'Penicillin', letter to *British Medical Journal*, 2 (1941), 386

'Some Uses of Nigrosin in Bacteriology', *Journal of Pathology and Bacteriology*, 53 (1941), 293–6

'A Pneumococcus which Required Carbon Dioxide for its Growth', *Lancet*, 1 (1941), 110

(with L. Colebrook, E.E. Lewis, R. Mowlem), 'Discussion on Chemotherapy and Wound Infection', *Proceedings of the Royal Society of Medicine*, 34 (1941), 337–50

'Bacteriological Examination of Wounds', in H. Bailey (ed.), *Surgery of Modern Warfare*, Edinburgh, E. and S. Livingstone, 1941, pp. 141–9

(with G.M. Findlay, W. Yorke), 'The Mode of Action of Chemotherapeutic Agents', *Biochemical Journal*, 36 (1942), 1–2

'A Simple Method of Using Penicillin: Tellurite and Gentian Violet for Differential Culture', *British Medical Journal*, 1 (1942), 547–8

'*In vitro* Tests of Penicillin Potency', *Lancet*, 1 (1942), 732–3

'Penicillina', *Prensa Médica Argentina*, 29 (1942), 1163–73

'The Prevention of Pyogenic Infections of the Nose and Throat', *Journal of Laryngology and Otology*, 58 (1943), 296–304

'Streptococcal Meningitis Treated with Penicillin: Measurement of the Bacteriostatic Power of Blood and Cerebrospinal Fluid', *Lancet*, 2 (1943), 434–8

'The Use of Paper and Cellophane Discs for the Preparation of Museum Specimens of Mould Cultures', *Proceedings of Linnaean Society of London*, 155 (1943), 5–6

(with A.T. Glenny, P. Hartley), 'Discussion on Active Immunity – General Considerations', *Proceedings of the Royal Society of Medicine*, 36 (1943), 145–9

'A descoberta da penicilina', *Revista Medica de Pernambuco*, 14 (1944), 253–8

'A descoberta da penicilina', *Brasil-Médico*, 58 (1944), 220–2

'Penicillin in Venereal Diseases', *British Journal of Venereal Diseases*, 20 (1944), 133–6

'The Discovery of Penicillin', *British Medical Bulletin*, 2 (1944), 4–5

'Penicillin for Selective Culture and for Demonstrating Bacterial Inhibitions', *British Medical Bulletin*, 2 (1944), 7–8

'The Discovery of Penicillin', *Bulletin of the United States Army Medical Department*, 77 (1944), 54–8

'El descubrimento de la penicillina', *Dia Medico*, 16 (1944), 498–500

'La penicillina para cultivo selectivo y para demonstrar inhibiciones bacterianas', *Revista de la Sanidad de Policia*, 4 (1944), 259–63

'La penicillina para cultivo selectivo y para demonstrar inhibiciones bacterianas', *Dia Medico*, 16 (1944), 506–7

'El descubrimento de la penicillina', *Gaceta Medica Espanola*, 18 (1944), 255–6

'El descubrimento de la penicillina', *Medicina Mexico*, 24 (1944), 195–9

'Discovery of Penicillin', *General Practitioner of Australia and New Zealand*, 15 (1944), 43–4

'Micro-Methods of Estimating Penicillin in Blood Serum and Other Body Fluids',

Lancet, 2 (1944), 620–1

(with M.Y. Young, J. Suchet, A.J.E. Rowe), 'Penicillin Content of Blood Serum after Various Doses of Penicillin by Various Routes', *Lancet*, 2 (1944), 621–4

'Discussion on Penicillin', *Proceedings of the Royal Society of Medicine*, 37 (1944), 101–12

'El descubrimento de la penicillina', *Revista de la Sanidad de Policia*, 4 (1944), 187–90

(with G. Smith), 'Some Methods for the Study of Moulds', *Transactions of the British Mycological Society*, 27 (1944), 13–19

'The Uses and Limitations of Penicillin', *Transactions of the Medical Society of London*, 64 (1944), 142–9

'Penicillin: the Robert Campbell Oration', *Ulster Medical Journal*, 13 (1944), 95–108

'Micro-Methods of Estimating Penicillin in the Blood Serum and Other Body Fluids', *American Journal of Clinical Pathology*, 15 (1945), 1–6

'The Discovery of Penicillin', *Caribbean Medical Journal*, 7 (1945), 147–50

'Antiseptics: the Lister Memorial Lecture', *Chemistry and Industry*, 3 (1945), 18–23

'Short Note on Penicillin', *Clinica nuova*, 1 (1945), 133–5

'Micro-métodos para la determinación de penicilina en la suero sanguineo y otros liquidos organicos', *Dia Medico*, 17 (1945), 354–6

(with M.Y. Young, J. Suchet, A.J.E. Rowe), 'Concentración de penicilina en el suero sanguíneo después de la administracíon de diversas dosis por diferentes vías', *Dia Medico*, 17 (1945), 841–5

'A descoberta da penicilina', *Hora Médica*, 1 (1945), 39–41

'Penicillin, its Discovery, Development and Uses in the Field of Medicine and Surgery: the Harben Lectures, 1944', *Journal of the Royal Institute of Public Health and Hygiene*, 8 (1945), 36–49, 63–71, 93–105

'Penicillin', *Journal of the Royal Naval Medical Service*, 31 (1945), 73–82

'The Story of Penicillin', *Medical Annals of the District of Columbia*, 14 (1945), 393–9

'La Découverte de la pénicilline', *Semaine des Hôpitaux de Paris*, 21 (1945), 509–10

'Penicillin in Neuro-Syphilis', *Anais do 1 Congresso Inter-Americano de Medicina*, Rio de Janeiro, 1 (7–15 September 1946), 15–17

'L'uso della penicillina', *Bollettino dell'Istituto Sieroterapico Milanese*, (1946), 11–15

'The Assay of Penicillin in the Days before it was Concentrated', *Bulletin of the Health Organisation, League of Nations*, 12 (1946), 250–2

'Antiseptics, Old and New', *Bulletin of the United States Army Medical Department*, 5 (1946), 544–50

'Antiseptics, Old and New', *Proceedings of the Staff Meetings of the Mayo Clinic*, 21 (1946), 67–75

Chemotherapy, Yesterday, Today and Tomorrow, the Linacre Lecture, Cambridge, Cambridge University Press, 1946

'Progressi nella cura specifica delle infezioni bacteriche', *Minerva Medica*, 2 (1946), 404–9

'Descoberta e uso da penicilina', *Resentha clínica-cientifica*, 15 (1946), 179–86

(ed.), *Penicillin: its Practical Application*, London, Butterworth, 1946

'Louis Pasteur', *British Medical Journal*, 1 (1947), 517–22 (with J.R. May, A.E. Voureka), 'Some Problems in the Titration of Streptomycin', *British Medical Journal*, 1 (1947), 627–30

'Influence of Penicillin on the Coagulation of Blood, with Especial Reference to Certain Dental Operations', *British Medical Journal*, 2 (1947), 242–3

'The Role of Penicillin in Surgical Practice', *Journal International de Chirurgie*, 7 (1947), 184–7

(with C. Smith), 'Estimation of Penicillin in Serum, Use of Glucose, Phenol Red and Serum Water', *Lancet*, 1 (1947), 401–2

'Die Geschichte des Penicillins', *Wiener Klinische Wochenschrift*, 59 (1947), 337–40

'Die Awendung des Penicillins', *Wiener Klinische Wochenschrift*, 59 (1947), 505–10

'Nobel Lecture on Penicillin, 11 December 1945', in *Les Prix Nobel en 1945*, Stockholm, P.A. Norstedt, 1947, pp. 155–64

'Le Role de la pénicilline en pratique chirurgicale', *Journal de Chirurgie*, 64 (1948), 97–9

'Comé debe usarse la penicilina', *Medicina Colonial*, 12 (1948), 3–20

'La historia de la penicilina', *Anales de Medicina y Cirugia*, 24/39 (1948), 141–52

'Discurso del Profesor Fleming en la inauguracion del Departamento de Investigacion del Hospital Municipal de Enfermedades Infecciosas de Barcelona, algunos aspectos de las heridas septicas, el lisozima, el empleo de la penicilina', *Revista Instituto de Biologia y Sueroterapia* (1948), 123–90

(with A. Voureka), 'Staining of Flagella', *Journal of General Microbiology*, 3 (1949), p. xxiii

(with W.H. Hughes, I.R.H. Kramer), 'Morphological Changes in Some Bacteria Grown in the Presence of Penicillin', *Journal of General Microbiology*, 3 (1946), pp. xxiii–xxiv

'Nuovi orientamenti nella terapia con antibiotici', *Rivista dell'Istituto Sieroterapico Italiano Sezione Seconda*, 24 (1949), 53–9

'Hommage à Jules Bordet au nom des savants étrangers', *Annales de l'Institut Pasteur*, 79 (1950), 495–8

'Motilité de cils de *Proteus vulgaris*', *Annales de l'Institut Pasteur*, 79 (1950), 604–11

'Sir Ernest Graham Little', *British Medical Journal*, 2 (1950), 952

(with A. Voureka, J.R.H. Kramer, W.H. Hughes), 'The Morphology and Motility of *Proteus vulgaris* and Other Organisms Cultured in the Presence of Penicillin', *Journal of General Microbiology*, 4 (1950), 257–69

'Further Observations on the Motility of *Proteus vulgaris* Grown on Penicillin Agar', *Journal of General Microbiology*, 4 (1950), 457–63

'Antibiotic Theory: an Introductory Article', *Medicine Illustrated*, 4 (1950), 477–8

'Current Therapeutics: Modern Penicillin Therapy', *Practitioner*, 165 (1950), 639–45

(ed.), *Penicillin: its Practical Application*, 2nd edn, London, Butterworth, 1950

(with A.C. Ogilvie), 'Syringe Needles and Mass Inoculation Technique', *British Medical Journal*, 1 (1951), 543–6

'Success: Rectorial Address', *Student* (Edinburgh University Magazine), 47/8 (1952)

'Review of the Development of Antibiotics', *Acta Medica Scandinavica*, 146 (1953), 65–6

'Antibiotics', *Medicine Illustrated*, 7 (1953), 285–8

'Twentieth-Century Changes in the Treatment of Septic Infections: Shattuck Lecture', *New England Journal of Medicine*, 248 (1953), 1037–45

'Conferencias del Alexander Fleming en la Escuela de medicina de la Universidad de la Habana', *Revista Cubana de Laboratorio Clinica*, 7 (1953), 79–104

'El uso de los antibioticos', *Revista Cubana de Tuberculosis*, 17 (1953), 72–5

'Some Side Issues in Antibiotic Therapy', *World Medical Association Bulletin*, 5 (1953), 27

'La Thérapeutique par les antibiotiques', *Gazette des Hôpitaux*, 6 (1954), 95

'A Test to Show the Relative Toxicity of a Chemical to Bacteria and to Human Leucocytes', *International Archives of Allergy*, 5 (1954), 160–2

'The Wright Fleming Institute of Microbiology', *St Mary's Hospital Gazette* (1954), 150–2

ARTICLES AND BOOKS RELATING TO ALEXANDER FLEMING AND THE HISTORY OF PENICILLIN

Abraham, E.P., Chain, E., Fletcher, C.M., Florey, H.W., Gardner, A.D., Heatley, N.G., and Jennings, M.A., 'Further Observations on Penicillin', *Lancet*, 2 (16 August 1941), 177–88

Abraham, Edward P., 'Selective Reminiscences of beta-lactam Antibiotics: Early Research on Penicillin and Cephalosporins', *Bioessays*, 12/12 (1990), 601–6

Abstracts of Third International Congress of Microbiology, 1936, New York, Third International Congress of Microbiology, 1940

Adams, David Parrish, *The Greatest Good to the Greatest Number: Penicillin Rationing on The American Home Front, 1940–1945*, New York, P. Lang, 1991

Alexandra, Duchess of Fife (Princess Arthur of Connaught), *A Nurse's Story*, London, privately published, 1954

Allison, V.D., 'Personal Recollections of Sir Almroth Wright and Sir Alexander Fleming', *Ulster Medical Journal*, 43/2 (1974), 89–98

Aub, J., *et al.*, *Management of the Cocoanut Grove Burns at the Massachusetts General Hospital*, Philadelphia, J.B. Lippincott, 1943

Barcat, J.A., 'Churchill, Fleming y la penicilina', *Medicina*, 54/2 (1994), 175–6

Barkov, A., and Tsyferov, G., 'Doctor Fleming and his Magic Drug', *Meditsinskaia Sestra*, 26 (1967), 53–6

Bauman, Robert P., Jackson, Peter, and Lawrence, Joanne T., *From Promise to Performance: a Journey of Transformation at SmithKline Beecham*, Boston, Harvard Business School Press, 1997

Baumler, Ernst, *Paul Ehrlich, Scientist for Life*, New York, Holmes and Meier, 1984

Bettley, J., 'Post voluptatem Misericordia: the Rise of the London Lock Hospitals', *London Journal*, 10/2 (1984), 167–75

Bickel, Lennard, *Rise up to Life: a Biography of Howard Walter Florey who gave Penicillin to the World*, London, Angus and Robertson, 1972

Biographical Memoirs of Members of the Royal Society, London, Royal Society, 1956–64

Biourge, R. *Des moissures du group Penicillium link*, Louvain, privately published, 1923

Brock, Thomas D., *Robert Koch: a Life in Medicine and Bacteriology*, Madison, Wisc., Science Tech Publishers, 1988

Brown, Kevin, 'Private Alexander Fleming', *St Mary's Gazette*, 99/2 (1993), 29–31

——. 'Better Late than Never: a New Honour for Sir Alexander Fleming', *St Mary's Gazette*, 99/3 (1993), 25–6

——. 'Almroth Wright and Alexander Fleming *en déshabille*', *St Mary's Gazette*, 100/3 (1994), 51–2

——. 'Sir Alexander Fleming beyond Penicillin', *Society of General Microbiology Quarterly*, 22/1 (1995), 4–5

——. 'Penicillin for All', *St Mary's Gazette*, 102/3 (1996), 25–9

——. 'The Inoculation Department at Boulogne', *St Mary's Gazette*, 103/1 (1997), 32–5

——. 'The Doctor's Dilemma a Play for Today?' *St Mary's Gazette*, 104/2 (1998), 49–52

——, and Eveleigh, Douglas E., 'Preservation of Fungal Herbarium Cultures: the Sale of an Alexander Fleming *Penicillium notatum* Preserved Medallion', *Society for Industrial Microbiology News*, 47/3 (1997), 116–18

——. *Alexander Fleming and the Development of Penicillin*, London, Alexander Fleming Laboratory Museum, 2000

——. *Alexander Fleming Laboratory Museum: a Guide*, London, Alexander Fleming Laboratory Museum, 2000

Bud, Robert, *The Uses of Life: a History of Biotechnology*, Cambridge, Cambridge University Press, 1993

——. 'Penicillin and the New Elizabethans', *British Journal for the History of Science*, 31 (September 1998), 305–33

Burdon-Sanderson, John, *The Thirteenth Report of the Medical Officer of the Privy Council, 1870*, London, HMSO, 1871

Burns, Marlene, and van Dijck, Piet W., 'The Development of the Penicillin Production Process in Delft, the Netherlands, during World War II, under Nazi Occupation', *Advances in Applied Microbiology*, 51 (2002), 185–99

——, Bennett, J.W., and van Dijck, Piet W.M., 'Code name Bacinol', *American Society of Microbiology News*, 69/1 (2003), 25–31

Bustinza Lachiondo, Florencio, *De Pasteur à Fleming*, Madrid, Plus-Ultra, 1945

——. *Diez años de amistad con Sir Alexander Fleming*, Madrid, Editorial MAS, 1961

Bynum, W.F., *Science and the Practice of Medicine in the Nineteenth Century*, Cambridge, Cambridge University Press, 1994

Cannon, S., *Nature's Revenge: Why Antibiotics can Breed Disease*, London, Virgin, 1995

Cartwright, F.F., *Development of Modern Surgery*, London, Arthur Barker, 1967

Chain, E., Florey, H.W., Gardner, A.D., Heatley, N.G., Jennings, M.A., Orr-Ewing, J., and Saunders, A.G., 'Penicillin as a Chemotherapeutic Agent', *Lancet* (24 August 1940), 226–8

Chen, Wai, 'The Laboratory as Business: Sir Almroth Wright's Vaccine Programme and the Construction of Penicillin', in A. Cunningham and P. Williams (eds), *The Laboratory Revolution in Medicine*, Cambridge, Cambridge University Press, 1992

——. *Comment Fleming n'a pas inventé la penicilline*, Paris, Synthelabo, 1996

Churchill, Winston S., *The Second World War: Closing the Ring*, London, Cassell, 1952

Clark, Ronald William, *The Life of Ernst Chain. Penicillin and Beyond*, London, Weidenfeld and Nicolson, 1985

Clarke, Hans T., Johnson, John R., and Robinson, Robert (eds), *The Chemistry of Penicillin*, Princeton, Princeton University Press, 1949

Clodfelter, M., *Warfare and Armed Conflicts: a Statistical Reference to Casualty and Other Figures, 1618–1991*, Jefferson, NC, McFarland, 1992

Coates, J.B., *Surgery in World War II, Activities of the Surgical Consultants*, Washington, DC, Office of Surgeon General, 1962

Colebrook, Leonard, *Almroth Wright, Provocative Doctor and Thinker*, London, Heinemann, 1954

——. 'Sir Alexander Fleming', *Biographical Memoirs of Fellows of the Royal Society*, vol. 2, London, Royal Society, 1956, pp. 117–27

Collier, L.H., *History of the Medical Research Club, 1891–1991*, London, privately published, 1991

Cope, V. Zachary, *History of St Mary's Hospital Medical School*, London, Heinemann, 1954

——. *Almroth Wright, Founder of Modern Vaccine Therapy*, London, Nelson, 1966

Dalio, P., 'Vicenzo Tiberio e la scoperta della penicillina, una grande conquista a cavallo di due secoli', *Minerva Medica*, 73 (1982), 2005–9

Davenport-Hines, R.P.T., and Slinn, Judy, *Glaxo: a History to 1962*, Cambridge, Cambridge University Press, 1992

Davies, Caleb W., '*Penicillium notatum*: a Glimpse of the Past', *St Mary's Gazette*, 98/3 (1992), 27

De Kruif, Paul, *Life among the Doctors*, London, Jonathan Cape, 1949

De Soville, C., and De Brouwer, C., 'Nobel Chronicle: Fleming and Gratia', *Lancet*, 354/9174 (17 July 1999), 258

Debré, Patrice, *Louis Pasteur*, Paris, Flammarion, 1994

Diggins, Francis W.E., 'The True History of Penicillin, with Refutation of the Misinformation in Literature', *British Journal of Biomedical Science*, 56 (1999), 83–93

——. 'The Discovery of Penicillin: so Many Get it Wrong', *Biologist*, 47/3 (2000), 115–19

Dubos, R.J., *Louis Pasteur: Freelancer of Science*, London, Gollancz, 1951

Duchesne, E.A., 'Contribution à l'étude de la concurrence vitale chez les microorganismes: antagonisme entre les moissures et les microbes', unpublished thesis, École du Service de Santé Militaire, Lyons, 1897

Duckett, Serge, 'Ernest Duchesne and the Concept of Fungal Antibiotic Therapy', *Lancet*, 354 (1999), 2068–71

Dunnill, Michael, *The Plato of Praed Street: the Life and Times of Almroth Wright*,

London, Royal Society of Medicine, 2000

Elder, Albert (ed.), *The History of Penicillin Production*, New York, American Institute of Chemical Engineers, Chemical Engineering Progress Symposium, 66/100 (1970)

Ferry, Georgina, *Dorothy Hodgkin: a Life*, London, Granta Books, 1998

Fleming, Amalia, *A Piece of Truth: Lady Fleming on the Colonels' Greece*, London, Jonathan Cape, 1972

Fleming, Robert, *Sir Alexander Fleming: a Personal Story of his Life*, privately printed, 1958

Fletcher, C.M., 'First Clinical Use of Penicillin', *British Medical Journal*, 289 (1984), 22–9

Florey, H.W., Chain, E.B., and Heatley, N.G., *Antibiotics: a Survey of Penicillin, Streptomycin and Other Antimicrobial Substances from Fungi, Actinomycetes, Bacteria and Plants*, Oxford, Oxford University Press, 1949

Florey, M.E., and Florey, H.W., 'General and Local Administration of Penicillin', *Lancet*, 1 (27 March 1943), 387–97

Foster, W.D., *History of Medical Bacteriology and Immunology*, London, Heinemann, 1970

Fraenkel, G.J., 'Rockefeller, Florey and the Penicillin Connection', *Annals of Diagnostic Pathology*, 3/3 (1999), 195–8

Frankland, A.W., 'Perspective: Penicillin History and Allergy', *Immunology and Allergy Practice*, 14/10 (1992), 21–3

——. 'Aerobiology and Allergy – an Autobiography', *Aerobiologia*, 12 (1996), 58

——, and Wainwright, Milton, 'More Mysteries from Fleming's Plate', *Journal of Medical Biography*, 2 (1994), 61–2

Fraser, Ian, 'Random Recollections: Penicillin and the Normandy Landings', *Annals of the Royal College of Surgeons of England*, 77 (1995), 198–201

Gambardella, G.A., *Science and Innovation: the American Pharmaceutical Industry during the 1980s*, Cambridge, Cambridge University Press, 1995

Garner, James Stuart, 'The Great Experiment: the Admission of Women Students to St Mary's Hospital Medical School, 1916–1925', *Medical History*, 42/1 (1998), 68–88

Garrod, L., and O'Grady, F., *Antibiotics and Chemotherapy*, Edinburgh, E. and S. Livingstone, 1971

Geison, Gerald L., *Private Science of Louis Pasteur*, Princeton, Princeton University Press, 1995

Gibbs, Dennis D., 'Sir Alexander Fleming in Stained Glass: St James' Church, Sussex Gardens', *Journal of Medical Biography*, 5/3 (1997), 177

Goldsmith, Margaret Leland, *The Road to Penicillin: a History of Chemotherapy*, London, Lindsay Drummond, 1946

Goodlee, R.J., *Lord Lister*, London, Macmillan, 1917

Greene, Graham, *The Third Man*, London, Heinemann, 1950

Handfield-Jones, R.M., *History of the Sancta Maria Lodge, no. 2682, 1897–1960*, London, privately published, 1960

Hare, Ronald, *The Birth of Penicillin, and the Disarming of Microbes*, London, Allen and Unwin, 1970

——. 'New Light on the Discovery of Penicillin', *Medical History*, 26 (1982), 1–24

——. 'The Scientific Activities of Alexander Fleming Other than the Discovery of Penicillin', *Medical History*, 27 (1983), 347–72

Harris, Henry, 'Howard Florey and the Development of Penicillin', *Notes and Records of the Royal Society of London*, 53/2 (1999), 243–52

Hawthorne, Fran, *The Merck Druggernaut: the Inside Story of a Pharmaceutical Giant*, Hoboken, John Wiley, 2003

Heaman, Elsbeth A., *St. Mary's: the History of a London Teaching Hospital*, Montreal and Kingston, McGill–Queen's University Press, 2003

Herrell, Wallace Edgar, *Penicillin and Other Antibiotic Agents*, Philadelphia, W.B. Saunders, 1945

Hillebrandt, David, 'The Circle of Medical History', *Lancet*, 355/9215 (6 May 2000), 1656

Hoare, Philip, *Spike Island: the Memory of a Military Hospital*, London, Fourth Estate, 2001

Hobby, Gladys L., *Penicillin: Meeting the Challenge*, New Haven, Yale University Press, 1985

Hughes, William Howard, *Alexander Fleming*, London, Priory Press, 1974

Imperial Chemical Industries, *Penicillin: a Brief History*, London, ICI, 1944

Keating, Peter, 'Vaccine Therapy and the Problem of Opsonins', *Journal of the History of Medicine*, 43 (1988), 281–2

Kennedy, Carol, *ICI: the Company that Changed our Lives*, London, Paul Chapman Publishing, 1993

Kerr, David Innes, *The London Lock Hospital, a Charitable Hospital for Venereal Disease, 1746–1952*, London, Royal Society of Medicine, 1999

Kingston, William, 'Antibiotics, Invention and Innovation', *Research Policy*, 29 (2000), 679–710

Kyle, R.A., and Shampo, M.A., 'Ernest Augustin Clement Duchesne', *Journal of American Medical Association*, 240/9 (1978), 847

La Torre, G., and Martines, V., 'Vicenzo Tiberio, precursore degli studi sulla penicillina', *Annali d'igiene*, 8/3 (1996), 325–7

Lacken, George, *The Story of Penicillin*: London, Pilot Press, 1945

Lazell, H.G., *From Pills to Penicillin: the Beecham Story*, London, Heinemann, 1975

Lechevalier, H.A., *The Development of Applied Microbiology at Rutgers*, New Brunswick, NJ, Rutgers University Press, 1982

——. 'The Waksman Institute of Microbiology, 1954–1984', *Journal of Rutgers University Libraries*, 50 (June 1988), 20–45

Liebenau, Jonathan, 'The British Success with Penicillin', *Social Studies of Science*, 17 (1987), 69–86

——. *Medical Science and Medical Industry: the Formation of the American Pharmaceutical Industry*, London, Macmillan, 1987

Lovell, Richard, *Churchill's Doctor: a Life of Lord Moran*, London, Royal Society of Medicine Press, 1992

Ludovici, Laurence James, *Fleming, Discoverer of Penicillin*, London, Dakers, 1952

Macfarlane, Gwyn, 'Howard Florey at Work', *New Scientist* (27 September 1979), 990–2

——. *Howard Florey: the Making of a Great Scientist*, Oxford, Oxford University Press, 1979

——. *Alexander Fleming: the Man and the Myth*, London, Chatto and Windus, 1984

Mahoney, T., *The Merchants of Life: an Account of the American Pharmaceutical Industry*, New York, Harper, 1959

Marks, Harry, *The Progress of Experiment, Science and Therapeutic Reform in the United States, 1900–1990*, Cambridge, Cambridge University Press, 1997

Martinez, Alonso, E., *Adventures of a Doctor*, London, Hale, 1962

Masters, David, *Miracle Drug: the Inner History of Penicillin*, London, Eyre and Spottiswoode, 1946

Mateles, Richard I., *Penicillin: a Paradigm for Biotechnology*, Chicago, Candida Corporation, 1998

Maurois, André, *Les Silences du Colonel Bramble*, Paris, Grasset, 1921

——. *Discours du Docteur O'Grady*, Paris, Grasset, 1922

——. *The Life of Sir Alexander Fleming, Discoverer of Penicillin*, London, Cape, 1959

——. 'Wright et Fleming', *Histoire de la médicine*, 9/2 (1959), 5–53

Mines, Samuel, *Pfizer: an Informal History*, New York, Pfizer, 1978

Moberg, C.L., 'Penicillin's Forgotten Man, Norman Heatley', *Science*, 253 (1991), 734–5

Neushul, Peter, 'Science, Government and the Mass Production of Penicillin', *Journal of the History of Medicine and the Allied Sciences*, 48 (1993), 371–95

——. 'Fighting Research: Army Participation in the Clinical Testing and Mass Production of Penicillin during the Second World War', in R. Cooter, M. Harrison and S. Sturdy (eds), *War, Medicine and Modernity*, Stroud, Sutton, 1998, pp. 203–24

Nobel Foundation, *Les Prix Nobels en 1945*, Stockholm, Nobel Foundation, 1947

Nobel, W.C., *Coli, Great Healer of Men: the Biography of Leonard Colebrook*, London, Heinemann, 1974

Notter, Armand, 'Difficultés d'industrialisation de la pénicilline', *Histoire des sciences médicales*, 25 (1991), 31–8

Obituaries of Notable Fellows of the Royal Society, London, Royal Society, 1947

Osserman, E.F., Canfield, R.E., and Beychock, S. (eds), *Lysozyme*, New York, Academic Press, 1974

Papagostas, G., and Gaté, J., *Les Associations microbiennes*, Paris, Doin et Cie, 1928

Parascandola, John (ed.), *History of Antibiotics: a Symposium*, Madison, Illinois, American Institute for the History of Pharmacy, 1980

——. 'John Mahoney and the Introduction of Penicillin to Treat Syphilis', *Pharmacy in History*, 43/1 (2001), 3–13

Porritt, A.E., *History of the Second World War, United Kingdom Medical Services, Surgery*, London, HMSO, 1953

Raper, Kenneth, 'The Penicillin Saga Remembered', *American Society for Industrial Microbiology News*, 44/12 (1978), 645–53

Ratcliff, John Drury, *Yellow Magic: the Story of Penicillin*, New York, Random House, 1945

Rodengen, Jeffrey L., *The Legend of Pfizer*, Fort Lauderdale, Write Stuff Syndicate, 1999

Rolinson, G.N., 'Forty Years of beta-lactam Research', *Journal of Antimicrobial Chemistry*, 41/6 (1998), 589–603

Rowland, John, *The Penicillin Man: the Story of Sir Alexander Fleming*, London, Lutterworth Press, 1957

Royal Society, *Penicillin Fifty Years after Fleming: a Royal Society Discussion Organized by Sir James Baddiley and E.P. Abraham, held on 2 and 3 May 1979*, London, Royal Society, 1980

Ryan, F., *Tuberculosis: the Greatest Story Never Told*, Boston, Little, Brown, 1992

Sava, George, *The Conquest of Disease: the Story of Penicillin*, London, McDonald, 1946

Scoutaris, Milton, 'Moldy Mary and the Illinois Fruit and Vegetable Company', *Pharmacy in History*, 38/4 (1996), 175–7

Shama, Gilbert, and Reinarz, Jonathan, 'Allied Intelligence Reports on Wartime German Penicillin, Research and Production', *Historical Studies in the Physical and Biological Sciences*, 32/2 (2002), 347–68

Shaw, George Bernard, *The Doctor's Dilemma*, London, Constable, 1913

Sheehan, John C., *The Enchanted Ring: the Untold Story of Penicillin*, Cambridge, Mass., MIT Press, 1982

Shipton, Rachel C., *A Bibliography of Sir Alexander Fleming, 1881–1955*, London, St Mary's Hospital Medical School, 1993

Silverstein, A.M., *A History of Immunology*, New York, Academic Press, 1989

Smith, F.B., *The People's Health, 1830–1910*, London, Croom Helm, 1979

Sokolov, Boris Fedorovich, *Penicillin: a Dramatic Story*, London, Allen and Unwin, 1946

Spink, W.W., 'Penicillin and the Fleming Myth: on Reading the Life of Sir Alexander Fleming', *Minnesota Medicine*, 42 (1959), 1447–50

Steftee, C.H., 'Alexander Fleming and Penicillin: the Chance of a Lifetime', *North Carolina Medical Journal*, 53/6 (1992), 308–10

Sternbach, G.L., and Varon, J., 'Alexander Fleming: the Spectrum of Penicillin', *Journal of Emergency Medicine*, 10/1 (1992), 89–91

Stewart, I., *Organising Scientific Research for War: the Administrative History of the Office of Scientific Research and Development*, Boston, Little, Brown, 1948

Stollerman, G.H., 'The Global Impact of Penicillin: Then and Now', *Mount Sinai Journal of Medicine*, 60/2 (1993), 112–19

Sturchio, Jeffrey L. (ed.), *Value and Visions: a Merck Century*, Rahway, Merck, 1991

Swan, H.T., and Wainwright, Milton, 'C.G. Paine and the Earliest Surviving Clinical Records of Penicillin Therapy', *Medical History* 30 (1986), 42–56

Swann, John P., 'The Search for Synthetic Penicillin during World War II', *British Journal for the History of Science*, 16 (1983), 154–90

——. 'The Discovery and Early Development of Penicillin', *Medical Heritage*, 1/5 (1985), 375–86

Tansey, E.M., and Reynolds, Lois A. (eds), *Post Penicillin Antibiotics: from Acceptance to Resistance?* London, Wellcome Trust, 2000

Tauber, A.I., and Chenyak, L., *Metchnikoff and the Origins of Immunology*, Cambridge, Cambridge University Press, 1991

Tischler, M., 'Drug Discovery, Background and Foreground', *Clinical Pharmacology and Therapeutics*, 14 (1973), 479–86

Vallery-Radot, R., *La Vie de Pasteur*, Paris, Hachette, 1906

Wainwright, Milton, 'Fleming Did Discover Penicillin', *Society for General Microbiology Quarterly*, 15/2 (1988), 30–1

——. *Miracle Cure: the Story of Penicillin and the Golden Age of Antibiotics*, Oxford, Basil Blackwell, 1990

——. 'Fleming's Early Search for Antibiotics Other than Penicillin', *Society for General Microbiology Quarterly*, 18/3 (1991), 46–7

——. 'The Mystery of the Plate: Fleming's Discovery and Contribution to the Early Development of Penicillin', *Journal of Medical Biography*, 1 (1993), 59–65

——. 'Roger Reid's Early Contribution to the Study of Penicillin', *Journal of Medical Biography*, 4/1 (1996), 14–17

——. 'St Mary's Other Man of Penicillin', *St Mary's Gazette*, 103/2 (1997), 41–3

——. 'A Response to Some Criticisms of Fleming's Role in the Discovery of Penicillin', *St Mary's Gazette*, 103/3 (1997), 31–4

——. 'Fleming's Unfinished', *Perspectives in Biology and Medicine*, 45/4 (2002), 529–38

Waksman, Selman, *Microbial Antagonisms and Antibiotic Substances*, New York, Commonwealth Fund, 1945

——. *My Life with the Microbes*, New York, Simon and Schuster, 1958

Waller, John, *Fabulous Science: Fact and Fiction in the History of Scientific Discovery*, Oxford, Oxford University Press, 2002

——. *The Discovery of the Germ: Twenty Years that Transformed our Understanding of Disease*, Cambridge, Icon Books, 2002

Webb-Johnson, Lord, *Annals of the Royal College of Surgeons*, London, Royal College of Surgeons, 1950

Weight, Richard, *Patriots: National Identity in Britain, 1940–2000*, London, Macmillan, 2002

Weatherall, Miles, 'An End to the Search for Drugs', *Nature*, 296 (1982), 387–90

——. *In Search of a Cure: a History of Pharmaceutical Discovery*, Oxford, Oxford University Press, 1990

Williams,Trevor Illtyd, *Howard Florey: Penicillin and After*, Oxford, Oxford University Press, 1984

Wilson, David, *Penicillin in Perspective*, London, Faber, 1976

Worboys, Michael, 'Vaccine Therapy and Laboratory Medicine in Edwardian Britain', in John V. Pickstone (ed.), *Medical Innovations in Historical Practice*, Manchester, Manchester Institute of Technology, 1992

Wright, Almroth Edward, *Technique of the Teat and Capillary Glass Tube*, London, Constable, 1912

——. *Unexpurgated Case against Woman Suffrage*, London, Constable, 1913

——. *Prolegomena to the Logic which Searches for Truth*, London, Heinemann, 1941

——. *Brief Survey of the History and Development of the Inoculation Department, St Mary's Hospital, W2*, London, privately published, 1945

——. *Alethetropic Logic*, London, Heinemann, 1953

Wright, J.W.L., *Sancta Maria Lodge, no. 2682: a Short Centenary History*, London, privately published, 1997

Zachary, G.P., *Endless Frontier: Vannevar Bush, Architect of the American Century*, New York, Free Press, 1997

Zetridou, P. C., and Psemenou, H. P., *Ελλήνιδες* (*Women of Greece in the Second World War*), Athens, Historical and Laographical Society of Thessaly, 1950

Index

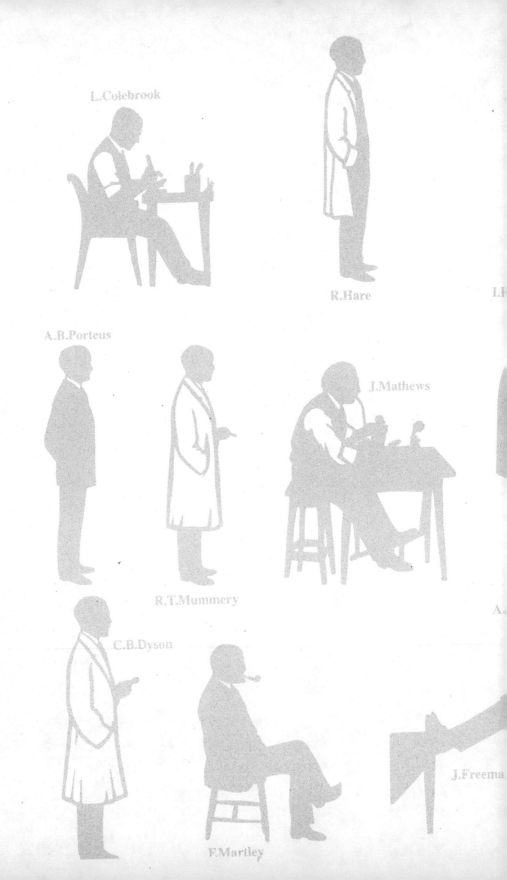

L.Colebrook

R.Hare

I.H

A.B.Porteus

J.Mathews

R.T.Mummery

A.

C.B.Dyson

F.Martley

J.Freema